GRANTS
&
AWARDS

AVAILABLE TO
AMERICAN
WRITERS

A PUBLICATION OF PEN AMERICAN CENTER

EDITOR: JOHN MORRONE

PRINCIPAL RESEARCHER: VICTORIA VINTON

COPY EDITOR: ANNA JARDINE

Grants and Awards Available to American Writers
21st Edition 2000-2001
© 2000 PEN American Center
Printed in the United States of America
ISBN: 0-934638-16-0

A publication of
PEN American Center
568 Broadway
New York, NY 10012-3225
www.pen.org

Cover: Jackie McKee

First printing: August 2000

CONTENTS

Grants and Awards   1
Appendix: State Arts Councils   277
Index of Awards   283
Index of Organizations   298
Index of Categories 307

A Note on Using this Book

Because the term *writer* covers many categories, we felt that we should break it down into the following eight:

Fiction	Ⓕ
Poetry	Ⓟ
Drama	Ⓓ
Journalism	Ⓙ
General Nonfiction	Ⓝ
Children's Literature	Ⓒ
Translation	Ⓣ
Screenwriting	Ⓢ

Most prizes which apply to more than two of these categories will be designated by the symbol Ⓜ. These symbols are located in the left-hand margin of each page next to the award description.

Residences for writers are designated by the symbol Ⓡ.

Awards for which one may not apply directly on his own behalf are designated in the text of each entry as "By Internal Nomination Only" and the symbol Ⓝ.

The appendix provides a guide to state commissions and agencies on writers-in-residence, poets-in-the-schools, and arts and humanities. Three indexes list awards, organizations, and categories. The category index uses the above symbols to identify each category.

Deadlines given are, for the most part, confirmed for 2000 and 2001. Writers should always reconfirm deadlines before submitting applications.

Editor's Note

The 2000-2001 edition of PEN's *Grants and Awards Available to American Writers* is still the most comprehensive directory of domestic and foreign grants for use by American writers in the United States and abroad. First published in 1969 as a pamphlet, and now updated as a book every two years by PEN American Center, the association of literary writers, *Grants and Awards* is a low-cost, one-volume directory for writers of all income brackets, at work in all genres.

Grants and Awards' principal researcher, Victoria Vinton, has listed primarily competitions that offer a cash stipend of $500 or more, and/or publication of a manuscript or production of a dramatic or performance work. Occasionally, an award is included even though its stipend is less than $500, because we believe it confers a special distinction in the field it honors. Some of the prizes offered by established literary magazines are given only to authors of works that have appeared in those publications during the past year or season; therefore, no deadline is stated. Also listed are grants that are not exclusively for writers, but whose purposes are defined broadly enough that writers are among the pool of eligible applicants. Some of these are research grants or fellowships sponsored by foundations or academic institutions; the main criterion used in deciding whether to list them is the likelihood that the grant will allow recipients to produce writing of a literary, rather than a purely technical, nature.

What's new in the 2000-2001 edition? As of the last edition, *Grants and Awards* began to list sponsoring organizations' fax numbers, e-mail addresses, and Web sites; many more appear this time around, as organizations frequently encourage applicants to fax or e-mail inquiries about their programs, and may even allow web browsers to download application forms directly. Please note, however, that in most cases formal applications are not accepted electronically. If you are obtaining documents electronically from the organizations listed in this book, ascertain the method by which you are expected to file an application before you do so.

A total of 234 new awards from 142 organizations are included in this edition; 53 discontinued programs have been dropped from the last edition. The total number of grants and awards listed in this edition continues to exceed 1,000. That's the good news. But in order to keep *Grants and Awards* to a manageable length, something had to go. We no longer list award programs strictly for Canadian writers, and we mention only those Canadian awards for which U.S. writers may apply. Canadian nationals and landed immigrants should consult the booklet *Awards, Competitions, and Prizes*, published by the Writers Union of Canada (most recent revision 1997). Like *Grants and Awards*, the booklet is modestly priced (CAN$9, which covers taxes and shipping) and includes a directory of arts councils in the Canadian provinces. To order a copy, contact the Writers Union of Canada, 24 Ryerson Avenue, Toronto, Ontario M5T 2P3; fax 416-703-0826.

Grants and Awards continues to list programs in foreign countries for which American writers are eligible. These are listed under the alphabetized name of the country or, if the scope of the prize encompasses more than one country, under INTERNATIONAL.

To assist readers in finding awards that may be of particular relevance, we have coded most entries according to the area of writing involved. See "A Note on Using This Book" for a detailed description of the codes used within.

Attention, writers for the silver screen! Because we have noticed a sizeable increase in the number of awards for screenwriting, a new category has been added to our list of coded entries. Whereas awards for screenwriters were included previously with those for other dramatic works (coded as D), we have split the category in two and the code S will specifically alert readers to a program that rewards a screenwriter with a prize or a production opportunity.

Attention, also, journalists. Scholarships intended for journalists continue to proliferate, and we have included information on quite a few of them. While many more exist in addition to those listed, we have chosen not to be exhaustive, because scholarships often give smaller (and variable) cash stipends and sometimes limit applicants to very localized groups (usually defined geographically).

The category Writers' Residences—indicated by the symbol R—refers mainly to retreats, colonies, or other residences where writers may work undisturbed, and to which access is won by competitive application. Not coded as such are teacher-in-residence, playwright-in-residence, or similar positions that involve academic responsibilities or oblige the writer to lead workshops, lectures, or readings.

The symbol IN refers to those prizes or fellowships for which writers may not apply; recipients are selected by a jury or an appointed panel. As a courtesy to the sponsoring organizations, which cannot answer the numerous inquiries received, the words *By Internal Nomination Only* appear at the end of descriptions of such awards, and the usual information on restrictions, deadlines, and person to whom to apply, does not appear. We stress that applications for these awards are neither accepted nor even considered. Please note, furthermore, that several large and well-known foundations are not listed in *Grants and Awards* at their own request, because they do not solicit nominations and they wish to discourage pointless applications.

Many organizations have elaborate application forms and very specific guidelines, which the entries here, in the interest of brevity, summarize and condense. We suggest that as a matter of course prospective applicants contact the sponsor of a grant or award before sending books, manuscripts, or other material. Because deadline dates are subject to change, we urge applicants to confirm them with the sponsoring organizations. Always include a self-addressed, stamped envelope (SASE) with any inquiry, application, or submission; this is standard practice. Some awards are not given annually, or not given at all in 2000 or 2001, but if the foundation or association is active and will administer prizes in the future, we have listed it. Wherever we have been informed that a reading fee is required for submissions, we have noted it.

This edition of *Grants and Awards* remains current until mid-2001, when the twenty-second edition will be published. Users should bear in mind that no directory of this nature can be definitive. Other sources to consult are the annual editions of *Study Abroad* and the Theater Communications Group's *Dramatists Sourcebook* (one of several directories designed specifically for playwrights and other scriptwriters). Monthly or bimonthly writers' magazines such as *Poets and Writers Magazine, The Writer,* and *Writers Digest* provide updated information. Especially useful are the newsletters and occasional publications of the American Society of Journalists and Authors, the Authors League, the Dramatists Guild, and Editorial Freelancers Association. *ARIS,* the Academic Research Information System Newsletter, offers information on scholarly residences and fellowships, and the *AWP Newsletter*, published by Associated Writing Programs, is particularly helpful in obtaining information on writers' residences, for summer or for academic year, and on writers' conferences. The Modern Language Association publishes the *MLA-ADE Job Information List* four times annually; some of the positions enumerated there may be of definite interest to writers.

For writers living in—or passing through—the New York metropolitan area, the library of The Foundation Center (79 Fifth Avenue, New York, NY 10003) makes available to grant-hunters extensive, reliable, up-to-date, and well-organized data on foundations offering grants, awards, and fellowships. Write to the Center for locations of its regional offices.

Every state government has a council or commission on the arts, usually located in the capital city. These agencies often sponsor grants, fellowships, or short-term residences, such as poets-in-the-schools programs, for which writers may apply. Accordingly, these programs are usually available only to residents of the state and pertain to arts and cultural matters of the region. Some of the more notable are listed in this book. The appendix gives the addresses of state arts councils in the United States, Puerto Rico, and the U.S. Virgin Islands.

For writers interested in writing abroad or researching a subject that necessitates foreign travel, the cultural attaché of the country concerned—usually at the embassy in Washington, DC, or in New York City—may provide information on periods of advanced study, research, and international literary awards.

The revisions in this edition are based on replies to a survey conducted between August 1999 and February 2000, supplemented by material from the latest references in the field and from readers' responses. PEN American Center thanks the many foundations, universities, publishers, professional organizations, and foreign and U.S. government agencies that furnished the bulk of information for this publication. PEN assumes no responsibility for the conduct of the organizations listed, and invites readers to report on their experiences with any of them. Additional entries, suggestions for the improvement of subsequent editions, and feedback on the sponsoring organizations now included, are greatly appreciated. Correspondence should be addressed to: PEN American Center, 568 Broadway, New York, NY 10012-3225; fax: 212-334-2181; e-mail: JM@PEN.ORG

John Morrone
May 2000

GRANTS AND AWARDS

A Contemporary Theatre
The Eagles Building
700 Union Street
Seattle, WA 98101-2330
Web site: http://www.acttheatre.org
Fax: 206-292-7670

Ⓓ The *ACT/Hedgebrook Women Playwrights Festival* selects four women playwrights for a staged reading of unproduced work, with audience feedback. After the reading, the playwrights receive a one-week residence at Hedgebrook to work on revisions, based on the response to the reading with two dramaturgs also in residence, plus a stipend of $500. Selected literary managers, artistic directors, and established playwrights are asked to nominated playwrights for the program. Self-nominations are not accepted. Send SASE for additional information.

Available to: Women playwrights
Deadline: Inquire
Apply to: ACT/Hedgebrook Women Playwrights Festival, above address

Academy of American Poets
584 Broadway, Suite 1208
New York, NY 10012
E-mail: iamos@dti.net
Web site: http://www.poets.org

Ⓟ The *American Poets Fund*, established by Peter I. B. Lavan, assists poets of demonstrated ability who are in immediate and urgent financial need. Grants from this fund may not be used to promote, improve, or enhance the literary talent or reputation of the recipient, but are intended solely to reduce financial burdens. Direct applications are not accepted. Academy chancellors, fellows, and award winners may nominate poets by writing to the executive director of the Academy.

Available to: U.S. citizens
Deadline: Ongoing
Apply to: See above

ⓘ The *Fellowship of the Academy of American Poets* is awarded in recognition of "distinguished poetic achievement." One fellowship of $20,000 is awarded annually. *By Internal Nomination Only.*

Ⓟ Ⓣ The *Harold Morton Landon Translation Award* is given for a published translation of poetry into English from any language. This may be a book-length poem, a collection of poems, or a verse-drama translated into verse. One prize of $1,000 is awarded annually. Collaborations by two or more translators are accepted; anthologies of work by a number of translators are not. Self-published books are ineligible. Write, e-mail, or visit the Web site for additional information.

Available to: U.S. citizens
Deadline: Manuscripts accepted January 1–December 31
Apply to: Harold Morton Landon Translation Award, above address

Ⓟ The *James Laughlin Award* is given annually for a poet's second book of poetry. The Academy awards a cash prize of $5,000 directly to the poet and purchases 7,000 copies of the winning book for distribution to its members. Only manuscripts already under contract with publishers from May 1 of the previous year to April 30 of the current year are considered for this award. Write, e-mail, or visit the Web site for guidelines and required entry form.

Available to: American poets who have already published one volume of poetry in a standard edition (40 pages or more; print run of 500 or more)
Deadline: April 30
Apply to: James Laughlin Award, above address

Ⓟ The *Lenore Marshall Poetry Prize* of $10,000, administered in conjunction with *The Nation*, is given annually for the most outstanding book of poems published in the United States during the previous calendar year. Books must be in a standard edition (40 pages or more in length and 500 or more copies); self-published books are not eligible. To enter, publishers should send four copies of the book to the Academy. Write, e-mail, or visit the Web site for additional information.

Available to: U.S. citizens
Deadline: Submissions accepted April 1–June 1
Apply to: Lenore Marshall Poetry Prize, above address

Ⓟ Ⓣ The *Raiziss/de Palchi Translation Award* consists of a $5,000 book prize or a $20,000 fellowship, given in alternate years, for the translation into English of modern or contemporary Italian poetry. The book prize is awarded to a living translator for a published translation of a significant work. The fellowship is awarded to a U.S. citizen engaged in a translation; the winner also receives a residence at the American Academy in Rome. Send SASE, e-mail, or visit the Web site for guidelines and application.

Available to: U.S. citizens
Deadline: November 1 in odd-numbered years for book prize; September 1–November 1 in even-numbered years for fellowship
Apply to: Raiziss/de Palchi Translation Award, above address

[IN] The *Tanning Prize*, endowed by the painter Dorothea Tanning, annually awards $100,000 in recognition of outstanding and proven mastery in the art of poetry. *By Internal Nomination Only.*

Ⓟ The *Walt Whitman Award* is given annually for a manuscript of 50 to 100 pages of original poetry in English by a poet who has not published a book of poems in a standard edition (40 pages or more; print run of 500 or more). The winner receives a cash prize of $5,000, a one-month residence at the Vermont Studio Center, and publication by Louisiana State University Press. The Academy purchases 8,000 copies of the book for distribution to its members. There is a $20 entry fee. Send SASE, e-mail, or visit the Web site for guidelines and required entry form.

Available to: U.S. citizens
Deadline: Manuscripts accepted September 15–November 15
Apply to: Walt Whitman Award, above address

Academy of Motion Picture Arts and Sciences
Nicholl Fellowships
8949 Wilshire Boulevard
Beverly Hills, CA 90211
E-mail: nicholl@oscars.org
Web site: http://www.oscars.org/nicholl

Ⓢ Up to five *Don and Gee Nicholl Screenwriting Fellowships*, of $25,000 each, are available annually for original, full-length feature scripts of 100 to 130 pages, with the understanding that the recipients will complete a new feature screenplay during the fellowship year. Entries must be in English (no translations) and must display exceptional craft and engaging storytelling. Writers must not have sold or optioned a feature screenplay or teleplay, or earned more than $5,000 for writing one. Send business-size SASE January–April or visit the Web site year-round for further information. There is a $30 entry fee.

Available to: See above
Deadline: May 1
Apply to: Nicholl Fellowships, above address

Acadia National Park
PO Box 177
Bar Harbor, ME 04609

® The *Artist-in-Residence Program* offers professional writers and other artists the opportunity to pursue their particular art form in the inspiring landscape of the park. Participants receive housing for two-week periods in spring and fall, in return for which they are asked to donate to the park collection a piece of work representative of their style and their stay. They are also asked to appear before the public during their residence, for instance in a demonstration, talk, exploratory hike, or performance. Write for additional information and guidelines.

Available to: No restrictions
Deadline: Applications accepted November 1–January 1
Apply to: Coordinator, Artist-in-Residence Program, above address

The Actors' Fund of America
729 Seventh Avenue, 10th floor
New York, NY 10019
Web site: http://www.actorsfund.org

5757 Wilshire Boulevard
Los Angeles, CA 90036

203 North Wabash, Suite 1308
Chicago, IL 60601

The Actors' Fund of America, a nonprofit organization founded in 1882, provides for the social welfare of entertainment professionals, including writers and actors. Headquarters and the Aurora Residence are located in New York City, with regional offices in Los Angeles and Chicago. Nursing and retirement homes are in Englewood, New Jersey. In addition to providing emergency grants for essentials such as food, rent, and medical care, the Actors' Fund operates comprehensive programs to meet the critical needs of entertainment professionals throughout their lives: nursing and retirement homes, senior and disabled programs, mental health and chemical dependency services, services to employable professionals, a health insurance resource center, the Phyllis Newman Women's Health Initiative, an AIDS initiative, and affordable housing. Professionals who earn their living in legitimate theater, film, radio, television, music, dance, and variety may be eligible.

Available to: See above
Deadline: Ongoing
Apply to: Any Actors' Fund office, above addresses

Actors' Playhouse at the Miracle Theatre
280 Miracle Mile
Coral Gables, FL 33134

© Ⓓ The *National Children's Theatre Festival* offers a cash prize of $1,000, plus paid production, travel, and housing to attend and participate in the festival, for a play and a musical. Submissions must be unpublished and original. Plays must be for young people ages twelve to seventeen, 45 to 60 minutes long, with a cast limit of six (actors may play multiple roles), and minimal sets suitable for touring. Musicals should be for children ages five to twelve, 45 to 60 minutes long, with a cast limit of eight, and minimal sets suitable for touring. Work dealing with social issues, including multiculturalism in today's society, is preferred. There is a $10 entry fee. Write for guidelines and entry form.

Available to: No restrictions
Deadline: September 1
Apply to: National Children's Theatre Festival, above address

Actors Theatre of Louisville
316–320 West Main Street
Louisville, KY 40202-4218
Web site: http://www.actorstheatre.org

Ⓓ The *National Ten-Minute Play Contest* awards $1,000 to the best 10-minute play submitted. The winning play may be considered for production by Actors Theatre of Louisville. Plays submitted must not have had a previous Equity production. Playwrights may submit only one 10-minute script, no more than 10 pages, typed and fastened. The author's name and address must appear on the title page only. No scripts will be returned.

Available to: U.S. citizens and residents
Deadline: December 1
Apply to: National Ten-Minute Play Contest, above address

Agricultural History Society
Center for Agricultural History
618 Ross Hall
Iowa State University
Ames, IA 50011-1202
E-mail: rdhurt@iastate.edu
Web site: http://www.iastate.edu/~history_info/aghissoc.htm
Fax: 515-294-5620

Ⓝ Three awards are given annually to writers: the *Theodore Saloutos Award* of $500, to the author of the best book published on U.S. agricultural history, broadly conceived; the *Vernon Carstensen Award* of $200, for the best article published by a scholar in the quarterly journal *Agricultural History*; and the *Everett Edwards Award* of $200, for the best article in agricultural history submitted by a graduate student.

Available to: No restrictions
Deadline: End of calendar year
Apply to: R. Douglas Hurt, Editor, *Agricultural History*, above address

Alabama State Council on the Arts
201 Monroe Street, Suite 110
Montgomery, AL 36130-1800
E-mail: randy@arts.state.al.us
Web site: http://www.arts.state.al.us
Fax: 334-240-3269

Ⓜ Fellowships in fiction, poetry, nonfiction, and playwriting of $5,000 and $10,000 are available annually to writers who have been residents of Alabama for at least two years.

Available to: See above
Deadline: March 1
Apply to: Randy Shoults, Literature Program Manager, above address

Alaska State Council on the Arts
411 West Fourth Avenue, Suite 1E
Anchorage, AK 99501-2343
Fax: 907-269-6601
E-mail: info@aksca.org
Web site: http://www.aksca.org

Ⓜ *Career Opportunity Grants* of up to $1,000 are awarded to cover travel costs and additional expenses for writers to take advantage of impending opportunities that will significantly advance their work or careers.

Available to: Alaska residents
Deadline: First of the month prior to activity
Apply to: Above address

Edward F. Albee Foundation
14 Harrison Street
New York, NY 10013

® The Albee Foundation offers writers and visual artists one-month residences at its center in Montauk, Long Island, from June through September. Admission is based on "talent and need." Residents are given housing but must provide their own meals. Write for guidelines.

Available to: No restrictions
Deadline: Applications accepted January 1–April 1
Apply to: Above address

Alleyway Theatre
1 Curtain Up Alley
Buffalo, NY 14202-1911

Ⓓ The *Maxim Mazumdar New Play Competition* annually offers a cash prize and production for an unproduced full-length play. A cash prize and production at Alleyway's yearly one-act festival, Buffalo Quickies, are offered also for a one-act. Work with an unconventional setting that explores the boundaries of theatricality is preferred. There is a $5 entry fee per playwright; only one submission is allowed in each category. Send SASE for return of script.

Available to: No restrictions
Deadline: July 1
Apply to: Maxim Mazumdar New Play Competition, above address

Alligator Juniper
Prescott College
301 Grove Avenue
Prescott, AZ 86301

Ⓜ The *Alligator Juniper Writing Contest* annually offers $500 each for fiction, nonfiction, and poetry. The winning entries are published in *Alligator Juniper*, the literary journal of Prescott College. Writers should submit a story or an essay, no longer than thirty pages; poets may submit up to five pages of poetry. The $10 entry fee covers an issue of the journal. Send SASE for guidelines.

Available to: No restrictions
Deadline: Submissions accepted from May 1–October 1
Apply to: Writing Contest, above address

American Academy of Arts and Letters
633 West 155th Street
New York, NY 10032

Awards and honors are conferred for work of distinction with the purpose of furthering literature and the fine arts and stimulating them in the United States. Academy members are eligible for non-monetary awards. *Applications are not accepted for any of the following. By Internal Nomination Only.*

ⒾⓃ *Academy Awards* are given to "honor and encourage distinguished artists, composers, and writers who are not members of the Academy." Eight awards in literature, of $7,500 each, are given annually.

ⒾⓃ The *Award of Merit Medal of the American Academy of Arts and Letters* consists of a medal and a cash prize of $5,000 given annually, in rotation, to an outstanding person in the United States representing the novel, the short story, poetry, drama, painting, or sculpture.

ⒾⓃ The *Michael Braude Award for Light Verse* of $5,000 is given biennially for light verse written in English, regardless of the writer's country of origin.

The *Witter Bynner Award for Poetry* of $2,500 is given annually to a young poet.

The *Gold Medal of the American Academy of Arts and Letters* is given each year, in rotation, for distinguished achievement in two categories of the arts: belles lettres and criticism, and painting; biography and music; fiction and sculpture; history and architecture (including landscape architecture); poetry and music; drama and graphic art.

The *Howells Medal of the American Academy of Arts and Letters* is given once every five years in recognition of the most distinguished work of American fiction published during that period.

The *Sue Kaufman Prize for First Fiction* of $2,500 is given annually for the best published first novel or collection of short stories of the preceding year.

The *Addison M. Metcalf Award in Literature* of $5,000 is given every year to a young writer of great promise.

The *Arthur Rense Poetry Prize* of $20,000 is given periodically to an exceptional poet.

The *Rome Fellowship in Literature* is given for a year's residence at the American Academy in Rome. This annual award is subsidized by the American Academy in Rome and the Academy of Arts and Letters. Recipients are selected by the American Academy of Arts and Letters.

The *Richard and Hilda Rosenthal Foundation Award* of $5,000 is granted annually for an American work of fiction published during the preceding twelve months that, though not a commercial success, is a considerable literary achievement.

The *Mildred and Harold Strauss Livings* provide writers of English prose literature with an annual stipend to cover living expenses so that they can devote their time exclusively to writing. The most recent Livings, each amounting to $50,000 annually, were awarded in 1998 to two writers for a period of five years. Recipients must agree to resign positions of paid employment during the term of the Livings, which will be given again in 2003.

The *Harold D. Vursell Memorial Award* of $5,000 was established in 1978 to single out recent writing in book form that merits recognition for the quality of its prose style. It may be given for fiction, biography, history, criticism, belles lettres, memoir, or journal, or for a translation rendered in distinguished and exceptional English prose.

The *Morton Dauwen Zabel Prize* of $5,000 is given every year, in rotation, to an American poet, writer of fiction, or critic.

American Academy in Berlin
14 East 60th Street, Suite 604
New York, NY 10022
E-mail: amacberlin@msn.com
Web site: http:www.amacberlin.com
Fax: 212-588-1758

® The *Berlin Prize Fellowships* are awarded to scholars, artists, and professionals who will benefit from a residential fellowship in Berlin. Candidates may come from a range of academic disciplines or fields of practice: the arts, architecture, history, philosophy, public policy, law and society, music, journalism, film, and others. Most fellows have a concurrent association with a Berlin institution, such as a museum, library, archive, or university. Benefits include a stipend ranging from $15,000 to $25,000 per semester, round-trip airfare, housing at the Hans Arnhold Center in Wannsee, and meals. Appointments are open to university faculty members, artists, and practicing professionals at early, middle, or senior levels of achievement. Write, e-mail, or visit the Web site for further information.

Available to: U.S. citizens or permanent residents

Deadline: February 1
Apply to: Above address

American Academy of Religion
825 Houston Mill Road, Suite 300
Atlanta, GA 30329
E-mail: aar@emory.edu
Web site: http://www.aar-site.org/scripts/AAR/members/resgrant.html

Ⓝ The *AAR Research Grants Program* provides support to AAR members for important aspects of research such as travel to archives and libraries, research assistance, field work, and release times. Grants range from $500 to $5,000 and may not be used for dissertation research or travel to the AAR annual meeting. Each proposal is judged on the basis of the project's contribution to scholarship in religious studies and the significance of that contribution for advancing the understanding of religion or discussion between religion and other humanistic and social science disciplines. Unaffiliated scholars and scholars in small institutions, departments, or programs without research support are encouraged to apply. Write or visit the Web site for additional information and application procedures.

Available to: AAR members
Deadline: August 1
Apply to: AAR Research Grants Program, above address

American Academy in Rome
7 East 60th Street
New York, NY 10022-1001
Web site: http://www.aarome.org

Ⓡ The Academy's *Rome Prize Competition* offers up to thirty fellowships with stipends of $9,000 to $17,800 for individuals of exceptional promise or achievement in architecture, landscape architecture, conservation and preservation, design, literature, musical composition, visual arts, archaeology, classical studies, history of art, modern Italian studies, and postclassical humanistic studies. Fellows receive free housing, a study or studio, and full access to library and other facilities. Applicants should be U.S. citizens with a bachelor's or master's degree, depending on the field of application. Some fellowships are open to postdoctoral candidates. There is no formal application process for the prize in literature; nominations for that award are made only by members of the American Academy of Arts and Letters (see listing above). Applications for other fields may be downloaded from the Web site.

Available to: See above
Deadline: November 15
Apply to: Programs Department, above address

American Antiquarian Society
185 Salisbury Street
Worcester, MA 01609-1634
E-mail: jdm@mwa.org
Fax: 508-754-9069

Ⓡ *Long-Term Postdoctoral Fellowships* provide support for four-to-twelve-month residences in the Society's library and carry stipends of up to $35,000. These include the *AAS–National Endowment for the Humanities Fellowships*, with a maximum stipend of $30,000, and the *Mellon Postdoctoral Research Fellowships*, with a maximum stipend of $35,000. The latter is awarded for an academic year (nine or ten months).

Ⓡ *Short-Term Fellowships* provide support for one to three months' residence in the Society's library and carry stipends of $950 per month. These include the *Kate B. and Hall J. Peterson Fellowship* and the *Legacy Fellowship*, for research on any topic supported by the collections; the *Stephen Botein Fellowships*, for research in the history of the book in American culture; the *AAS–American Society for Eighteenth-Century Studies Fellowships*, for research on projects related to the American eighteenth century; the *American Historical Print Collectors Society Fellowship*, for research on American prints of the eighteenth and nineteenth centuries or for projects using prints as primary documentation; the *Joyce A. Tracy Fellowship*, for research on newspapers and magazines or for projects using these as primary documentation; the *Reese Fellowship* for bibliographical research and projects in the history of the book in American culture; the *AAS–Northeast Modern Language Association Fellowship* for research in American literary studies through 1876; and the *Richard F. and Virginia P. Morgan Fellowship* for research on Ohio history or utilizing Ohio-printed materials in bibliography, the history of the book, or both. Application packets, with full details about the fellowships, including restrictions that apply, must be requested before an application is made. Write, e-mail, or fax for materials.

Available to: See above
Deadline: January 15
Apply to: Above address

® At least three *Visiting Fellowships for Historical Research by Creative and Performing Artists and Writers* will be awarded, for four-to-eight-week residences at the Society. The stipend is $1,200 per four-week period, plus an allowance for travel expenses. (There are no funds available for housing, which is, however, available in the Society's Goddard-Daniels House. Room rents range from $295 to $495 per week.) The Society seeks fellows whose goals are to produce works on pre-twentieth-century American history intended for the general public rather than for academic or educational communities. Research and study carried out under these fellowships may focus on virtually any subject within the general area of American history and culture before 1877. The end products of research developed under these fellowships may include but are not limited to historical novels, historical nonfiction designed for general audiences of adults or children, plays or screenplays, and magazine or newspaper articles. Write for additional information and guidelines.

Available to: No restrictions
Deadline: October (inquire for exact date)
Apply to: James David Moran, above address

American Association for the Advancement of Science
1200 New York Avenue
Washington, DC 20005
E-mail: media@aaas.org

Ⓙ The *AAAS Science Journalism Awards* are given "for outstanding journalism on the sciences and their engineering and technological applications in newspapers, general-circulation magazines, radio, and television." Entries are judged on the basis of initiative, originality, scientific accuracy, clarity of interpretation, and value in promoting the understanding of science by the public. There are five awards, of $2,500 each: for writing in newspapers with a circulation of more than 100,000; for writing in newspapers with a daily circulation of less than 100,000; for writing in general-circulation magazines; for radio writing; and for television writing. Entries must have been published in a newspaper or magazine or aired in the United States during the contest year, which runs from July 1 through June 30 of the following year.

Available to: See above
Deadline: August 1
Apply to: Office of News and Information, AAAS Science Journalism Awards, above address

American Association of University Women
2201 North Dodge Street
Iowa City, IA 52243-4030

The AAUW Educational Foundation offers a variety of fellowships and grants to help women reach their personal and professional goals, including: *American Fellowships*, which support women doctoral candidates writing dissertations and scholars seeking postdoctoral/research leave funds; *Career Development Grants*, for women in the early stages of graduate studies preparing to reenter the work force, change careers, or advance their current career; and *International Fellowships*, for full-time graduate or postgraduate study or research abroad. Stipends vary. Write for additional information and application procedures.

Available to: American women

Deadline: Varies according to program (inquire)
Apply to: AAUW Educational Foundation, above address

American Booksellers Association
828 South Broadway
Tarrytown, NY 10591
E-mail: jill@bookweb.org
Web site: http://www.bookweb.org

[IN] The *Abby Award* annually offers a $5,000 prize for the adult and children's book "hidden treasures" that members of the American Booksellers Association most enjoyed recommending to their customers during the previous year. ABA members may nominate any trade book published within the calendar year for the award; members elect the winner from the five titles that receive the most nominations. There is no application process. *By Internal Nomination Only.*

American Chemical Society
1155 16th Street, NW
Washington, DC 20036

ⓙ The *James T. Grady–James H. Stack Award for Interpreting Chemistry for the Public* is given to recognize, encourage, and stimulate outstanding reporting directly to the American public that increases knowledge and understanding of chemistry, chemical engineering, and related fields. This information must have been disseminated through the press, radio, television, film, lecture, or book or pamphlet for the lay public. The award, which consists of $3,000 and a gold medal, is given annually. Recipients must be nominated by a colleague for a career accomplishment.

Available to: No restrictions
Deadline: February 1
Apply to: James T. Grady–James H. Stack Award, above address

American Council of Learned Societies
228 East 45th Street
New York, NY 10017
E-mail: Grants@acls.org
Web site: http://www.acls.org
Fax: 212-949-8058

The Council offers various types of grants for which scholars may qualify, when doing research in the humanities and humanities-related social sciences.

Fellowships are given for holders of a doctorate or its equivalent tenable in the United States or abroad, with specialized fellowships for dissertation or postdoctoral work in American art, Eastern European studies, Chinese studies, and contemplative practice. Stipends and fellowship tenure periods vary by program. Contact ACLS for additional information.

Available to: U.S. citizens and permanent residents
Deadline: Varies (inquire for exact dates)
Apply to: Office of Fellowships, above address

American Dreamer Independent Filmworks
PO Box 20457
Seattle, WA 98102
E-mail: american_dreamer@bigfoot.com
Web site http://adfilmworks.com
Fax: 206-320-7724

ⓢ The *American Dreamer Script Competition* offers an acquisition award of $5,000 for each writing sample accepted as an outstanding production option. Submissions may be in the form of a completed or unfinished screenplay, treatment, or step outline. There is a $50 entry fee. Write, e-mail, or visit the Web site for guidelines and application packet.

Available to: Writers at least 18 years old

Deadline: July 4, 2000; inquire for 2001
Apply to: American Dreamer 2000, above address

American Historical Association
400 A Street, SE
Washington, DC 20003
E-mail: aha@theaha.org
Web site: http://www.theaha.org
Fax: 202-544-8307

Albert J. Beveridge Grants of up to $1,000 are offered annually to AHA members to support research in the history of the Western Hemisphere.

Available to: AHA members
Deadline: February 1
Apply to: Above address

The *J. Franklin Jameson Fellowship*, co-sponsored by the Library of Congress and the AHA, awards a stipend of $10,000 to a young historian for significant scholarly research in the collections of the Library.

Available to: No restrictions
Deadline: January 15
Apply to: Above address

Michael Kraus Research Grants of up to $800 are offered to AHA members for research in American colonial history, with particular reference to the intercultural aspects of American and European relations.

Available to: AHA members
Deadline: February 1
Apply to: Above address

Littleton–Griswold Research Grants of up to $1,000 are offered to AHA members to support research in American legal history and the field of law and society.

Available to: AHA members
Deadline: February 1
Apply to: Above address

The *NASA Fellowship* annually provides applicants of unusual ability the opportunity to engage in significant and sustained advanced research in NASA aerospace science, technology, management, or policy. The fellowship awards a stipend of $25,000 to postdoctoral candidates and $16,000 to predoctoral.

Available to: U.S. citizens
Deadline: February 15
Apply to: Above address

Bernadette E. Schmitt Research Grants of up to $1,000 are offered annually to AHA members to support research in the history of Europe, Africa, and Asia.

Available to: AHA members
Deadline: September 1
Apply to: Above address

Cash stipends for the following awards vary from year to year. For exact amounts, query the American Historical Association. Updated applications/guidelines are available approximately two months before the submission deadline; obtain current guidelines before submission. Do not send books directly to the AHA for consideration. Current guidelines will provide addresses of judging committee members.

Ⓝ The *Herbert Baxter Adams Prize* is awarded for an author's first book on ancient, medieval, or early modern European history.

Available to: U.S. and Canadian residents

Deadline: May 15
Apply to: Above address

(N) The *George Louis Beer Prize* is awarded annually in recognition of outstanding historical writing by a U.S. citizen on European international history since 1895.

Available to: U.S. citizens
Deadline: May 15
Apply to: Above address

(N) The *Albert J. Beveridge Award* is given annually for the best book on the history of the Americas (the United States, Canada, or Latin America) from 1492 to the present.

Available to: No restrictions
Deadline: May 15
Apply to: Above address

(N) The *Paul Birdsall Prize* is awarded biennially for a major work on European military history and strategic history.

Available to: U.S. or Canadian citizens
Deadline: May 15, 2000 (inquire for 2002)
Apply to: Above address

(N) The *James Henry Breasted Prize* is offered annually for the best book in any field of history before the year 1000.

Available to: No restrictions
Deadline: May 15
Apply to: Above address

(N) The *Albert B. Corey Prize in Canadian–American Relations* is awarded biennially for the best book on the history of Canadian–American relations or the history of both countries. The prize is awarded jointly by the Canadian Historical Association and the AHA.

Available to: No restrictions
Deadline: May 15
Apply to: Above address

(N) The *Premio del Rey* is awarded in even-numbered years for the best book in English on Hispanic history and culture in Spain and/or other Hispanic countries before 1516.

Available to: No restrictions
Deadline: May 15, 2000
Apply to: Above address

(N) The *John H. Dunning Prize* is awarded in odd-numbered years for an author's first or second book on any subject relating to U.S. history.

Available to: No restrictions
Deadline: May 15, 2001
Apply to: Above address

(N) The *John K. Fairbank Prize in East Asian History* is awarded annually for an outstanding book on the history of China proper, Chinese Central Asia, Japan, Korea, Mongolia, or Vietnam since 1800.

Available to: No restrictions
Deadline: May 15
Apply to: Above address

(N) The *Herbert Feis Award*, funded by a grant from the Rockefeller Foundation, is given annually for the best book, article, or policy paper by an independent scholar or public historian.

Available to: No restrictions
Deadline: May 15
Apply to: Above address

(N) The *Morris O. Forkosch Prize* is given annually for the best work published on modern British,

British imperial, and British Commonwealth history by a U.S. citizen.

Available to: U.S. citizens
Deadline: May 15
Apply to: Above address

Ⓝ The *Leo Gershoy Award* is given annually to the author of the most outstanding work in English on any aspect of seventeenth- and/or eighteenth-century European history.

Available to: No restrictions
Deadline: May 15
Apply to: Above address

Ⓝ The *Clarence H. Haring Prize* is awarded every five years to the Latin American who has published the most outstanding book of Latin American history during the preceding five years.

Available to: Latin American historians
Deadline: May 15, 2001
Apply to: Above address

Ⓝ The *J. Franklin Jameson Prize* is a quinquennial award for outstanding achievement in the editing of historical sources; it will be granted next in 2005.

Available to: No restrictions
Deadline: May 15, 2005
Apply to: Above address

Ⓝ The *Joan Kelly Memorial Prize in Women's History* is offered annually for the best work in women's history and/or feminist theory.

Available to: No restrictions
Deadline: May 15
Apply to: Above address

Ⓝ The *Waldo G. Leland Prize*, offered for the most outstanding reference tool in the field of history, is given quinquennially. The award will be given next in 2001.

Available to: No restrictions
Deadline: May 15, 2001
Apply to: Above address

Ⓝ The *Littleton–Griswold Prize* is offered annually for the best book on any subject in the history of American law and society.

Available to: No restrictions
Deadline: May 15
Apply to: Above address

Ⓝ The *Helen and Howard R. Marraro Prize* is given for the best work on any epoch of Italian history or cultural history or on Italian–American relations.

Available to: U.S. and Canadian residents
Deadline: May 15
Apply to: Above address

Ⓝ The *James Harvey Robinson Prize* is awarded in even-numbered years for the teaching aid that has made the greatest contribution to the teaching of history.

Available to: No restrictions
Deadline: May 15, 2002
Apply to: Above address

Ⓝ The *Wesley–Logan Prize* is given annually for an outstanding book on any aspect of the dispersion, settlement, and adjustment of peoples originally from Africa, or their return.

Available to: No restrictions
Deadline: May 15
Apply to: Above address

American Institute of Indian Studies
University of Chicago
1130 East 59th Street
Chicago, IL 60637
E-mail: aiis@uchicago.edu
Web site: http://humanities.uchicago.edu/orgs/aiis/

The American Institute of Indian Studies annually offers *Senior Research Fellowships* (postdoctoral), *Senior Scholarly Development Fellowships*, *Junior Fellowships* (doctoral), and *Senior Performing Arts Fellowships* for research in India. Award funds are made available in foreign currency only. Requirements vary; query the Institute before applying. (Also available is a limited intensive-language program in India; contact the Institute for further information and deadline.)

> Available to: U.S. citizens at the doctoral or postdoctoral level and foreign nationals enrolled at the doctoral level or teaching full-time (postdoctoral) at American colleges or universities. U.S. and Indian government employees are ineligible.
> Deadline: July 1
> Apply to: Above address

American Institute of Physics
Public Information Division
One Physics Ellipse
College Park, MD 20740
E-mail: kheinema@aip.org
Fax: 301-209-0846

Ⓝ The *Writing Awards in Physics and Astronomy* are given to stimulate and recognize distinguished writing that improves public understanding of physics and astronomy. Entries must be articles, booklets, or books written in English. Material from professional scientific, technical, and trade publications is not eligible. Three prizes of $3,000 each are awarded annually in journalism, science writing, children's literature, and broadcast media.

> Available to: U.S., Canadian, and Mexican residents
> Deadlines: Journalism: February 6; science: July 23; children's literature: July 24; broadcast media: August 6
> Apply to: Above address

American Jewish Archives
3101 Clifton Avenue
Cincinnati, OH 45220
E-mail: aja@huc.edu
Web site: http://www.huc.edu/aja

Fellowships for active research or writing at the American Jewish Archives are offered to doctoral and postdoctoral candidates in American Jewish studies and to unaffiliated, independent, and senior scholars. Stipends are sufficient to cover living expenses while in residence in Cincinnati. Write, e-mail, or visit the Web site for further information and application guidelines.

> Available to: No restrictions
> Deadline: April 1
> Apply to: Administrative Director, above address

The American Legion
Public Relations Division
700 North Pennsylvania Street
Indianapolis, IN 46204
E-mail: pr@legion.org
Web site: http://www.legion.org

Ⓙ The *American Legion Fourth Estate Award* is given for the best work published or broadcast during the calendar year that "covers an issue of national interest and contributes to the

American way of life." A stipend of $2,000 accompanies the award to defray the recipient's expenses in accepting the award at the American Legion National Convention in September. Each entry must include a cover letter explaining the entry, and documentation or evidence of the entry's impact on the community, state, or nation. Write or visit the Web site for additional information.

Available to: No restrictions
Deadline: January 31
Apply to: Fourth Estate Award, above address

American Library Association
50 East Huron Street
Chicago, IL 60611
E-mail: awards@ala.org
Web site: http://www.ala.org

Ⓜ The *Gay, Lesbian, Bisexual, and Transgendered (GLBT) Book Award* is given annually to English-language books of exceptional merit relating to gay, lesbian, bisexual, and transgendered experience. Awards are made in literature, which includes novels, short stories, poetry, and drama, and in nonfiction, which includes biography, history, criticism, reference works, fine arts, and other traditional nonfiction genres. Each winner receives a commemorative plaque and a cash stipend to be determined by the GLBT Round Table of the American Library Association. Nominations for books published between December 1 of the previous year and November 30 of the current year may be made by the general public, librarians, or members of the GLBT Round Table. Write, e-mail, or visit the Web site for additional information.

Available to: No restrictions
Deadline: November 30
Apply to: GLBT Book Award, GLBT Round Table, above address

Ⓒ The *Coretta Scott King Award* is given annually by the Social Responsibilities Round Table (SRRT) of the American Library Association to honor African-American authors and illustrators for "outstanding contributions to children's and young adult literature that promote understanding and appreciation of the culture and contribution of all people to the realization of the American Dream." Winners receive a framed citation, an honorarium, and a set of the *Encyclopaedia Britannica* or *World Book Encyclopedia*. The SRRT also offers the *Coretta Scott King/John Steptoe Award for New Talent*, which is given to a black author and a black illustrator at the beginning of their careers. Candidates for the New Talent award cannot have published more than three books. Write, e-mail, or visit the Web site for additional information.

Available to: African-Americans
Deadline: Inquire
Apply to: Coretta Scott King Award or Coretta Scott King/John Steptoe Award, SRRT, above address

Ⓝ The *Eli M. Oboler Memorial Award* biennially offers $1,500 for a published work in English or in English translation dealing with issues, events, or questions in the area of intellectual freedom. Nominated books must be published in the two-year period prior to the year in which the award is granted.

Available to: No restrictions
Deadline: December 1
Apply to: Eli M. Oboler Memorial Award, Office for Intellectual Freedom, IRFT Staff Liaison, above address

Ⓕ The *Bill Boyd Library Literature Award* of $10,000 is given for the best book-length work of fiction set in a period when the United States was at war. The award recognizes the service of American veterans and military personnel and encourages the writing and publishing of outstanding war-related fiction. Publishers or authors should submit six copies of the work; the book must have been published during the year prior to the submission deadline. Write for additional information.

Available to: No restrictions
Deadline: December 1
Apply to: ALA Awards Program, Member Programs and Services, above address

American Literary Review
University of North Texas
English Department
Denton, TX 76203-1307
Web site: http://www.engl.unt.edu/alr

Ⓕ Ⓟ The *American Literary Review Short Fiction Contest* awards $500 and publication for a short story of 10,000 words or less in odd-numbered years. In even-numbered years, the review sponsors its *Poetry Contest.* There is a $10 reading fee, for which each entrant will receive a copy of the spring issue of the *Review,* in which the winning story or poem appears. Send SASE or visit the Web site for guidelines.

Available to: No restrictions
Deadline: October 1
Apply to: Short Fiction or Poetry Contest, above address

American Literary Translators Association
University of Texas at Dallas
Box 830688 (MC 35)
Richardson, TX 75083-0688
Fax: 972-883-6303

Ⓣ The ALTA *National Translation Award,* funded by the Larry McMurtry Center for the Arts and Humanities and the Simon H. Rifkind Center for the Humanities, offers a cash prize of at least $2,000 for an English translation of a book-length work of fiction, poetry, drama, or creative nonfiction published during the calendar year. Literary criticism and philosophy are not eligible. Publishers must provide an original-language version of all books selected as finalists by August 1; finalists will be excluded from further consideration if no original-language version is provided. Translations of contemporary works receive preference, although important retranslations or first-time translations of older works are also considered if they make significant contributions to literature. Publishers should submit a letter of nomination and three copies of each nominated book. Write for additional information.

Available to: No restrictions
Deadline: March 31
Apply to: ALTA National Translation Award, above address

American Musicological Society
201 South 34th Street
Philadelphia, PA 19104-6313
E-mail: ams@sas.upenn.edu
Web site: http://www.sas.upenn.edu/music/ams

Ⓝ The *Philip Brett Award* of $500 is given each year to honor an exceptional musicological work in the field of gay, lesbian, bisexual, or transgender/transsexual studies completed during two academic years in any country and in any language. This work may be a published article, book, edition, annotated translation, paper read at a conference, teaching material, or other scholarly product. Write for additional information.

Available to: No restrictions
Deadline: July 1
Apply to: Consult AMS directory for name and address of committee chairperson

Ⓝ The *Alfred Einstein Award* is given annually for a musicological article of exceptional merit by a scholar in the early stages of his or her career. The article must have been published during the preceding calendar year, in any country and in any language. The award consists of $400 and a certificate signed by the president of the Society.

Available to: U.S. and Canadian citizens or permanent residents
Deadline: June 1
Apply to: Consult AMS directory for name and address of committee chairperson

Ⓝ The *Otto Kinkeldey Award* is given each year for the work of musicological scholarship deemed by a committee of scholars to be the most distinguished published during the previous year in any language and in any country. The award consists of $400 and a certificate signed by the president of the Society.

Available to: U.S. and Canadian citizens and permanent residents
Deadline: None
Apply to: Consult AMS directory for name and address of committee chairperson

Ⓝ The *Paul A. Pisk Prize* of $1,000 is awarded annually to a music graduate student for a scholarly paper, which will be read at the annual meeting of the Society. Write for guidelines.

Available to: No restrictions
Deadline: Inquire
Apply to: Consult AMS directory for name and address of committee chairperson

American Poetry Review
1721 Walnut Street
Philadelphia, PA 19103

Ⓟ The *American Poetry Review/Honickman First Book Prize* awards $3,000 and publication of a book-length volume of poems to a poet who has never published a book of poems. The winning volume will be distributed by Copper Canyon Press through Consortium. There is a $20 entry fee. Send SASE for guidelines.

Available to: U.S. citizens
Deadline: Submissions accepted August 1–October 31
Apply to: APR/Honickman First Book Prize, above address

Ⓟ The *S. J. Marks Memorial Poetry Prize* of $500 is awarded annually for a writer's first appearance in *American Poetry Review* during the preceding calendar year.

Available to: See above
Deadline: Ongoing
Apply to: Submit manuscripts to above address with SASE

Ⓟ The *Jerome J. Shestack Poetry Prizes* of $1,000 are awarded annually to each of two poets whose work has appeared in the *Review* during the preceding calendar year.

Available to: Poets whose work has appeared in *APR*
Deadline: Ongoing
Apply to: Submit manuscripts to above address with SASE

American Political Science Association
1527 New Hampshire Avenue, NW
Washington, DC 20036-1206
E-mail: apsa@apsanet.org
Web site: http://www.apsanet.org
Fax: 202-483-2657

Ⓙ The *APSA Congressional Fellowship Program,* funded in part by MCI WorldCom, is designed to bring academics, political reporters, and scholars to Washington to work as legislative aides on Capitol Hill. The fellowship period is divided into three general parts: a month-long orientation (early November to early December); a congressional office assignment (early December to mid-April); and for many, a second assignment (mid-April to mid-August). Fellows receive a stipend of $30,000 plus travel allowance. Interested journalists must have a bachelor's degree and two to ten years' full-time professional experience in newspaper, magazine, radio, or television reporting; scholars must have completed a Ph.D. in the last fifteen years or be near completion. Preference is given to applicants without extensive experience in Washington. Write, e-mail, or visit the Web site for additional information.

Available to: See above
Deadline: December 1
Apply to: Director, Congressional Fellowship Program, above address

American Psychiatric Association
Division of Public Affairs/Media Awards
1400 K Street, NW
Washington, DC 20005

Ⓙ The *Robert T. Morse Writers Award* of $1,000 is given annually to popular newswriters or
groups of writers who have covered the mental health/illness field over an extended
period or who have written an exemplary article or series for the general public on mental
health/illness topics and the role of psychiatry. For the next award, articles must have
been published between August 1, 1999, and July 31, 2000. Write for additional information
and entry form.

Available to: No restrictions
Deadline: August 31
Apply to: Robert T. Morse Writers Award, above address

American Research Center in Egypt
30 East 20th Street, Suite 401
New York, NY 10003-1310

The *American Research Center in Egypt Fellowship Program* is designed to "promote a fresh and
more profound knowledge of Egypt and the Near East through scholarly research and to
aid in the training of American specialists in Middle Eastern studies in academic disciplines
that require familiarity with Egypt." Fellowships are for three-to-twelve-month periods
and include the *Islamicist-in-Residence Program,* for a postdoctoral scholar wishing to spend
up to a year in Cairo carrying out a specific research project, and the *Kress Fellowship in
Egyptian Art and Architecture* of $15,000 for a predoctoral student. Write for additional
information and application form.

Available to: Pre- and postdoctoral scholars (predoctoral must be U.S. citizens; postdoctoral
may be U.S. citizens, or foreign citizens who have held a teaching position at a U.S.
university for a minimum of three years)
Deadline: October 1
Apply to: Above address

American–Scandinavian Foundation
115 East 65th Street
New York, NY 10021
E-mail: grants@amscan.org
Web site: http://www.amscan.org
Fax: 212-249-3444

To encourage research and increase understanding between the United States and Denmark,
Finland, Iceland, Norway, and Sweden, the Foundation administers fellowships and grants
for qualified university graduates to undertake study projects that make a stay in Scandinavia
essential. Approximately twenty-five awards, ranging from $3,000 to $18,000, are given annually.

Available to: U.S. citizens and permanent residents
Deadline: November 1 (for the following academic year)
Apply to: Exchange Division, above address

Ⓣ The *ASF Translation Prize* is offered annually by the Foundation for the best translation into
English of poetry, fiction, drama, or literary prose by a Scandinavian author born after
1800. The award includes $2,000, publication in an issue of *Scandinavian Review*, and a
bronze medallion. The *Inger Sjöberg Award* of $500 is given to the runner-up. For rules
and instructions, write to the Foundation.

Available to: No restrictions
Deadline: June 1
Apply to: Translation Prize, above address

American Society of Church History
PO Box 8517
Red Bank, NJ 07701

Ⓝ The *Frank S. and Elizabeth D. Brewer Prize* offers $1,000 to assist an author in publishing a first book-length manuscript on church history. The winning manuscript will be published in a manner acceptable to the Society. If competing essays are of equal quality, preference is given to topics relating to the history of Congregationalism.

    Available to: First-book authors
    Deadline: November 1
    Apply to: Henry W. Bowden, Secretary, Frank S. and Elizabeth D. Brewer Prize, above address

American Society of Composers, Authors, and Publishers
One Lincoln Plaza
New York, NY 10023

Ⓙ The *ASCAP–Deems Taylor Awards* are given in two categories: best nonfiction book and best nonfiction newspaper or magazine article about music and/or its creators. Works may be biographical or critical, reportorial or historical, but not textbooks, how-to guides, or fiction.They must have been published in the United States in English during the calendar year under review. The book award is $500 and a plaque; the article award, $250 and a plaque.

    Available to: No restrictions
    Deadline: April 30
    Apply to: ASCAP–Deems Taylor Awards, above address

American Society for Eighteenth-Century Studies
Wake Forest University
PO Box 7867
Winston-Salem, NC 27109
E-mail: asecs@wfu.edu
Fax: 336-727-4697

Ⓝ The *James L. Clifford Prize* of $500 is awarded annually for an outstanding article appearing in a festschrift, or a journal or other serial publication. The article must be a study of some aspect of eighteenth-century culture of interest to any eighteenth-century specialist, regardless of discipline. The article may be nominated by a member of the Society, its author, or the editor of the publishing journal. Nominations must be accompanied by eight copies of the article.

    Available to: Society members
    Deadline: January 1
    Apply to: Byron R. Wells, Executive Director, above address

Ⓝ The *Louis Gottschalk Prize* of $1,000 is awarded annually for an outstanding historical or critical study on a subject of eighteenth-century interest. Eligible books are commentaries, critical studies, biographies, and critical editions, which may be written in any modern language; books that are primarily translations are not eligible. Books must have been published between the November 1 preceding and October 31 of the award year.

    Available to: Society members
    Deadline: November 15
    Apply to: Byron R. Wells, Executive Director, above address

American Society of Journalists and Authors Charitable Trust
1501 Broadway, Suite 302
New York, NY 10036

The *Llewellyn Miller Fund* is open to professional freelance writers of nonfiction books and magazine articles who are sixty or older, disabled, or in an extraordinary professional crisis, and in financial need. The Fund provides grants of up to $3,500. Proof of professional freelance work must be supplied.

Available to: See above
Deadline: None
Apply to: Murray Teigh Bloom, Chairman, above address

American Society of Magazine Editors
919 Third Avenue
New York, NY 10022

The *Magazine Internship Program,* a ten-week summer session during which students learn about magazines by working in the editorial offices of consumer magazines and business publications, is available to college students between their junior and senior years. Applicants must be journalism majors or liberal arts majors who have held responsible positions on a campus magazine, newspaper, or yearbook and have had at least one summer job or internship in journalism. Interns will be temporary employees of the magazines to which they are assigned and will be paid a minimum weekly stipend of $325 (before deductions). The emphasis of the program is on editing; at some magazines there may be some reporting and writing. Interns are responsible for their own travel, housing, food, and personal expenses; ASME will assist in making dormitory arrangements in New York and Washington, D.C. Applications are available through college deans, department heads, or professors.

Available to: See above
Deadline: December 15
Apply to: Magazine Internship Program, above address

American Translators Association
Honors and Awards Committee
225 Reinekers Lane #590
Alexandria, VA 22314
E-mail: ata@atanet.org
Web site: http://www.atanet.org
Fax: 703-683-6122

Ⓣ The *ATA German Literary Translation Prize* of $1,000 is awarded in odd-numbered years for translations from the German into English that have been published, as a single volume or as part of a collection, by an American publisher in the United States within the two years preceding the prize year. Submit two copies of the book and 10 pages of the German original.

Available to: No restrictions
Deadline: Inquire
Apply to: German Literary Translation Prize, above address

Ⓣ The *Lewis Galantiere Prize* of $1,000 is awarded in even-numbered years for distinguished published literary works translated from any language other than German into English. Submit two copies of the book and 10 pages of the original.

Available to: No restrictions
Deadline: Inquire
Apply to: Lewis Galantiere Prize, above address

Amherst Writers and Artists Press
PO Box 1076
Amherst, MA 01004
E-mail: awapress@javanet.com
Web site: http://www.javanet.com/~awapress

Ⓕ Ⓟ The *Peregrine Prize* consists of three awards: $500 and publication in *Peregrine* for a short story; $500 and publication in *Peregrine* for a poem; and $100 and publication in *Peregrine* for the "Best of the Nest," which is given to a western Massachusetts writer. Winners will receive two copies of the publication issue. Poets should send three poems, no more than 70 lines total. Fiction writers should send a manuscript of no more than 3,000 words. The entry fee is $10. Send SASE or visit the Web site for guidelines.

Available to: See above for "Best of the Nest"
Deadline: April 1
Apply to: Peregrine Prize, above address

Amy Foundation
PO Box 16091
Lansing, MI 48901
E-mail: Amyfoundtn@aol.com
Web site: http://www.amyfound.org
Fax: 517-323-7293

(N)   The *Amy Foundation Writing Awards* offer a $10,000 first prize, a $5,000 second prize, a $4,000 third prize, a $3,000 fourth prize, a $2,000 fifth prize, plus ten prizes of $1,000 each, for "creative, skillful writing that presents in a sensitive, thought-provoking manner the biblical position on issues affecting the world today." Submitted articles must have been published in a secular, nonreligious publication during the preceding calendar year.

Available to: No restrictions; U.S. citizens preferred
Deadline: January 31
Apply to: Writing Awards, above address

Anamnesis Press
PO Box 51115
Palo Alto, CA 94303
E-mail: anamnesis@compuserve.com (for queries only)
Web site: http://ourworld.compuserve.com/homepages/anamnesis
Fax: 510-481-7193

(P)   The annual *Anamnesis Poetry Chapbook Award Competition* offers a prize of $1,000, chapbook publication, and 20 author's copies. Poets should submit a manuscript of 20 to 30 pages, with an entry fee of $15. No e-mail submissions accepted. Send SASE or visit the Web site for guidelines.

Available to: No restrictions
Deadline: Submissions must be postmarked by March 15 (notification in June)
Apply to: Poetry Chapbook Award, above address

Mary Anderson Center for the Arts
101 St. Francis Drive
Mount St. Francis, IN 47146
E-mail: maca@iglou.com
Fax: 812-923-3200

(R)   Residences at the Center, which is a fifteen-minute drive north of Louisville, Kentucky, are available from one week to three months for seven writers and visual artists concurrently. Residents pay what they can afford, with a suggested minimum of $30 per day. Residence fellowships are sometimes available. Private studio/bedroom and communal kitchen and dining room are provided, as are meals. Write for further information and guidelines.

Available to: No restrictions
Deadline: Ongoing
Apply to: Debra Carmody, Executive Director, above address

Anhinga Press
PO Box 10595
Tallahassee, FL 32302
Web site: http://www.anhinga.org
Fax: 850-442-6323

(P)   The *Anhinga Prize for Poetry* is awarded annually for a book-length manuscript of original poetry in English. The winner receives $2,000 and publication by Anhinga. There is a $20 reading fee. Send SASE for application instructions.

Available to: No restrictions
Deadline: Submissions accepted January 1–March 31
Apply to: Above address

Another Chicago Magazine
3709 North Kenmore
Chicago, IL 60613
Web site: http://www.anotherchicagomag.com

Ⓕ Ⓟ The *Chicago Literary Awards* offer $1,000 each for an unpublished short story and a poem, plus publication in *Another Chicago Magazine*, a semi-annual journal of fiction, poetry, essays, and art. Writers may submit stories of no more than 6,500 words or up to three poems of no more than 300 lines total. The entry fee is $10. Send SASE for guidelines.

Available to: No restrictions
Deadline: Submissions must be postmarked by December 15
Apply to: Chicago Literary Awards, above address

Anthology of New England Writers
PO Box 483
Windsor, VT 05089
E-mail: newvtpoet@aol.com

Ⓕ Ⓟ The New England Writers Free Verse Contest offers the *Robert Penn Warren Awards* of $500, $200, and $150. The Short Fiction Contest offers the *Marjory Bartlett Sanger Award* of $500. Free-verse submissions should be no longer than 30 lines; short fiction entries no more than 1,000 words. There is a $6 entry fee for three poems or one piece of short fiction; $5 each for two or more entries.

Available to: No restrictions
Deadline: June 15
Apply to: Frank Anthony, above address

Apostle Islands National Lakeshore
Route 1, Box 4
Bayfield, WI 54814
Web site: http://www.nps.gov/apis
Fax: 715-779-3049

Ⓡ Apostle Islands National Lakeshore and the Chequamegon Bay Area Arts Council sponsor an *Artist-in-Residence* program for creative artists with accomplishment, integrity, and the ability to relate to the park through their work. Residences of two to three weeks are offered to one writer, poet, visual artist, or choreographer at a time in a rustic lakeside cabin on Sand Island, from late June through mid-September. Each artist must bring his or her own supply of food, and each should contribute to the park a piece of work representative of the stay, and share experiences with the public by demonstration, talk, or other means during the stay. Write or visit the Web site for additional information and application.

Available to: No restrictions
Deadline: January 15
Apply to: Above address

Archaeological Institute of America
656 Beacon Street, 4th floor
Boston, MA 02215-2010
E-mail: aia@bu.edu
Fax: 617-353-6550

The *Anna C. and Oliver C. Colburn Fellowship* of $14,000 is awarded biennially to an incoming or student associate member of the American School of Classical Studies in Athens. Candidates must apply concurrently to the American School for associate membership.

Available to: U.S. or Canadian citizens or permanent residents
Deadline: Inquire for 2002
Apply to: Colburn Fellowship, above address

The *Kenan T. Erim Award*, established by the American Friends of Aphrodisias, awards $4,000 annually to an American or international research and/or excavating scholar working on Aphrodisias material.

Available to: No restrictions
Deadline: November 1
Apply to: Erim Award, above address

The *Olivia James Traveling Fellowships* of $22,000 are awarded for an academic year to students desiring to travel and study in Greece, the Aegean Islands, Sicily, southern Italy, Asia Minor, or Mesopotamia. The classics, sculpture, architecture, archaeology, and history are the most suitable areas of study. The word "student" does not mean only individuals registered in academic institutions.

Available to: U.S. citizens or permanent residents
Deadline: November 1
Apply to: James Fellowship, above address

The *Harriet and Leon Pomerance Fellowship* is awarded for work on an individual project of a scholarly nature relating to Aegean Bronze Age archaeology. Preference is given to candidates whose project requires travel to the Mediterranean. One fellowship carrying a stipend of $4,000 is available annually.

Available to: U.S. and Canadian residents
Deadline: November 1
Apply to: Pomerance Fellowship, above address

Ariadne Press
4817 Tallahassee Avenue
Rockville, MD 20853

Ⓕ A *Fiction Prize* awards $500 and publication by Ariadne Press for a novel in the literary/mainstream tradition. Manuscripts should be between 175 and 350 pages; short story collections are not eligible. There is a $50 reading fee, which covers a brief critique. Manuscripts will not be returned. Enclose SASE for announcement of winner and finalists.

Available to: No restrictions
Deadline: Inquire
Apply to: Fiction Prize, above address

Arizona Commission on the Arts
417 West Roosevelt
Phoenix, AZ 85003
E-mail: general@ArizonaArts.org
Web site: http://az.arts.asu.edu/artscomm
Fax: 602-256-0282

Ⓜ Poetry, playwriting, and fiction fellowships, of no less than $5,000 and no more than $7,500, are available in rotating years to Arizona residents at least eighteen years of age who are not students.

Available to: See above
Deadline: Inquire
Apply to: Jill Bernstein, Literature Director, above address

Arizona Theatre Company
Box 1631
Tucson, AZ 85702

Ⓓ The *National Hispanic Playwriting Contest* awards $1,000 and possible inclusion in ATC's

Genesis: New Play Reading series for a full-length play or adaptation by a playwright of Hispanic heritage residing in the United States, its territories, or Mexico. Plays may be in English or in Spanish with an English translation. The contest is sponsored in association with the Centro Cultural Mexicano de Phoenix. Write for guidelines.

Available to: See above
Deadline: October 31
Apply to: National Hispanic Playwriting Contest, above address

Arrowhead Regional Arts Council
101 West Second Street, Suite 204
Duluth, MN 55802-2086
E-mail: ARACouncil@aol.com
Web site: http://members.aol.com/ARACouncil
Fax: 218-722-4459

Ⓜ The Council annually offers *Individual Artists Fellowships* of $4,500 to writers in the seven-county Arrowhead region of Minnesota. Write for further information.

Available to: Residents of the Arrowhead region of Minnesota
Deadline: Inquire
Apply to: Individual Artists Fellowships, above address

Ⓜ *Career Development Grants* are offered to Arrowhead region writers. These provide financial support to developing and established regional artists who wish to take advantage of impending, concrete opportunities to advance their work or careers. Applicants may request grants of up to $1,000.

Available to: Residents of the Arrowhead region of Minnesota
Deadline: July, November, and April (inquire for exact date)
Apply to: Career Development Grants, above address

Artist Trust
1402 Third Avenue, Suite 404
Seattle, WA 98101-2118
Web site: http://www.artisttrust.org

Ⓜ Fellowships of $5,500 are available to Washington State residents. Awards in literature are given in odd-numbered years; in theater, including playwriting, in even-numbered years. Artists must participate in a community meet-the-artist event developed with a sponsor in a town or city other than their own. Send SASE or visit the Web site for guidelines and application.

Available to: See above
Deadline: Inquire (generally spring/early summer)
Apply to: Above address

Ⓜ The *GAP (Grants for Artist Projects) Program* provides support of up to $1,200 for artist-generated projects, which may be the development, completion or presentation of new work. All disciplines and interdisciplinary projects are eligible. Send SASE or visit the Web site for guidelines and application.

Available to: Washington State residents
Deadline: Inquire (generally midwinter)
Apply to: GAP, above address

Arts & Letters Journal of Contemporary Culture
Campus Box 44
Georgia College & State University
Milledgeville, GA 31061
E-mail: mlammon@mail.gcsu.edu
Web site: http://al.gcsu.edu

Ⓜ The *Arts & Letters Prizes Competition* offers $1,000 and publication in *Arts & Letters*, a journal of contemporary culture, in three categories: poetry, fiction (short stories), and drama (one-act plays). All submissions will be considered for publication. There is a $15 submission fee, which covers a two-issue subscription to the journal. Send SASE, e-mail, or visit the Web site for guidelines.

Available to: No restrictions
Deadline: Submissions accepted January 1–April 30
Apply to: Arts & Letters Prizes, above address

ArtServe Michigan
17515 West Nine Mile Road, Suite 250
Southfield, MI 48075
E-mail: artist@ArtServeMichigan.com
Web site: http://www.artservemichigan.org
Fax: 248-557-8581

Ⓜ ArtServe Michigan (formerly known as the Arts Foundation of Michigan), in partnership with the Michigan Council for Arts and Cultural Affairs, offers *Creative Artists Grants* of up to $7,000 in fiction, nonfiction, poetry, playwriting, and screenwriting. Funding is not available to those enrolled in degree or certificate programs. Write or e-mail for additional information.

Available to: Michigan residents
Deadline: Inquire
Apply to: Mark Packer, Program Director, above address

Ⓜ The *Artists in Michigan Program* pairs Creative Artists Grant recipients and other artists, including writers, with selected arts and human service agencies to reach underserved populations or nontraditional arts audiences in Michigan communities. ArtServe pays artist fees associated with these projects.

Available to: Michigan residents
Deadline: Inquire
Apply to: Mark Packer, Program Director, above address

Ashland Poetry Press
Ashland University
Ashland, OH 44805

Ⓟ The *Richard Snyder Poetry Award* annually offers $500 and publication in a paperback edition of 1,000 copies for a book-length collection of original poems. Poets should submit a manuscript of 50 to 80 pages, with no more than one poem per page, and a $15 reading fee. Send SASE for guidelines.

Available to: No restrictions
Deadline: January 15, 2000 (inquire for 2001)
Apply to: Richard Snyder Poetry Award, above address

Asian American Writers Workshop
37 St. Marks Place, Suite B
New York, NY 10003
E-mail: qwriter@hotmail.com
Web site: http://www.aaww.org

Ⓕ The *Van Lier Fellowships,* of $5,500 each, are offered in 2000 and 2001 to unpublished Asian-American novelists under age thirty who live in New York City. Send SASE, e-mail, or visit the Web site for further information and guidelines.

Available to: See above
Deadline: Inquire (probably late spring)
Apply to: Van Lier Fellowships, above address

Asian Cultural Council
437 Madison Avenue
New York, NY 10104
E-mail: acc@accny.org
Web site: http://www.asianculturalcouncil.org

® The Asian Cultural Council helps support residences in Japan for American artists interested in pursuing creative projects. Preference is given to performing and visual artists, though playwrights and writers will be considered. Duration of residence is usually one to six months.

Available to: U.S. citizens
Deadline: February 1
Apply to: Ralph Samuelson, Director, above address

Isaac Asimov Award
University of South Florida
School of Mass Communications
4202 East Fowler, CIS 1040
Tampa, FL 33620-7800
Web site: http://www.sfsite.com/asimovs/

Ⓕ The *Isaac Asimov Award for Undergraduate Excellence in Science Fiction and Fantasy Writing* annually offers $500 and consideration for publication in *Asimov's Science Fiction* magazine for a science fiction or fantasy short story by a full-time college undergraduate. The winner receives an expense-paid trip to the annual Conference on the Fantastic in Fort Lauderdale, Florida, in mid-March. There is a $10 entry fee for up to three submissions, payable to the Asimov Award. Send SASE for guidelines.

Available to: See above
Deadline: December 15
Apply to: Asimov Award, above address

Associated Press
50 Rockefeller Plaza
New York, NY 10020
Web site: http://www.ap.org

Ⓙ The *Associated Press Summer Minority Internship Program* is a twelve-week training period for up to seventeen black, Hispanic, Asian, and Native American college students in the United States. At the time of application, candidates must be enrolled full-time as juniors, seniors, or graduate students. Each intern will work in an AP bureau under the supervision of a designated trainer and will be paid a weekly wage based on classifiable experience. Interns who successfully complete the program are offered full-time news positions. Applications are not mailed out; the application-testing process takes place only at an AP bureau or designated test site. Visit the Web site or write to the nearest AP office to verify eligibility and schedule a test.

Available to: See above
Deadline: Tests scheduled early September to mid-February
Apply to: Director of Recruiting, above address

Associated Writing Programs
Tallwood House, MS-1E3
George Mason University
Fairfax, VA 22030
E-mail: awp@gmu.edu
Web site: http://awpwriter.org
Fax: 703-993-4302

Ⓜ The *AWP Award Series*, for poetry, short fiction, the novel, and creative nonfiction, are offered by the AWP and university and independent presses that have combined efforts to publish a number of book-length manuscripts every year. The competitions are open to all authors writing in English, and manuscripts are welcome from published as well as unpublished writers. Mixed-genre manuscripts are not accepted. Winning works appear through prearranged agreements with four university presses; AWP acts as a literary agent to try to place finalists' manuscripts. Authors receive a standard royalty from books sold. A $2,000 honorarium is given in each category; winners of the novel contest receive $10,000 and a standard royalty contract. The judges accept work being considered by other publishers if the author states to whom the manuscript has been submitted and agrees to inform the AWP if the work is accepted by another publisher. The reading and handling fee is $10 for AWP members, $20 for nonmembers. Send SASE or visit the Web site for guidelines.

Available to: No restrictions
Deadline: Submissions accepted January 1–February 28
Apply to: Award Series (specify genre), above address

® Three *AWP/Prague Summer Seminars Fellowships* are awarded each year, to a fiction writer, a nonfiction writer, and a poet who have not published a full-length book. Fellows receive full support and tuition to attend the Prague Summer Seminars, held in July. Travel and food expenses are their own responsibility. There is a $5 handling fee. Write, e-mail wlavende@uno.edu, or visit http://www.uno.edu/prague for guidelines.

Available to: No restrictions
Deadline: December (inquire for exact date)
Apply to: AWP/Prague Summer Seminars Fellowship (specify genre), above address

Association of American Colleges and Universities
1818 R Street, NW
Washington, DC 20009
Web site: http://www.aacu-edu.org

Ⓝ The *Frederic W. Ness Book Award* of $2,000 is given for a book published between July 1 of the preceding year and June 30 of the current year that contributes to the understanding and improvement of liberal education. Books by multiple authors and histories of colleges are ineligible.

Available to: No restrictions
Deadline: September 15
Apply to: Frederic W. Ness Book Award, above address

Association for Asian Studies
1021 East Huron
Ann Arbor, MI 48104-1628
E-mail: postmaster@aasianst.org
Web site: http:www.aasianst.org
Fax: 734-665-3801

Ⓝ The *John Whitney Hall Book Prize* of $1,000 is given for an outstanding book in English on Japan or Korea published during the year preceding the prize deadline. Nominated books may address either contemporary or historical topics in any field of the humanities or the social sciences. Translations from Japanese or Korean into English are eligible only if they include a substantial introduction, annotation, and critical apparatus. Books must be nominated by publishers (trade or university presses); nominations by authors are not accepted. Write for additional information and addresses of prize committee members.

Available to: No restrictions
Deadline: June 30
Apply to: Above address for list of prize committee members

Ⓝ The *Joseph Levenson Book Prizes*, of $1,500 each, are awarded annually to two outstanding scholarly works that further broad understanding of China. One award is given for books on China before 1900 and the other for books on twentieth-century China. A copy of each entry must be sent to each member of the appropriate committee. Write for additional information and addresses of prize committee members

Available to: No restrictions
Deadline: June 15
Apply to: Above address for list of prize committee members

Ⓣ The *A. K. Ramanujan Book Prize for Translation* of $1,000 is given every other year to recognize and encourage translations from South Asian languages into English. Special consideration will be given to innovative work that reaches a wide audience. Books must have been published during the two-year period preceding the prize deadline. A copy of each entry must be sent to each member of the committee. Write for additional information and addresses of prize committee members.

Available to: No restrictions
Deadline: Inquire for 2001
Apply to: Above address for list of prize committee members

Association for the Care of Children's Health
7910 Woodmont Avenue, Suite 300
Bethesda, MD 20814

© The *Joan Fassler Memorial Book Award* offers $1,000 for a book that makes an "outstanding contribution to children's literature dealing with hospitalization, disease, disabling conditions, death, and dying." The book must have been published in English in the award year.

Available to: No restrictions
Deadline: December 1
Apply to: Joan Fassler Memorial Book Award, above address

Association of Jesuit Colleges and Universities
One Dupont Circle, Suite 405
Washington, DC 20036
E-mail: blkrobe@aol.com
Web site: http://www.mu.edu/dept/ASN
Fax: 202-862-8523

Ⓝ The *National Jesuit Book Award Competition*, sponsored by Alpha Sigma Nu, the national Jesuit Honor Society, offers four cash prizes, of $1,000 each, to the best nonfiction books in categories that alternate on a three-year cycle. The 2000 award will be in the sciences, the 2001 in the professional fields, and the 2002 in the humanities. Application forms are available at local ASN chapters or from the above-listed Web site.

Available to: Full-time or part-time faculty or administrators or anyone with emeritus status at a U.S. Jesuit college or university
Deadline: March 1
Apply to: National Jesuit Book Award, above address

Association of Jewish Libraries
15 East 26th Street, Room 1034
New York, NY 10010-1579

© The *AJL Sydney Taylor Book Awards* honor outstanding children's books of positive Jewish content published during the calendar year. A prize of $1,000 is offered in each of two categories: picture books, and books aimed at grade three and above. If an award involves separate author and illustrator, the prize money is divided. Books must be submitted by the publisher.

Available to: No restrictions
Deadline: January 15
Apply to: AJL Sydney Taylor Book Awards, c/o Linda Silver, 3729 Meadowbrook Boulevard, University Heights, OH 44118

© The *AJL Sydney Taylor Manuscript Award* of $1,000 is given to the author of a new children's book with universal appeal of Jewish content for readers ages eight to eleven. Manuscripts should be between 64 and 200 pages long. Writers must have no previously published books. Send SASE to the address below for additional information and application form, or fax 770-671-8380.

Available to: No restrictions
Deadline: January 15
Apply to: AJL Sydney Taylor Manuscript Award, c/o Paula Sandfelder, 1327 Wintercreek Lane, Dunwoody, GA 30338

Association for Library Services to Children
American Library Association
50 East Huron Street
Chicago, IL 60611
E-mail: awards@ala.org
Web site: http://www.ala.org

© The *John Newbery Medal* is awarded annually to the author of the most distinguished contribution to American literature for children published in the United States during the preceding year. Authors and publishers are invited to submit books to the medal committee for review during the ALA midwinter meeting. No cash award is given; winners receive a medal. The high prestige of the Newbery Medal in the field of children's literature warrants its inclusion here.

Available to: U.S. citizens or residents
Deadline: January (inquire for exact date)
Apply to: John Newbery Medal, above address

Astraea National Lesbian Action Foundation
116 East 16th Street, 7th floor
New York, NY 10003
E-mail: info@astraea.org
Web site: http://www.astraea.org
Fax: 212-982-3321

Ⓕ Ⓟ The *Lesbian Writers' Fund Awards* offer several grants of $10,000 each to emerging lesbian writers in fiction and poetry who have published at least once in a magazine, literary journal, or anthology. Write or visit the Web site for guidelines and application.

Available to: U.S. resident lesbian writers
Deadline: Early March (inquire for exact date)
Apply to: Lesbian Writers' Fund Awards, above address

Atlanta Review
PO Box 8248
Atlanta, GA 31106
E-mail: dveach@auctr.edu
Web site: http:www.atlantareview.com

Ⓟ The *Atlanta Review International Poetry Competition* awards a $2,000 first prize, a $500 second prize, and a $250 third prize for unpublished poems of any length or style. Many entrants are published in *Atlanta Review*, which appears in 120 countries. An entry fee of $5 is required for the first poem, and $2 for each additional poem. Enclose SASE for notification of winners.

Available to: No restrictions
Deadline: May 1
Apply to: International Poetry Competition, above address

Atlantic Center for the Arts
1414 Art Center Avenue
New Smyrna Beach, FL 32168
Web site: http://www.atlantic-centerarts.org
Fax: 904-427-5669

Ⓡ The Atlantic Center for the Arts *Master Artists-in-Residence Program* provides a three-week residence for writers and artists at a sixty-nine-acre ecological preserve in eastern Florida. Associates spend half their time working with master artists in meetings, workshops, casual conversations, and recreational activities, and are free to spend other time on their own projects. The residence fee is $300, with another $500 needed for housing. Scholarships are available on a limited basis, according to need, to writers already accepted into the

Program. Write or visit the Web site for additional information and guidelines.

Available to: No restrictions
Deadline: Inquire
Apply to: Above address

Austin Film Festival
1604 Nueces
Austin, TX 78701-1106
E-mail: ausfilm@aol.com
Web site: http://www.austinfilmfestival.org

Ⓢ The *Austin Film Festival Screenwriters Competition* offers two first prizes of $4,000, one for an adult film and one for a family film screenplay. A $1,000 prize is offered for a comedy screenplay. Winners participate in the AFF Mentor Program and are reimbursed for round-trip airfare to/from Austin and up to four nights' accommodation at a Festival hotel; they also receive a complimentary all-access pass to the Festival and Screenwriters Conference. There is a $40 submission fee. Send SASE, e-mail, or visit the Web site for guidelines and entry form.

Available to: No restrictions
Deadline: May 15
Apply to: Screenwriters Competition, above address

Austin Writers' League
1501 West 5th Street, Suite E-2
Austin, TX 78703
E-mail: awl@writersleague.org
Web site: http://www.writersleague.org
Fax: 512-499-0441

Ⓜ The Austin Writers' League distributes state funds in literature for the Texas Commission on the Arts to foster growth and excellence of the literary arts in Texas. The League provides professional opportunities for Texas writers and supports projects that expand public participation in the literary arts. Grants may be given for projects (up to $3,000) or for operations (up to $6,000); funds must support activities based in Texas. Write for guidelines.

Available to: Texas writers and Texas-based organizations
Deadline: December 15
Apply to: Above address

Ⓜ The *Violet Crown Book Awards* honor outstanding books published by Austin Writers' League members. The   awards offer a $1,000 cash stipend and a trophy in fiction, in nonfiction, and in literary work (poetry, essays, short stories). Books must have been published between the July 1 preceding and June 30 of the award year. A $10 entry fee is required. Membership in the League is $40 annually; writers may join when submitting their entry.

Available to: League members
Deadline: June 30
Apply to: Violet Crown Book Awards, above address

Ⓒ The *Teddy Book Award* honors an outstanding children's book published by an Austin Writers' League member. The award consists of a $1,000 cash stipend and a trophy. Books may be fiction or nonfiction, picture book to young adult, and books must have been published between the February 1 preceding and January 31 of the award year. A $10 entry fee is required. Membership in the League is $40 annually; writers may join when submitting their entry.

Available to: League members
Deadline: January 31
Apply to: Teddy Book Award, above address

AUSTRALIA
Arts Management Pty, Ltd.
Station House, Rawson House
790 George Street
Sydney NSW 2000
Australia
E-mail: vbraden@ozemail.com.au
Fax: 61-2-9211-7762

Ⓓ Ⓕ The *Miles Franklin Award*, of $28,000 Australian, is offered annually for a published novel that best presents Australian life "in any of its phases." If no novel is judged of sufficient literary merit, the award may be given to the author of a play.

Available to: No restrictions
Deadline: January 31 for work published in the preceding year
Apply to: Above address

Authors League Fund
330 West 42nd Street
New York, NY 10036
Fax: 212-564-8363

The Fund makes interest-free loans to professional published authors and produced playwrights in need because of illness, misfortune, or other temporary emergency. The Fund does not make grants. Write for information and application.

Available to: See above
Deadline: None
Apply to: Susan Drury, Administrator, above address

Authors in the Park
PO Box 85
Winter Park, FL 32790-0085
E-mail: foley@magicnet.net
Fax: 407-275-8688

Ⓕ The *Authors in the Park Short Story Contest* offers a $1,000 first prize, a $500 second prize, and a $250 third prize for unpublished short stories written in English, with a 5,000-word maximum. Winners are announced in *Fine Print*, a short story collection, by December. Send SASE or e-mail for guidelines before submitting.

Available to: No restrictions
Deadline: April 30
Apply to: Short Story Contest, above address

The Backwaters Press
3502 North 52nd Street
Omaha, NE 68104-3506

Ⓟ The *Backwaters Prize* of $1,000 and publication by the Press is awarded for a previously unpublished manuscript of poetry, up to 80 pages. There is a $20 entry fee. Send SASE for guidelines.

Available to: No restrictions
Deadline: June 1
Apply to: Backwaters Prize, above address

Ⓕ The *Omaha Prize* of $1,000 and publication by the Press is awarded for a previously unpublished novel, up to 350 manuscript pages. Collections of short stories are not eligible. There is a $20 entry fee. Send SASE for guidelines.

Available to: No restrictions
Deadline: November 1
Apply to: Omaha Prize, above address

Baker's Plays
PO Box 699222
Quincy, MA 02269-9222

Ⓓ The *High School Playwriting Contest* offers a first prize of $500 and publication in Baker's Plays *Best Plays from High School* series for a full-length or one-act play by a high school student. Plays should be suitable for production on high school stages and preferably should be about "the high school experience." Student playwrights must be sponsored by a high school drama or English teacher. A second prize of $250 and a third prize of $100 are also awarded. Write for further information and guidelines.

Available to: High school students
Deadline: January 31
Apply to: High School Playwriting Contest, above address

bananafish
PO Box 381332
Cambridge, MA 02238-1332
E-mail: bananafi@aol.com
Fax: 617-868-0017

Ⓕ The *bananafish Short Story Contest* offers a first prize of $1,000, a second of $250, and a third of $100 for a short story. All winning entries will be published in *bananafish*. There is a $10 reading fee, $5 for subscribers. Send SASE for guidelines.

Available to: No restrictions
Deadline: Submissions accepted January 1–February 28
Apply to: Short Story Contest, above address

Bank Street College of Education
Children's Book Committee
610 West 112th Street
New York, NY 10025
E-mail: bookcom@bnkst.edu
Web site: http://www.bnkst.edu

ⒾⓃ The Children's Book Committee of Bank Street College annually confers three awards, carrying a stipend of $500 each. The *Josette Frank Award* honors an outstanding book of children's fiction in which children or young people deal in a positive and realistic way with difficulties in their world and grow emotionally and morally. The *Flora Stieglitz Straus Award* is given for a distinguished work of children's nonfiction that fulfills the ideals of the award's namesake, who led the Committee for more than seventy-five years, and that serves as an inspiration to young people. The *Claudia Lewis Award* is given for the best children's poetry book of the year. There is no application process. *By Internal Nomination Only.*

Banks Channel Books
PO Box 4446
Wilmington, NC 28406
Fax: 910-762-4677

Ⓕ The *Carolina Novel Award* biennially offers $1,000 (advance against royalties) and publication by Banks Channel Books for a novel by a legal resident of North Carolina or South Carolina. There is a $35 reading fee. Send SASE for guidelines.

Available to: North or South Carolina residents
Deadline: July 31, 2000
Apply to: Carolina Novel Award, above address

Bantam Doubleday Dell
Books for Young Readers
1540 Broadway
New York, NY 10036

Ⓒ The *Marguerite de Angeli Prize* is awarded annually to encourage the writing of fiction, either contemporary or historical, for children, in the spirit of the works of Marguerite de Angeli. Manuscripts must be between 40 and 144 pages, and suitable for readers seven to ten years of age. The award consists of a $1,500 cash prize and a $3,500 advance against royalties when the winning manuscript is published. Send SASE for guidelines.

> Available to: U.S. or Canadian writers who have not previously published a novel for middle-grade readers
> Deadline: Manuscripts must be postmarked April 1–June 30
> Apply to: Marguerite de Angeli Prize, above address

© The *Delacorte Press Prize for a First Young Adult Novel* offers a book contract for hardcover and paperback editions, a $1,500 cash prize, and a $6,000 advance against royalties. Manuscripts should be book length, 100 to 224 typed pages; they should have a contemporary setting and be suitable for ages twelve to eighteen. Write for complete submission guidelines.

> Available to: U.S. and Canadian writers who have not previously published a young adult novel
> Deadline: Manuscripts must be postmarked October 1–December 31
> Apply to: Delacorte Press Prize, above address

Barnard College
3009 Broadway
New York, NY 10027-6598

℗ The *Barnard New Women Poets Prize* offers an honorarium of $1,000 and publication by Beacon Press for a book-length manuscript of poems by a woman who has not yet published a book. Poets who have published chapbooks or similar works with fewer than 500 copies are eligible. Write for guidelines before submission.

> Available to: Women poets
> Deadline: October 15
> Apply to: Barnard New Women Poets Prize, above address

Barnes & Noble
122 Fifth Avenue
New York, NY 10011
E-mail: kruden@bn.com

Ⓕ The *Discover Great New Writers Award* annually offers $10,000 to the best first novel by an American author whose work has appeared in the Discover Great New Writers program during the year. Publishers should submit a minimum of three galley copies (one manuscript if galleys are not available) by an author making a strong literary debut. Work should be submitted prior to the book's publication date according to a seasonal schedule, which has four yearly deadlines. Author submissions are not accepted. Write or e-mail for additional information and deadlines.

> Available to: Authors whose work has appeared in the Discover Great New Writers program
> Deadline: Inquire
> Apply to: Kelle Ruden, Manager & Editor, Discover Great New Writers, above address

The Bear Deluxe Magazine
PO Box 10342
Portland, OR 97296-0342
E-mail: Orlo@teleport.com

Ⓕ The *Edward Abbey Short Fiction Award* offers $500 and publication in *The Bear Deluxe*, an environmental/creative arts journal, for an unpublished work of fiction of fewer than 4,000 words. There is a $5 entry fee. Send SASE for guidelines.

> Available to: No restrictions
> Deadline: Submissions must be postmarked by the first Tuesday after Labor Day
> Apply to: Edward Abbey Short Fiction Award, above address

Bear Star Press
185 Hollow Oak Drive
Cohasset, CA 95973

Ⓟ The *Dorothy Brunsman Poetry Prize* awards $1,000 for a poetry manuscript, 50–65 pages, by a writer living in the western/Pacific states (including Alaska and Hawaii). Send SASE for guidelines.

Available to: Poets living in the western United States (including Alaska and Hawaii)
Deadline: Inquire
Apply to: Above address

Bellagio Study and Conference Center. *See* **Rockefeller Foundation**

Bellingham Review
Mail Stop 9053
Western Washington University
Bellingham, WA 98225
Web site: http://www.ac.wwu.edu/~bhreview/

Ⓝ The *Annie Dillard Award for Nonfiction* offers $1,000 and publication for an essay in any style and on any subject, maximum 10,000 words. The entry fee is $10 for each essay. Send SASE for guidelines.

Available to: No restrictions
Deadline: March 1
Apply to: Annie Dillard Award, above address

Ⓟ The *49th Parallel Poetry Award* offers $1,000 and publication for an original poem. Poets may submit poems of any length. There is a $10 entry fee, which covers a one-year subscription to *Bellingham Review*. Send SASE for guidelines.

Available to: No restrictions
Deadline: December 1
Apply to: 49th Parallel Poetry Award, above address

Ⓕ The *Tobias Wolff Award for Fiction* offers $1,000 and publication for a short story or a novel excerpt no longer than 10,000 words. A $250 second prize and a $100 third prize are also awarded. The fee is $10 for the first entry, $5 per entry thereafter. All entrants will receive a two-issue subscription to *Bellingham Review*. Send SASE for guidelines.

Available to: No restrictions
Deadline: March 1
Apply to: Tobias Wolff Award, above address

The Beloit Poetry Journal
24 Berry Cove Road
Lamoine, ME 04605
Web site: http://www.bpj.org

Ⓟ The *Chad Walsh Poetry Award* annually offers a cash prize ($4,000 in 1999) for a poem or group of poems published in the *Journal* in the preceding year.

Available to: Poets published in *The Beloit Poetry Journal*
Deadline: Ongoing
Apply to: Above address

Berea College
Appalachian Center
CPO 2336
Berea, KY 40404
E-mail: Gordon_McKinney@Berea.edu

Ⓜ The *Weatherford Award*, of $500, is given annually to recognize the writer whose published work "best describes and analyzes the challenges, personalities, and qualities of the

Appalachian South." Eligible are a book-length or shorter works of fiction, nonfiction, or poetry first published during the year for which the award is given. Send SASE for guidelines.

Available to: No restrictions
Deadline: December 31 of publication year
Apply to: Chair, Weatherford Award Committee, above address

Berkshire Conference of Women Historians
c/o Barbara Winslow, Secretary-Treasurer
124 Park Place
Brooklyn, NY 11217
E-mail: 74641.401@compuserve.com
Web site: http://www-berks.aas.duke.edu

Ⓝ The *Publication Awards* offer a $1,000 prize for the best published book and a $500 prize for the best published article in any field of historical scholarship by a U.S. or Canadian woman. Publishers are notified of the competition and asked to submit eligible works, but submissions by authors are also welcome.

Available to: U.S. or Canadian women historians
Deadline: January 15
Apply to: Above address for list of award committee members

Bertelsmann USA
1540 Broadway, 33rd floor
New York, NY 10036-4098
E-mail: bwoesp@bmge.com
Fax: 212-930-4783

Ⓜ The *World of Expression Scholarship Program* offers a $10,000 first prize, a $7,500 second prize, a $5,000 third prize, ten fourth-place prizes of $2,500 each, and twenty fifth-place prizes of $1,000 to New York City high school seniors in two categories, literary and musical composition. Literature submissions may consist of poems, fiction, dramatic work, or personal essays no longer than 10 pages and/or 2,500 words. Monetary awards will be paid by the World of Expression Foundation to each winner's choice of institution of postsecondary education. Write or e-mail for guidelines and application.

Available to: New York City high school seniors
Deadline: February 1
Apply to: World of Expression Scholarship Program, above address

Beverly Hills Theatre Guild
2815 North Beachwood Drive
Los Angeles, CA 90068

Ⓓ The *Julie Harris Playwright Competition* awards an annual cash prize of $5,000 for the best play submitted by a U.S. playwright. An additional $2,000 is available to help finance a showcase production if the award-winning play is presented in the Los Angeles area within one year of receiving the award. The second-place *Janet and Maxwell Salter Award* offers a prize of $2,000, and the third-place *Dr. Henry and Lilian Nesburn Award* offers $1,000. Entries must be original full-length plays (minimum of 90 minutes) that have not been published, have never had an Equity or non-Equity production for which actors or authors were paid or admission was charged, and are not under option. Musicals, one-act plays (shorter than 90 minutes), adaptations, translations, plays that have won any other competition, and plays that have entered previous Beverly Hills Theatre Guild competitions are ineligible. Send SASE for rules and an application.

Available to: U.S. citizens
Deadline: Submissions accepted August 1–November 1
Apply to: Above address

Ⓒ Ⓓ The *Beverly Hills Theatre Guild Plays for Children's Theatre Competition* annually awards a prize of $750 for plays suitable for children in grades 6 to 8 (middle school) that are no more than 60 minutes long and a prize of $250 for plays suitable for children in grades 3 to 5 that are no more than 30 minutes long. Send SASE for guidelines and entry form.

Available to: U.S. citizens
Deadline: February 28
Apply to: Above address

Beyond Baroque Literary/Arts Center
681 Venice Boulevard
Venice, CA 90291
Web site: http://www.beyondbaroque.org

(P) Beyond Baroque periodically sponsors chapbook contests. In 1998, the *Beyond Baroque Poetry Chapbook Contest* awarded $500 and publication by Beyond Baroque Books in a 500-copy run for a poetry manuscript no longer than 20 pages. The winner was invited to read at the Center. Criteria and guidelines may change; contact the Center directly for updated information. The Center offers free weekly workshops in poetry and fiction year-round, including Los Angeles's longest-running poetry session, the Wednesday Night Workshop, and a regular program of readings by some 500 poets and fiction writers a year. Write or visit the Web site for additional information.

Available to: No restrictions
Deadline: Inquire
Apply to: Poetry Chapbook Contest, above address

Birmingham-Southern College
Box 549003
Birmingham, AL 35254

(F) (P) The *Hackney Literary Awards* offer $5,000 in prizes for poetry and short stories and a $5,000 award for the novel. There is a $10 reading fee per poetry and short story entry and a $25 reading fee for novel entries. All submitted work must be original and unpublished. Send SASE for guidelines.

Available to: No restrictions
Deadlines: Submissions accepted October 1–December 31 for poetry and short stories; June 1–September 30 for novels
Apply to: Hackney Literary Awards, above address

The Bitter Oleander
4983 Tall Oaks Drive
Fayetteville, NY 13066-9776
E-mail: bones44@ix.netcom.com

(P) The *Frances Locke Memorial Poetry Award* offers $500 and publication in *The Bitter Oleander*, a twice-yearly magazine of essays, fiction, poetry, and reviews, for an unpublished poem. Poets may submit up to five poems with a $10 entry fee; $2 for each additional poem. Send SASE for guidelines.

Available to: No restrictions
Deadline: Submissions accepted March 1–June 15
Apply to: Frances Locke Memorial Poetry Award, above address

BkMk Press
University of Missouri at Kansas City
University House
5100 Rockhill Road
Kansas City, MO 64110-2499
E-mail: bkmk@umkc.edu
Fax: 816-235-2611

(P) The *John Ciardi Prize for Poetry* biennially offers $1,000 and publication by BkMk Press for the best collection of poetry, 48 to 96 pages in length, by a living American author. There is a

$20 reading fee. Send SASE or e-mail for guidelines.

Available to: U.S. citizens
Deadline: October 15, 2000; inquire for 2002
Apply to: John Ciardi Prize for Poetry, above address

Black Caucus of the American Library Association
c/o New York Public Library
Office of Adult Services
455 Fifth Avenue
New York, NY 10016
E-mail: chixon@nypl.org
Web site: http://www.bcala.org

Ⓕ Ⓝ The *Black Caucus of the American Library Association Literary Awards,* of $500 each, are given in recognition of excellence in adult fiction and nonfiction by African-American authors. Publishers may submit books published during the calendar year. The Caucus also annually presents a *First Novelist Award Citation* and an *Outstanding Contributions to Publishing Citation.* Write for guidelines.

Available to: African-American writers
Deadline: December 31
Apply to: Literary Awards, above address

Black Warrior Review
University of Alabama
PO Box 862936
Tuscaloosa, AL 35486-0027
Web site: http://www.sa.ua.edu/osm/bwr

Ⓕ Ⓟ *Black Warrior Review* will award $500 each to a poet and a fiction writer whose work has been published in either the fall or the spring issue of the *Review.* Winners will be selected by a prominent writer or critic; names of the recipients and the award judge will be announced in the fall issue of the *Review.*

Available to: See above
Deadlines: July 15 for fall issue; January 15 for spring
Apply to: Editor, above address

Susan Smith Blackburn Prize
3239 Avalon Place
Houston, TX 77019
Fax: 713-654-8184

Ⓓ The *Susan Smith Blackburn Prize* is given annually to women playwrights for full-length plays, unproduced or produced within one year of the deadline. The award carries a first prize of $5,000 and a signed and numbered de Kooning print; a second-place prize of $2,000; and $500 to each of the other finalists. Plays will be received only from recognized sources, which include professional regional and off-Broadway theaters and other organizations regularly reading new works. Send SASE to the above address for a listing of these sources. Applications by individual playwrights or their agents will not be considered.

Available to: Women playwrights of any nationality writing in English
Deadline: Submissions accepted in September only
Apply to: Emilie S. Kilgore, above address

Bloomington Playwrights Project
308 South Washington Street
Bloomington, IN 47401
E-mail: bppwrite@bluemarble.net
Web site: http://www.newplays.org

Ⓓ The *Reva Shiner Full-Length Play Contest* offers $500, a staged reading, and production for an unpublished, unproduced full-length play suitable for production in a sixty-five-seat theater, with simple sets. There is a $5 reading fee. Write, e-mail, or visit the Web site for guidelines.

Available to: No restrictions
Deadline: January 15
Apply to: Above address

Blue Mountain Center
PO Box 109
Blue Mountain Lake, NY 12812-0109

® The Blue Mountain Center offers fourteen four-week residences four times a year, from mid-June through late October. The residences are open to writers and provide free room and board; spouses must apply individually. Send a brief bio, work samples, reviews, and a project description to apply; specify preferred period of stay. There is a $20 application fee.

Available to: Established writers, particularly those whose work shows social and ecological concern
Deadline: February 1
Apply to: Admissions Committee, above address

Ⓜ ® The *Richard J. Margolis Award* of $2,000 plus a month-long residence at Blue Mountain Center is given annually to a poet, essayist, or journalist "whose work recalls Richard J. Margolis's warmth, humor, and concern for social issues." To nominate a writer, send three copies of at least two samples of work, published or unpublished, of no more than 30 pages total, and a short biographical note.

Available to: No restrictions
Deadline: July 1
Apply to: Richard J. Margolis Award, 101 Arch Street, 9th floor, Boston, MA 02110, attn: Harry S. Margolis

The Bogliasco Foundation
885 Second Avenue, Room 3100
New York, NY 10017
E-mail: bogfound@mindspring.com
Web site: http://www.liguriastudycenter.org

® The Liguria Study Center for the Arts and Humanities, located on the Italian Riviera in the town of Bogliasco, offers residential fellowships to qualified writers doing advanced creative work or scholarly research in archaeology, architecture, classics, dance, film or video, history, literature, music, philosophy, theater, or the visual arts. Fellowship applicants must demonstrate significant achievement in their disciplines, commensurate with their age and experience. Fellowships are from mid-September to the third week of December and from mid-February to the third week of May, with a typical duration of one month or half a semester. Bogliasco fellows are provided with living quarters and full board; they may be accompanied by spouses or equivalent companions during their stay. Write, e-mail, or visit the Web site for application.

Available to: See above
Deadline: February 1 for the fall/winter semester; May 1 for the winter/spring semester
Apply to: Above address

Borderlands Theater
PO Box 2791
Tucson, AZ 85702
E-mail: bltheater@aol.com
Fax: 520-882-7406

Ⓓ The *Border Playwrights Project* offers residences to writers of unproduced full-length plays that explore the U.S.–Mexico border and border culture or the concept of other borders, e.g., immigration or issues of class, race, and gender. Plays may be in English and/or

Spanish. Playwrights should send a synopsis, and SASE for response.

Available to: No restrictions
Deadline: Inquire
Apply to: Suzi List, Literary Coordinator, above address

Robert Bosch Foundation
c/o CDS International
871 United Nations Plaza, 15th floor
New York, NY 10017
E-mail: eandros@cdsintl.org
Web site: http://www.cdsintl.org/rbffprogram.html
Fax: 212-497-3535

ⓙ   The *Robert Bosch Foundation Fellowship Program* offers journalists and other young professionals the opportunity to participate in an intensive nine-month work/study program in Germany. Applicants must be U.S. citizens with a graduate degree and work experience; evidence of outstanding professional performance and/or academic achievement; and the ability to communicate well in German. Fellows receive round-trip transportation between their U.S. residence and Germany, a stipend of DM 3,500 per month for the duration of the program, tuition and fees for a language course (if needed), limited health and accident insurance, and financial support for an accompanying spouse. Write for additional information and application.

Available to: U.S. citizens
Deadline: October 15
Apply to: Fellowship Program, above address

Boston Authors Club
45 Chiltern Road
Weston, MA 02193

Ⓜ   The Boston Authors Club makes two annual awards of $500 each, one for an adult trade book, the other for a children's/young adult book. The book must be published in the year prior to the award, i.e., in 1999 for the year 2000. The author must live or have lived within 100 miles of Boston. Works of fiction, nonfiction, memoir, poetry, and biography are eligible; self-published works are not accepted. Two copies of the book, which will not be returned, should be submitted.

Available to: See above
Deadline: January 1
Apply to: Above address

The Boston Book Review
30 Brattle Street, 4th floor
Cambridge, MA 02138
E-mail: Kiril@BostonBookReview.org
Web site: http://www.bostonbookreview.org

Ⓘ Ⓝ   The *Boston Book Review Literary Awards*, consisting of the *Fisk Fiction Prize*, given in memory of Lilla Fisk Rand; the *Rea Nonfiction Prize*, given in memory of Anne Rea Jewell; and the *Bingham Poetry Prize*, given in memory of Belinda Bingham Pierce, offer $1,000 each to "celebrate excellent literary accomplishments" published in the calendar year. *By Internal Nomination Only.*

Boston Review
E53-407 MIT
Cambridge, MA 02139

Ⓕ Ⓟ   The *Boston Review Short Story Contest* and the *Boston Review Poetry Contest* annually award $1,000 to each contest winner and publication in *Boston Review*, a bimonthly journal of poetry, fiction, reviews, and articles. Fiction writers should submit an unpublished short story of no more than 4,000 words; poets may submit up to five unpublished poems, totaling no more than 10 pages. There is a $15 entry fee, which covers a one-year subscription to the *Review*. Send SASE for guidelines.

Available to: No restrictions
Deadline: June 1 for poetry; September 1 for short stories
Apply to: Short Story Contest or Poetry Contest, above address

Boulder Museum of Contemporary Art
1750 13th Street
Boulder, CO 80302
E-mail: bmoca@indra.net
Web site: http://www.bmoca.org
Fax: 303-447-1633

Ⓓ The BMCA *One-Act Festival* annually offers $250 and production to three one-act plays that have not been previously produced. Plays should be no longer than 30 minutes, have a maximum of five characters, have minimal set, prop, and lighting requirements, and be suitable for production in a black-box-style theater with seating for one hundred. There is a $15 entry fee. Send SASE for additional information and guidelines.

Available to: No restrictions
Deadline: March 15
Apply to: One-Act Festival Committee, above address

Boulevard
PMB 322, 4579 Laclede Avenue
St. Louis, MO 63108-2103

Ⓕ The *Boulevard Short Fiction Contest for Emerging Writers* awards $1,200 and publication in *Boulevard* for a short story of up to 7,500 words by a writer who has not yet published a book of fiction, poetry, or creative nonfiction with a nationally distributed press. The entry fee is $15 per story, with a two-story limit per author. Send SASE for guidelines.

Available to: No restrictions
Deadline: December 15
Apply to: Boulevard Short Fiction Contest for Emerging Writers, above address

Box Turtle Press
184 Franklin Street
New York, NY 10013

Ⓟ The *Mudfish Poetry Prize* annually offers $1,000 and publication in *Mudfish*, a journal of poetry and art published by Box Turtle Press. Poets may submit any number of poems; all entries will be considered for publication. The reading fee is $15 for up to three poems, $2 each for more. Send SASE for guidelines.

Available to: No restrictions
Deadline: Inquire
Apply to: Mudfish Poetry Prize, above address

Bread Loaf Writers' Conference
Middlebury College
Middlebury, VT 05753
E-mail: blwc@middlebury.edu
Web site: http://www.middlebury.edu/~blwc
Fax: 802-443-2087

Ⓡ The *Bread Loaf Writers' Conference* awards fellowships and scholarships to candidates applying to attend a session of the Conference. Candidates for fellowships must have a first original book published within three years of filing their application. Scholarship candidates must have published in major literary periodicals or newspapers. Send SASE for nomination and application procedures.

Available to: See above

Deadline: April 1
Apply to: Above address

(M) Bread Loaf also sponsors the *Bakeless Literary Publication Prizes*, an annual competition for new authors of poetry, fiction, and nonfiction. The prizes support emerging writers by sponsoring publication of their first books through Middlebury College/University Press of New England. Winners also receive fellowships to attend the Bread Loaf Writers' Conference. Send SASE for guidelines.

Available to: Emerging writers
Deadline: Manuscripts accepted January 1–March 1
Apply to: Bakeless Prizes, above address

Bright Hill Press
PO Box 193
Treadwell, NY 13846
E-mail: wordthurs@aol.com
Web site: http://www.nyslittree.org
Fax: 607-746-7274

(P) The *Bright Hill Press Poetry Award* annually offers $500, publication, and 25 copies for a full-length manuscript of poetry. Poets should submit manuscripts of 48 to 64 pages with a $15 fee per entry; $10 for Word Thursdays/Bright Hill Press members. Send SASE or e-mail for guidelines.

Available to: No restrictions
Deadline: September 15
Apply to: Poetry Award, above address

Brody Arts Fund
California Community Foundation
606 South Olive Street, Suite 2400
Los Angeles, CA 90014-1526

(M) Up to five fellowships, of $5,000 each, are awarded to emerging writers residing in Los Angeles County. Those who are "rooted in and reflective of the diverse multicultural communities" of the county are preferred. The awards rotate among disciplines; contact the Fund for the year of the next literature cycle.

Available to: Los Angeles County residents
Deadline: Inquire
Apply to: Above address

Bronx Council on the Arts
1738 Hone Avenue
Bronx, NY 10461
E-mail: bronxarts@artswire.org
Web site: http://www.bronxarts.org

(M) The *BRIO (Bronx Recognizes Its Own) Fellowships* award $1,500 to Bronx artists in various disciplines, including fiction, poetry, playwriting/screenwriting, and nonfiction. The Council provides technical assistance to writers through the Bronx Writers Center, a workspace that offers computers, on-line capability, fax machine, copier, resource library, and fiction and poetry collections, and that accommodates spoken-word performances, writing workshops, and a literary calendar. Write for guidelines and application.

Available to: Bronx residents
Deadline: Mid-March (inquire for exact date)
Apply to: BRIO Fellowships, above address

John Carter Brown Library
Brown University
Box 1894
Providence, RI 02912
E-mail: JCBL_Fellowships@Brown.edu
Web site: http://www.JCBL.org

Approximately twenty-five *Research Fellowships* are offered annually by the John Carter Brown Library, which houses an outstanding collection of primary materials relating to the discovery, exploration, settlement, and development of the New World. Fellowship recipients are expected to be in continuous residence at the Library and to participate in the intellectual life of Brown University. Preference may be given to applicants able to take up the fellowship during the course of the academic year. Fellowships are of two types:

Long-Term Fellowships, supported principally by the National Endowment for the Humanities and the Andrew W. Mellon Foundation, and carrying stipends of $2,800 per month, are available for five months. Applicants must be U.S. citizens or have resided in the United States for three years immediately before the term of the fellowship. Graduate students are not eligible.

Short-Term Fellowships, carrying stipends of $1,200 per month, are available for two to four months. Eligible are U.S. and foreign citizens engaged in predoctoral, postdoctoral, or independent research.

Available to: See above
Deadline: January 15
Apply to: Research Fellowships, above address, or e-mail for application

Bucknell University
Stadler Center for Poetry
Lewisburg, PA 17837
E-mail: ciotola@bucknell.edu
Web site: http://www.departments.bucknell.edu/stadler_center/
Fax: 570-577-3760

Ⓟ The *Bucknell Seminar for Younger Poets* offers ten fellowships for graduating college seniors and talented undergraduates to write and receive guidance from established poets during a seminar in June and July. Readings and workshops are offered. Tuition, room, board, and space for writing are provided.

Available to: Graduating seniors and undergraduates from U.S. colleges
Deadline: March 1
Apply to: Send academic transcript, two recommendations, 10-to-12-page portfolio, and letter of self-presentation to Cynthia Hogue, Director, above address

Ⓡ The *Philip Roth Residence in Creative Writing* provides a studio on the Bucknell University campus, a fully equipped two-bedroom apartment, meals in the University Dining Service, and a stipend of $1,000 for a young writer with some record of accomplishment. The residence will coincide with the fall semester, from the last week in August to mid-December. In even-numbered years the residence will be awarded to a poet, in odd-numbered years to a fiction writer. Write for guidelines.

Available to: No restrictions
Deadline: March 1
Apply to: Cynthia Hogue, Director, Philip Roth Residence in Creative Writing, above address

Mary Ingraham Bunting Institute at Radcliffe
34 Concord Avenue
Cambridge, MA 02138
E-mail: Bunting_Fellowships@radcliffe.harvard.edu
Web site: http://www.radcliffe.edu/bunting
Fax: 617-495-8136

The *Bunting Fellowship Program* supports women scholars, artists, and activists of exceptional promise and demonstrated accomplishment who wish to pursue independent work in academic and professional fields and the creative arts. Appointments are full-time, for September 15–August 15, and require residence in the Boston area during the term. The fellowship stipend for the year is $40,000, with additional privileges. Applicants should have received their doctorate or appropriate terminal degree at least two years before appointment. Academic applicants without doctorates but with equivalent professional experience will be considered. Applicants in fiction and nonfiction must have a contract for the publication of a book-length manuscript, or must have had at least three short works published; publication in the last five years is highly desirable. Applicants in poetry must have had at least twenty poems or a book of poetry published in the last five years, and be in the process of completing a manuscript. Writers must wait three years to reapply after a previous application to the Institute. Write, e-mail, or visit the Web site for additional information.

Available to: See above
Deadline: October 1
Apply to: Bunting Fellowship Program, above address

Bush Artist Fellows Program
E-900 First National Bank Building
332 Minnesota Street
St. Paul, MN 55101

Ⓜ Grants are made to selected artists to enable them to set aside time for concentrating on the development of their artistic talent. Awards are made in seven categories, which rotate on a two-year cycle: visual arts, two-dimensional; visual arts, three-dimensional; choreography/multimedia/performance art; literature (fiction, creative nonfiction, poetry); music composition; scriptworks (playwriting and screenwriting); and film/video. Writers must meet certain prior-publication requirements. Fellowships are for twelve to eighteen months, with a stipend of $40,000. Students are not eligible.

Available to: Minnesota, North Dakota, South Dakota, and western Wisconsin residents, nonstudents, age twenty-five or older, who have been residents of the region for at least twelve of the preceding thirty-six months
Deadline: Inquire
Apply to: Above address

Buttonwood Press
PO Box 206
Champaign, IL 61824-0206
Web site: http://www.butwood.com

Ⓟ The *Magellan Prize for the Year 2002* will be given for an unpublished poetry manuscript of 60 to 100 pages. The winner will receive $1,000 and publication by Buttonwood. All entrants will receive a copy of the prize-winning book. There is a $20 reading fee. Send SASE or visit the Web site for guidelines.

Available to: No restrictions
Deadline: June 30, 2001
Apply to: Magellan Prize, above address

Witter Bynner Foundation for Poetry
PO Box 10169
Santa Fe, NM 87504
E-mail: bynner@mciworld.com
Fax: 505-986-8222

Ⓟ The Foundation offers grants in support of poetry translation and the process of translation, developing an audience for poetry, and uses of poetry. Applicants must be sponsored by a nonprofit organization, and a letter of intent must be submitted before an application form can be issued. Letters of intent are accepted from September 1 through January 1.

Available to: See above
Deadline: February 1 for application; September 1–January 1 for letter of intent
Apply to: Above address

California Arts Council
1300 I Street, Suite 930
Sacramento, CA 95814
E-mail: cac@cwo.com
Web site: http://www.cac.ca.gov
Fax: 916-322-6575

Ⓜ *Artists Fellowships* are given to exemplary California artists in recognition of outstanding artistic achievement. Fellowships are offered in various disciplines on a rotating basis; the next literature cycle is 2001–2002. Applicants must be legal residents of California for one year before the application deadline. Write, e-mail, or visit the Web site for further information and application.

Available to: See above
Deadline: Inquire
Apply to: Artists Fellowship Program, above address

The *Artists in Residence Program* provides funding for projects that emphasize long-term, in-depth interaction between professional California artists and an organizing group of participants through workshops and classes sponsored by schools, nonprofit organizations, units of government, social institutions, and tribal councils. The Program effectively forges a partnership among artists, sponsors, and the citizens of California. Funding varies according to the nature of the proposed project. Write, e-mail, or visit the Web site for further information and application.

Available to: See above
Deadline: Inquire
Apply to: Artists in Residence Program, above address

California Library Association
717 K Street, Suite 300
Sacramento, CA 95814-3477
E-mail: info@cla-net.org
Web site: http://www.cla-net.org/groups/beatty/beatty

© The *John and Patricia Beatty Award* offers $500 for a children's or young adult book "highlighting California, its culture, heritage and/or future. The California setting must be depicted authentically and must serve as an integral focus for the book." Any children's or young adult book, fiction or nonfiction, set in California and published in the United States during the calendar year preceding the presentation of the award is eligible. Write, e-mail, or visit the Web site for submission procedures.

Available to: No restrictions
Deadline: Inquire
Apply to: John and Patricia Beatty Award, above address

Camargo Foundation
125 Park Square Court
400 Sibley Street
St. Paul, MN 55101-1928
E-mail: camargo@jeromefdn.org

®   The Camargo Foundation offers fellowships consisting of free residence in fully furnished self-catering apartments in Cassis, France, to members of universities and college faculties, teachers in secondary schools, graduate students, and writers, photographers, visual artists, and musicians who are in an advanced stage of a project that will benefit from residence near Marseilles and Aix-en-Provence. Applicants must be working on subjects in the humanities relating to French and/or Francophone culture. Candidates are asked to submit an application form, a vita, and a detailed description of the project they wish to complete in France. Three letters of recommendation are also required. Write for additional information and application.

Available to: See above
Deadline: February 1
Apply to: Above address

Cambridge Arts Council
57 Inman Street, 2nd floor
Cambridge, MA 02139
E-mail: cac@ci.cambridge.ma.us
Web site: http://www.ci.cambridge.ma.us/~CAC
Fax: 617-349-4669

Ⓜ   *Arts Lottery Grants* are available for projects in the arts, humanities, interpretative sciences, and writing that are conducted in Cambridge and publicly benefit the local community. Applicants must live or work in Cambridge. Send SASE or e-mail for guidelines and application.

Available to: See above
Deadline: October 15
Apply to: Arts Lottery Grants, above address

Campbell Corner
Sarah Lawrence College
1 Mead Way
Bronxville, NY 10708-5999
Web site: http://www.slc.edu/campbellcorner

Ⓟ Ⓝ   Campbell Corner, a new language exchange forum on the Sarah Lawrence College Web site named for mythologist Joseph Campbell, sponsors the *Campbell Corner Poetry Prize* and the *Campbell Corner Essay Prize*. Each competition awards $2,500 and publication on the Corner's Literary Exchange. The winner of the poetry prize will also be invited, along with three finalists, to give a public reading at Sarah Lawrence College. Poets should submit one to three poems "resonating with the transcultural dialogue that Joseph Campbell's writing promotes," and essayists a 1,500-to-5,000-word essay on "transmissions and transgressions of the Holy," in three hard-copy sets and one disk in ASCII text format. There is no entry fee.

Available to: No restrictions
Deadline: March 15
Apply to: Phillis Levin, Department of English, 3101 Susquehanna Hall, University of Maryland, College Park, MD 20742, for poetry prize; Director of Graduate Studies, above address, for essay prize

CANADA
Banff Centre for the Arts
Box 1020, Station 28
107 Tunnel Mountain Drive
Banff, Alberta T0L 0C0
Canada
E-mail: registrars_office@banffcentre.ab.ca
Web site: http://www.banffcentre.ab.ca
Fax: 403-762-6345

Ⓙ The Banff Centre *Creative Nonfiction and Cultural Journalism Program* offers eight established nonfiction writers an opportunity to develop a major essay, memoir, or feature piece in the domain of arts and culture. The program consists of a month-long residence at the Centre for the selected writers, who work to complete original projects brought to Banff in draft form. Writers receive a $3,000 commission for their work ($1,000 paid on arrival for their first draft, and the balance on completion). There is a processing fee of $50 Canadian. Write, e-mail, or visit the Web site for additional information and application procedures.

Available to: No restrictions
Deadline: March (inquire for exact date)
Apply to: Office of the Registrar, above address

Ⓡ The *Leighton Studios for Independent Residencies* provide residence periods of one week to three months for senior-level writers, composers, and visual artists engaged in the creation of new work. Selection is ongoing. Interested artists are encouraged to apply at least six months before the start of the requested residence. Studio fees are $46.50 Canadian per day; artists may apply to the Centre for a discount. Write, e-mail, or visit the Web site for additional information.

Available to: Established artists
Deadlines: Ongoing
Apply to: Leighton Studios Registrar, above address

CANADA
Lionel Gelber Prize
Meisner Publicity
112 Braemore Gardens
Toronto, Ontario M6G 2C8
Canada
E-mail: meisner@interlog.com
Fax: 416-658-5205

Ⓝ The *Lionel Gelber Prize* is a $50,000 award presented annually to the author of the year's most outstanding work of nonfiction in international relations. The award, designed to encourage writers on international relations and to increase the audience for their books, is open to all nationalities. Six copies of each title must be submitted by the publisher. Books must be published between September 1 and August 31 of the following year, in English or English translation, and must be distributed or available for sale in Canada. Write or e-mail for additional information.

Available to: No restrictions
Deadline: May 31; for titles to be published between June 1 and August 31, submit bound galleys or spiral-bound typescript in lieu of finished book
Apply to: Prize Manager, above address

CANADA
Grain Magazine
Box 1154
Regina, Saskatchewan S4P 3B4
Canada
E-mail: grain.mag@sk.sympatico.ca
Web site: www.skwriter.com

Ⓜ The *Short Grain Writing Contest* annually offers a $500 first prize, a $250 second prize, and a
$125 third prize in each of four categories: Postcard Story, a work of narrative fiction in
500 words or less; Prose Poem, a lyric poem written as a prose paragraph of 500 words or
less; Dramatic Monologue, a self-contained speech given by a single character in 500
words or less; and Long Grain of Truth, a nonfiction creative prose piece of 500 words or
less. The winning works will be published in *Grain*, a quarterly literary journal published
by the Saskatchewan Writers Guild. The entry fee is $22 Canadian for a maximum of two
entries in one category. For an additional $5, you may enter an additional piece in any
category of your choice. You may enter as many times as you wish, in as many categories
as you wish. The entry fee covers a one-year subscription to *Grain* (entrants outside Canada
should add the equivalent of $4 Canadian for postage). Write, visit the Web site, or e-mail
for guidelines.

Available to: No restrictions
Deadline: January 31
Apply to: Short Grain Writing Contest, above address; e-mail entries not accepted

CANADA
Malahat Review
University of Victoria
PO Box 1700
Victoria, British Columbia V8W 2Y2
Canada
Web site: http://web.uvic.ca/~malahat/contests.htm
Fax: 604-721-7212

Ⓕ Ⓟ The *Malahat Review Long Poem Prize* and *Novella Prize* award $400 Canadian, plus payment
for publication at their regular rate of $30 for each published page, for a long poem and a
novella, respectively. The prizes are given in alternate years; the novella prize will be
awarded in 2000, the poetry prize in 2001. The $25 entry fee is payable in U.S. funds and
covers a one-year subscription to the *Review*. Send SASE or visit the Web site for guidelines.

Available to: No restrictions
Deadline: March 1, 2001, for Long Poem Prize; March 1, 2002, for Novella Prize
Apply to: Long Poem Prize or Novella Prize, above address

CANADA
PRISM international
Creative Writing Program
University of British Columbia
Buch E 462 - 1866 Main Mall
Vancouver, British Columbia V6T 1Z1
Canada
E-mail: prism@interchange.ubc.ca
Web site: http://www.arts.ubc.ca/prism
Fax: 604-822-3616

Ⓝ The *Maclean–Hunter Endowment Award for Literary Nonfiction* offers a first prize of $1,500 for
the best piece of literary nonfiction no longer than 25 pages. The winning entry will be
published in *PRISM international*, the university's literary magazine, and the writer will
receive an additional payment of $20 per page. The entry fee is $20 for one piece of
nonfiction, $5 for each additional piece; the entry fee covers a one-year subscription to
PRISM. Canadian residents may use Canadian funds, but entrants outside Canada should
use U.S. dollars to cover the international mailing costs. E-mail submissions are not
accepted. Write, e-mail, or visit the Web site for guidelines.

Available to: No restrictions
Deadline: September 30
Apply to: Maclean–Hunter Endowment Award, above address

Ⓕ The *PRISM international Short Fiction Contest* annually awards a $2,000 first prize and five $200 runner-up prizes for short stories no longer than 25 pages. The six winning stories will be published in the summer fiction contest issue; writers will receive an additional payment of $20 per page, plus $10 per page if chosen for the Web site. There is a $22 entry fee for one story, $5 for each additional story; the entry fee covers a one-year subscription to *PRISM*. Canadian residents may use Canadian funds, but entrants outside Canada should use U.S. dollars to cover the international mailing costs. E-mail submissions are not accepted. Write, e-mail, or visit the Web site for guidelines.

Available to: No restrictions
Deadline: Inquire (December or January)
Apply to: Short Fiction Contest, above address

CANADA
Saskatchewan Writers/Artists Colony
c/o Saskatchewan Writers Guild
PO Box 3986
Regina, Saskatchewan S4P 3R9
Canada
Web site: http://www.skwriter.com/colonies.html
Fax: 306-565-8554

Ⓡ The Saskatchewan Writers/Artists Colony offers residences to writers and visual artists at two retreats in Saskatchewan: St. Peter's Abbey (two weeks in February or six weeks in July/August) and Emma Lake (two weeks in August). The weekly fee is $125 Canadian for Guild members, or $175 Canadian for nonmembers. Writers from anywhere are welcome to apply. Write, fax, or visit the Web site for additional information and guidelines. Faxed applications are not accepted.

Available to: No restrictions
Deadline: December 1 for winter colony; May 1 for summer
Apply to: Above address

CANADA
University of British Columbia
Department of Theatre, Film and Creative Writing
Buch E-462
1866 Main Mall
Vancouver, British Columbia V6T 1Z1
Canada
E-mail: resprize@interchange.ubc.ca
Web site: http://www.arts.ubc.ca/crwr/resprize
Fax: 604-822-0231

Ⓓ Ⓡ The *UBC Creative Writing Residency Prize in Stageplay* offers $25,000 and a one-month residence at the University of British Columbia for an original, previously unproduced and unpublished full-length play. While on campus, the winning playwright will mentor creative-writing students, work with theater students and faculty on the development of the play for performance, and deliver the Stageplay Residency Lecture. The winning play will be published in *PRISM international*, UBC's literary magazine, and a public performance will be presented at the campus theater. There is a $50 entry fee, payable in U.S. dollars for entrants outside of Canada. Write, e-mail, or visit the Web site for guidelines.

Available to: No restrictions
Deadline: April 30, 2000; inquire for subsequent years
Apply to: Steven Galloway, Stageplay Prize Coordinator, above address

Carnegie Fund for Authors
1 Old Country Road
Carle Place, NY 11514

The Carnegie Fund offers grants-in-aid to qualified commercially published book authors who have suffered financial emergency as a result of illness or injury, their own or that of spouses or dependent children, or who have suffered some equivalent misfortune. Grant amounts vary according to need.

Available to: See above
Deadline: None
Apply to: Above address

Carolina Quarterly
CB #3520 Greenlaw Hall
University of North Carolina
Chapel Hill, NC 27599-3520

Ⓕ Ⓟ The *Charles B. Wood Award for Distinguished Writing* offers $500 for the best poem or short story by an emerging writer published during the year in *Carolina Quarterly*. All poems and short stories by emerging writers are considered.

Available to: *Carolina Quarterly* contributors
Deadline: None
Apply to: Above address

The Carter Center
453 Freedom Parkway
One Copenhill
Atlanta, GA 30307
E-mail: ccmph@emory.edu
Web site: http://www.cartercenter.org

Ⓙ Five *Rosalynn Carter Fellowships for Mental Health Journalism* are awarded annually to print and broadcast journalists to study a selected topic in mental health or mental illness. Fellows receive a grant of $10,000 to cover expenses, including travel, materials, and other incidentals. In addition, fellows make two expense-paid visits to The Carter Center, the first at the beginning of the fellowship year, when fellows meet with advisors to discuss project plans, the second at the end, when fellows present their completed projects. Write, e-mail, or visit the Web site for additional information and application procedures.

Available to: Print and broadcast journalists with at least two years' experience
Deadline: Inquire
Apply to: John Gates, Director, Rosalynn Carter Fellowships for Mental Health Journalism, above address

Case Western Reserve University
Department of Theater Arts
10900 Euclid Avenue
Cleveland, OH 44106-7077
Web site: http://www.cwru.edu/artsci/thtr/website/Home.htm

Ⓓ The *Marc A. Klein Playwriting Award* offers $500, full production, and an additional $500 during the rehearsal period to defray travel and living expenses, for a previously unpublished, unproduced full-length play, or evenings of thematically related one-acts by a student currently enrolled at a U.S. college or university. Musicals and children's plays are not eligible. Write for additional information and entry form.

Available to: See above
Deadline: May 15
Apply to: Marc A. Klein Playwriting Award, above address

Catawba College
Theatre Arts Department
Salisbury, NC 28144
E-mail: jepperso@catawba.edu
Fax: 704-637-4207

Ⓓ The *Peterson Emerging Playwright Competition* annually offers $2,000, full production, and transportation and room and board to attend rehearsals and performances for an unpublished, unproduced full-length play by an emerging playwright. Send SASE or e-mail for guidelines.

Available to: No restrictions
Deadline: March 15
Apply to: James R. Epperson, Chair, above address

Cave Canem Foundation
39 Jane Street #GB
New York, NY 10014
E-mail: micked@aol.com

Ⓟ The *Cave Canem Poetry Prize* awards a three-year fellowship to Cave Canem's summer workshop/retreat and publication by a distinguished small press (Graywolf Press for the 1999 winner) for a manuscript of poems by an African-American poet who has not yet had a book professionally published. Send SASE for additional information and guidelines.

Available to: African-American poets
Deadline: Inquire
Apply to: Cave Canem Prize, above address

CCS Entertainment Group
433 North Camden Drive, Suite 600
Beverly Hills, CA 90210
Web site: http://hollywoodawards.com

Ⓢ The *Christopher Columbus Screenplay Discovery Awards* option screenplays for up to $10,000. One screenplay will be selected monthly to receive rewrite notes and become a finalist as *Screenplay Discovery of the Year*. First-, second-, and third-place winners in the yearly competition will be offered film options by Breaking In Productions and will receive a gift certificate to the Hollywood Film Institute. Registration is $55 per script. Write for guidelines and release form.

Available to: No restrictions
Deadline: Last day of each month for monthly selection; August 1 for annual cycle
Apply to: Screenplay Discovery Awards, above address

Ⓕ Ⓝ The *Opus Magnum Discovery Awards* are given for completed, unpublished works of fiction and nonfiction suitable for film adaptation. First-, second-, and third-place winners will be offered film options for up to $10,000 by Breaking In Productions. Registration is $75 per manuscript. Write for guidelines and release form.

Available to: No restrictions
Deadline: Last day of each month
Apply to: Opus Magnum Discovery Awards, above address

CEC International Partners
12 West 31st Street
New York, NY 10001-4415
E-mail: artslink@cecip.org
Fax: 212-643-1996

ArtsLink Collaborative Projects offers grants of up to $10,000 to enable creative artists, including writers and translators, to work with counterparts in Central or Eastern Europe and the Newly Independent States of the former Soviet Union on projects that will enrich the artists' work and/or create new work that draws inspiration from experience in the country visited. Write for guidelines and application.

Available to: U.S. citizens or permanent residents
Deadline: January 18, 2000 (inquire for 2001)
Apply to: ArtsLink, above address

Centenary College of Louisiana
Department of English
PO Box 41188
Shreveport, LA 71134-1188

[IN] The *John William Corrington Award for Literary Excellence* offers up to $2,000 and a bronze medal in honor of lifetime achievement. The winner is chosen by a committee of the college's Student Government Association and the English faculty. There is no application process. *By Internal Nomination Only.*

Center for Book Arts
28 West 27th Street, 3rd floor
New York, NY 10001

(P) The Center for Book Arts *Poetry Chapbook Competition* offers a cash award of $500, a $500 reading honorarium, and publication of a letterpressed, limited-edition chapbook printed and bound by artists at the Center. Poets may submit typescripts of a collection of poems, totaling no more than 500 lines or 24 pages. There is a $15 reading fee for each submission. Send SASE for guidelines.

Available to: No restrictions
Deadline: December 1
Apply to: Poetry Chapbook Competition, above address

Center for Documentary Studies
Duke University
1317 West Pettigrew Street
Durham, NC 27705
Web site: http://cds.aas.duke.edu/l-t

(N) The *Dorothea Lange–Paul Taylor Prize* of $10,000 is given to fund collaborative work between a writer and a photographer in the formative or field-work stages of a documentary project. Submissions on any subject are welcome. At the end of one year, prizewinners are invited to the Center to make a public presentation based on their field-work. Applications are accepted from collaborators only; individual submissions will not be accepted. More than two people may apply, as long as one is a writer and one a photographer working with black-and-white or color still photography. There is a $10 application fee. Send SASE or visit the Web site for guidelines and application.

Available to: See above
Deadline: January 31
Apply to: Dorothea Lange–Paul Taylor Prize Committee, above address

Center for Environmental Journalism
University of Colorado
Campus Box 287
Boulder, CO 80309-0287
E-mail: cej@colorado.edu
Web site: http://campuspress.colorado.edu/CEJ/Scripps.html

(J) The *Ted Scripps Environmental Fellowship Program* blends classroom and field training at the University of Colorado's Center for Environmental Journalism to help professional journalists acquire knowledge to cover the environment more effectively and enrich public understanding. Five fellowships are awarded each year. Fellows receive tuition, fee payment, and a stipend of $33,000 for the nine-month academic year. Write for additional information.

Available to: U.S. citizens with a minimum of five years' full-time professional journalism experience
Deadline: March 1, 2000; inquire for 2001
Apply to: Len Ackland, Director, above address

Center for the Pacific Rim
University of San Francisco
2130 Fulton Street
San Francisco, CA 94117-1080
E-mail: admin@pacificrimvoices.org
Web site: http://pacificrimvoices.org
Fax: 415-422-5933

Ⓕ Ⓝ The *Kiriyama Pacific Rim Book Prize* annually awards $15,000 each for a book of fiction and one of nonfiction that promote "greater understanding among the nations and peoples of the Pacific Rim." Books must have been published in English, either originally or in translation, between November 1 of the preceding year and October 31 of the prize year. Books may be submitted as finished copies or bound galleys. Publishers may submit a maximum of three titles in each category. Write, e-mail, or visit the Web site for guidelines and required entry form.

Available to: No restrictions
Deadline: July 1
Apply to: Kiriyama Pacific Rim Book Prize, above address

Center Press
PO Box 17897
Encino, CA 91416
Web site: http://members.xoom.com/centerpress

Ⓜ The *Masters Literary Awards* annually offer a grand prize of $1,000 and possible publication in the Center Press Internet journal. Nominations for honorable mentions are made quarterly in fiction, poetry and song lyrics, and nonfiction; the grand-prize winner is selected from among the honorable mentions. Published and unpublished manuscripts alike are eligible. There is a $15 reading fee per entry. Send SASE or visit the Web site for guidelines and additional information.

Available to: No restrictions
Deadline: Ongoing (nominations made March 15, June 15, September 15, December 15)
Apply to: Masters Literary Awards, above address

Center for Southern Studies
Jacksonville State University
228 Stone Center
Jacksonville, AL 36265
E-mail: swhitton@jsucc.jsu.edu
Web site: http://www.jsu.edu/depart/english/southpla.htm
Fax: 205-782-5441

Ⓓ The *Southern Playwrights Competition* offers $1,000 and full-scale production for full-length plays that deal with the southern experience and have not received Equity production. Write, e-mail, or visit the Web site for guidelines and entry form.

Available to: Natives or residents of Alabama, Arkansas, Florida, Georgia, Kentucky, Louisiana, Mississippi, North Carolina, South Carolina, Tennessee, Virginia, and West Virginia
Deadline: February 15
Apply to: Steven J. Whitton, above address

Centrum
Fort Worden State Park
PO Box 1158
Port Townsend, WA 98368
Web site: http//www.centrum.org
Fax: 360-385-2470

® *Centrum Residencies,* varying in length from one week to two months, offer the opportunity for reflection and intense creative work. Housing consists of three modest cottages (two or three bedrooms each) and three apartments (two or three bedrooms each), for residences February through May and September through December. Write for additional information and guidelines.

Available to: No restrictions
Deadline: Inquire
Apply to: Above address

Cerritos College
The Original Theatre Works
Burnight Center
11110 Alondra Boulevard
Norwalk, CA 90650-6298

Ⓓ The *Lee Korf Playwriting Awards* annually offer $750 plus production. Plays with multicultural themes are encouraged. Send SASE for guidelines and application before submitting.

Available to: No restrictions
Deadline: September 1
Apply to: Lee Korf Playwriting Awards, attn: Gloria Manriquez, above address

Charlotte Writers Club
PO Box 220954
Charlotte, NC 28222-0954

Ⓕ The *Elizabeth Simpson Smith Award* of $500 is given for the best original unpublished short story of less than 4,000 words written by a North or South Carolina resident. Send SASE for guidelines.

Available to: Residents of North and South Carolina
Deadline: April 30
Apply to: Rebecca Schenck, Elizabeth Simpson Smith Award Chair, above address

Chattahoochee Review
Georgia Perimeter College
2101 Womack Road
Dunwoody, GA 30338-4497
Web site: http://www.gpc.peachnet.edu/~twadley/cr/prize.htm

Ⓝ The *Lamar York Prize for Nonfiction* offers $1,000 and publication in the *Chattahoochee Review,* a literary magazine, for an essay of up to 5,000 words. Scholarly, critical, and theoretical essays are not eligible; all other approaches and topics are welcome. There is a $10 reading fee. All entries will be considered for publication. Send SASE for guidelines.

Available to: No restrictions
Deadline: Submissions accepted October 1–January 15
Apply to: Lamar York Prize, above address

Chelsea Award Competition
c/o Richard Foerster, Editor
PO Box 1040
York Beach, ME 03910

Ⓕ Ⓟ *Chelsea* awards two annual prizes of $1,000 for the best unpublished work of short fiction (7,500 words or less) and the best group of four to six unpublished poems (500 lines or less) selected in anonymous competitions. Winning entries are published in *Chelsea*; all work entered is considered for publication. The $10 entry fee covers a one-year subscription to *Chelsea*. Send SASE for guidelines.

Available to: No restrictions
Deadlines: June 15 for fiction; December 15 for poetry
Apply to: Above address; all other business to Box 773, Cooper Station, New York, NY 10276

Chesterfield Film Company
1158 26th Street, PMB 544
Santa Monica, CA 90403
Web site: http://www.chesterfield-co.com
Fax: 310-260-6116

ⓈThe *Chesterfield Film Company/Writers' Film Project* annually selects up to five writers for a year-long screenwriting fellowship in Los Angeles, which offers a $20,000 stipend to cover living expenses. Each writer chosen creates two original feature-length screenplays with the advice of professional screenwriters and executive mentors. Writers meet in a workshop setting three to five times a week to consider story ideas, script outlines, and drafts. Current and former writing program students are encouraged to apply. Writers may submit short stories, novels, plays, or screenplays. The application fee is $39.50. Send SASE or visit the Web site for application materials.

Available to: No restrictions
Deadline: Inquire
Apply to: Writers' Film Project, above address

The Chicago Reporter
332 South Michigan Avenue, Suite 500
Chicago, IL 60604
Web site: http://www.chicagoreporter.com
Fax: 312-427-6130

ⒿThe *Chicago Reporter Minority Fellowship in Urban Journalism,* supported by the Robert R. McCormick Tribune Foundation of Chicago, is offered to a talented, aggressive minority journalist to work for a year as a full-time reporter at the *Reporter*, an award-winning investigative monthly. The fellowship offers a competitive salary and benefits, and opportunities for continuing education. Interested candidates should send a résumé and clippings of five articles they have written. Write or visit the Web site for additional information.

Available to: Minority journalists
Deadline: March 1
Apply to: Laura Washington, Editor and Publisher, above address

Chicago Tribune
435 North Michigan Avenue
Chicago, IL 60611

ⒻThe *Nelson Algren Awards for Short Fiction* offer a first prize of $5,000 and three runner-up prizes of $1,000 each for outstanding unpublished short stories by American writers. The winning stories will be published in the *Tribune*. Stories should be typed double-spaced, and between 2,500 and 10,000 words. Manuscripts will not be returned.

Available to: U.S. citizens
Deadline: January 31 (no submissions accepted before November 1)
Apply to: Nelson Algren Awards, Chicago Tribune Editorial Department, above address

Ⓕ ⓃThe *Heartland Prizes* award $5,000 each for a novel and a book of nonfiction embodying the spirit of the nation's heartland. Books published between the August 1 preceding the deadline year and July 31 of that year are eligible.

Available to: U.S. citizens
Deadline: July 31
Apply to: Heartland Prizes, above address

Children's Book Guild of Washington, D.C.
c/o Susan Hepler
2602 Valley Drive
Alexandria, VA 22302
Web site: http://www.childrensbookguild.org

IN   The *Washington Post/Children's Book Guild Nonfiction Award* offers $1,000 annually to the author
of an outstanding body of nonfiction work for children. There is no application process.
By Internal Nomination Only.

Children's Literature Association
PO Box 138
Battle Creek, MI 49016
E-mail: chla@mlc.lib.mi.us
Web site: http://www.ebbs.english.vt.edu/chla
Fax: 616-965-3568

©   The *Children's Literature Association Research Fellowships and Scholarships*, ranging from $250 to
$1,000, are given to support any activity related to serious literary criticism or original
scholarship of children's literature that will, presumably, lead to publication and contribute
significantly to the field. Awards may be used for transportation, living expenses, or
materials, but not for obtaining advanced degrees, researching or writing a thesis or
dissertation, writing textbooks, conducting pedagogical projects, or supplementing
summer salaries. Write for additional information and guidelines.

Available to: Scholars who have completed an advanced degree program
Deadline: February 1
Apply to: Above address

Children's Literature Research Collections
University of Minnesota
Elmer L. Andersen Library
222-21st Avenue, South
Minneapolis, MN 55455
E-mail: clrc@tc.umn.edu
Web site: http://www.lib.umn.edu/special/kerlan
Fax: 612-625-5525

©   The *Ezra Jack Keats/Kerlan Collection Memorial Fellowship* provides $1,500 to a talented aspiring
writer and/or illustrator of children's books who wishes to use the Kerlan Collection for
furthering his or her artistic development. Special consideration is given to those for
whom it would be difficult to finance the visit. The Kerlan Collection contains more than
66,000 children's books, primarily by twentieth-century American writers, and manuscript
and illustration material for at least 9,100 titles. Also included are more than 300 periodical
and more than 1,200 reference titles, as well as letters, posters, toys, photographs,
audiovisuals, publishers' catalogues, and a figurine collection.

Available to: No restrictions
Deadline: First business day in May
Apply to: Ezra Jack Keats/Kerlan Collection Memorial Fellowship Committee, above
address

The Children's Theatre Foundation of America
Box 8067
New Orleans, LA 70182
Fax: 504-866-0502

© ⒹThe *Aurand Harris Children's Theatre Fellowships* offer up to $2,500 to theatre artists, including
playwrights, to work on specific projects or professional development related to children's
theater. Send SASE for guidelines.

Available to: U.S. residents
Deadline: April 30
Apply to: Aurand Harris Fellowships, above address

Christopher Columbus Fellowship Foundation
2001 Jefferson Davis Highway, Suite 804
Crystal Plaza One
Arlington, VA 22202
E-mail: 105621.1575@compuserve.com
Web site: http://www.columbusfdn.org
Fax: 703-305-7692

The *Frank Annunzio Award* offers a $100,000 fellowship to a living individual American whose innovative thinking has led to a creative work, process, product, or other discovery that, time has shown, has made a significant and beneficial impact on society. Write for guidelines and required nomination form. Self-nominations are not accepted.

Available to: U.S. citizens
Deadline: June 30
Apply to: Judith Shellenberger, Executive Director, above address

Cincinnati Playhouse in the Park
Box 6537
Cincinnati, OH 45206
Web site: http://www.cincyplay.com

Ⓓ The *Lois and Richard Rosenthal New Play Prize* offers $10,000, a full production in the subsequent season, plus paid travel expenses for a residence in Cincinnati during rehearsals, for an unpublished full-length play that has not been produced professionally. Translations and adaptations are not eligible. Playwrights may submit only one script per year. Submit a two pages of synopsis, a character list and playwright bio, and five pages of sample dialogue; furnish cassette tape or CD for musicals. Materials will not be returned without SASE with correct postage.

Available to: No restrictions
Deadline: Submissions accepted July 1–December 31
Apply to: Rosenthal New Play Prize, above address

Cintas Foundation
c/o William Warren, President
Dewey Ballantine LLP
1301 Avenue of the Americas, Room 2900
New York, NY 10019

The *Cintas Fellowship Program* offers at least four grants of $10,000 each in architecture, music, literature, and the visual arts for Cuban professional artists living outside Cuba. Fellowships are awarded annually and rotate among genres and disciplines; they may not be used for study programs. Write for additional information and application.

Available to: Cuban citizens or individuals of Cuban descent living outside of Cuba
Deadline: March 15
Apply to: Cintas Fellowship Program, above address

City of Atlanta Bureau of Cultural Affairs
675 Ponce de Leon Avenue
Atlanta, GA 30308
Fax: 404-817-6827

Ⓜ *Artist Project Grants* are designed to support practicing professional artists, including writers, residing in Atlanta. Grants of up to $3,000 are offered for projects by poets, fiction writers, creative nonfiction writers, and playwrights who demonstrate a consistent level of high-quality work.

Available to: Atlanta residents
Deadline: December
Apply to: Nikki Tucker, Grants Administrator, above address

Ⓜ The *Mayor's Fellowships in the Arts* program annually awards $5,000 to a practicing professional artist who has resided in Atlanta for at least three consecutive years immediately prior to the deadline. The awards rotate among several artistic disciplines. The next literary arts fellowship will be awarded in 2002. Write for guidelines and application.

Available to: Atlanta residents
Deadline: Inquire for exact date and yearly discipline
Apply to: Nikki Tucker, Grants Administrator, above address

Civil War Institute
Gettysburg College
233 North Washington Street
Gettysburg, PA 17325
E-mail: civilwar@gettysburg.edu
Web site: http://www.gettysburg.edu
Fax: 717-337-6596

Ⓜ The *Lincoln Prize* annually awards $50,000 for the finest scholarly work on the era of the American Civil War published during the calendar year. Preference is given to work on Lincoln and the Civil War soldier, and work that addresses the literate general public. In rare instances the prize may go to a work of fiction, poetry, drama, or film. Ten copies of the work should be submitted to the Institute. Work that will not be in its final form until the end of the year may be submitted in galley form; copies of the published work must follow as soon as they are available.

Available to: No restrictions
Deadline: November 1
Apply to: Lincoln Prize, above address

Clackamas Literary Review
19600 South Molalla Avenue
Oregon City, OR 97045
Web site: http://www.clackamas.cc.or.us/Instruct/English/clr/index.htm

Ⓕ Ⓟ The *Willamette Award in Fiction and Poetry* offers $500 in each category and publication in the *Review* for a short story and a poem. Writers should submit one short story of no more than 10,000 words or one to three poems, along with a $10 reading fee. Send SASE or visit the Web site for further information.

Available to: No restrictions
Deadline: June 1
Apply to: Willamette Award (specify genre), above address

Claremont Graduate University
160 East 10th Street
Claremont, CA 91711-6160
Fax: 909-607-9103

Ⓟ The *Kate Tufts Discovery Award*, of $5,000, is given for "a first or very early work by a poet of genuine promise." Write for guidelines and entry form before submitting.

Ⓟ The *Kingsley Tufts Poetry Award* offers a $50,000 prize for a book of poems written in English by an emerging poet, "one who is past the very beginning but has not yet reached the acknowledged pinnacle of his or her career." The submitted text must be either published or completed during the calendar year, and may be submitted by the author or, with the author's consent, by a publisher, agent, or other representative. Work scheduled for publication after the deadline may be submitted in the form of typescript or proofs. Write for guidelines and entry form.

Available to: U.S. citizens or legal residents
Deadline: September 15
Apply to: Kate Tufts Poetry Award and Kingsley Tufts Poetry Award, above address

Clauder Competition for Excellence in Playwriting
PO Box 383259
Cambridge, MA 02238
Web site: http://www.theatrics.net/clauder_competition

Ⓓ The *Clauder Competition for Excellence in Playwriting* biennially offers a first prize of $3,000 and full production for full-length plays by New England playwrights that have not been produced professionally. Runners-up receive $500 and a staged reading. The next competition will be held in 2001. Send SASE for guidelines.

Available to: New England playwrights
Deadline: Inquire for 2001
Apply to: Above address

Cleveland Foundation
1422 Euclid Avenue, Suite 1400
Cleveland, OH 44115-2001
Web site: http://www.clevelandfoundation.org
Fax: 216-861-1729

Ⓜ The *Anisfield-Wolf Book Awards* "recognize recent books which have made important contributions to our understanding of racism or our appreciation of the rich diversity of human cultures." An award of $10,000 is given annually for books written in English and published in the preceding calendar year. If multiple winners are chosen in a given year, the $10,000 is divided equally among the winning books. Copies of eligible books should be sent directly to the panel of jurors.

Available to: No restrictions
Deadline: January 31
Apply to: Above address for list of current jurors

Cleveland Public Theatre
6415 Detroit Avenue
Cleveland, OH 44102
E-mail: cpt@en.com
Web site: http://www.clevelandartists.net/cpt
Fax: 216-631-2575

Ⓓ The *New Plays Festival* annually selects twelve to sixteen new works for three weeks of staged readings. Selected playwrights will be flown to Cleveland for the Festival. The script chosen as "Best of Festival" will receive the *Frank K. and Janet Levin Award*, of $500 to $1,000. Write, e-mail, or visit the Web site for further information.

Available to: No restrictions
Deadline: Inquire
Apply to: New Plays Festival, above address

Cleveland State University
Poetry Center
Department of English
Rhodes Tower, Room 1815
1983 East 24th Street
Cleveland, OH 44115-2440
E-mail: poetrycenter@popmail.csuohio.edu
Web site: http://www.ims.csuohio.edu/poetry/poetrycenter.html

Ⓟ The *Poetry Center Prize* annually awards $1,000 and publication in the CSU Poetry Series for a volume of original poetry. Other contest entries may be selected for additional volumes in the series. Submission should consist of a book-length manuscript (50 to 100 pages) with the poet's name, address, and phone number appearing on the cover sheet only. Previously published collections, including self-published books, are not eligible. There is a $20 submission fee. Send SASE for guidelines.

Available to: No restrictions
Deadline: Submissions accepted November 1–February 1
Apply to: Poetry Center Prize, above address

Coalition for the Advancement of Jewish Education
261 West 35th Street, Floor 12A
New York, New York 10001
E-mail: 500-8447@mcimail.com
Web site: http://www.caje.org
Fax: 212-268-4214

Ⓕ The *David Dornstein Memorial Creative Writing Contest for Young Adult Writers* offers a $750 first prize and a $250 second prize for a short story on a Jewish theme or topic by a writer age eighteen to thirty-five. If three winning stories are chosen, the first-place winner will receive $700, the second $200, and the third $100. CAJE will attempt to publish all winning stories in *Jewish Education News*. Writers may submit one unpublished story of 5,000 words or less by mail, fax, or e-mail. Send SASE or e-mail for guidelines.

Available to: No restrictions
Deadline: December 31
Apply to: David Dornstein Contest, above address

Coldwater Community Theater
c/o J. Richard Colbeck, Award Chairman
89 South Division
Coldwater, MI 49036

Ⓒ Ⓓ The *Robert J. Pickering Award for Playwriting Excellence* annually offers a cash prize plus production in the historic Tibbits Opera House in Coldwater for an unproduced full-length play or musical; plays for children are eligible. Send SASE for guidelines.

Available to: No restrictions
Deadline: December 31
Apply to: Above address

Colonial Players
108 East Street
Annapolis, MD 21401

Ⓓ The biennial *Promising Playwright Award* is given for a full-length play suitable for an arena stage by an aspiring playwright residing in any of the states descended from the original thirteen colonies (Connecticut, Delaware, Georgia, Massachusetts, New Hampshire, New Jersey, New York, North Carolina, Pennsylvania, Rhode Island, South Carolina, Virginia), West Virginia, or Washington, D.C. Plays should be limited to two sets and a cast of ten. The winner is awarded $750 plus production (playwright must be available to attend rehearsals). Send SASE for guidelines.

Available to: See above
Deadline: December 31, 2000 (no manuscripts accepted before September 1, 2000)
Apply to: Promising Playwright Award, above address

Colorado Council on the Arts and Humanities
750 Pennsylvania Street
Denver, CO 80203
E-mail: coloarts@artswire.org
Web site: http://www.aclin.org/code/arts
Fax: 303-894-2615

Ⓜ Several *Artist Fellowship Awards in Literature* of $4,000 are offered annually to Colorado writers to acknowledge outstanding achievement by artists in the state. Fellowships alternate yearly between poetry and fiction/creative nonfiction. Write, e-mail, or visit the Web site for guidelines and application.

Available to: Colorado residents
Deadline: Inquire
Apply to: Artist Fellowship Awards in Literature, above address

Colorado Review
Department of English
Colorado State University
Fort Collins, CO 80523
E-mail: creview@vines.colostate.edu
Web site: http://www.colostate.edu/depts/english/english_ns4.htm

Ⓟ The *Colorado Prize* offers a $1,500 honorarium and publication by the Center for Literary Publishing and University Press of Colorado for a book-length collection of poems. There is a $25 reading fee, which covers a one-year, three-volume subscription to *Colorado Review*. Send SASE for guidelines.

Available to: No restrictions
Deadline: Mid-January (inquire for exact date)
Apply to: Colorado Prize, above address

Ⓘ The *"Evil Companions" Literary Award* of $1,000 is given annually to a writer living in, writing about, or with ties to the American West. The award is named for the self-proclaimed "Evil Companions," a group of Denver journalists in the 1950s and 1960s. The winner is chosen by a committee of individuals from *Colorado Review*, the Tattered Cover Bookstore, and the Oxford Hotel. There is no application process. *By Internal Nomination Only.*

Columbia College
72 East 11th Street
Chicago, IL 60605
E-mail: csmith@papmail.colum.edu
Fax: 312-344-8077

Ⓓ The *Theodore Ward Prize for Playwriting* annually awards $2,000 plus production for a professionally unproduced full-length play by an African-American writer. The winner will receive transportation to/from Chicago and housing during the week of rehearsal before the first performance. A second prize of $500 plus a staged reading is also offered. Write for guidelines.

Available to: African-American writers
Deadline: Submissions accepted April 1–July 1
Apply to: Chuck Smith, Facilitator, Theodore Ward Prize for Playwriting, above address

Columbia University
Bancroft Prize Committee
Office of the President
202A Low Memorial Library
Mail Code 4310
New York, NY 10027

Ⓝ Two *Bancroft Prizes* are given annually for books in American history (including biography) and diplomacy; "American" refers to all the Americas, North, South, and Central. The prizes, $4,000 each, are for books first published in the year preceding that of the award. Submissions should include four copies of the book and a nominating letter.

Available to: No restrictions
Deadline: November 1
Apply to: Above address

Columbia University
Graduate School of Journalism
2950 Broadway
New York, NY 10027
E-mail: cabot@jrn.columbia.edu (for Maria Moors Cabot Prizes)
Web site: http://www.jrn.columbia.edu

Ⓙ The *Maria Moors Cabot Prizes* honor the advancement of freedom of the press and distinguished contributions to inter-American understanding. The prizes, awarded annually to two to four professional journalists for the body of their work, consist of a medal, an honorarium of $1,500, and travel expenses to/from the awards ceremony at Columbia. Greatest consideration is given to sustained work in covering events that affect the Americas. Write, e-mail, or visit the Web site for additional information and nomination procedures.

Available to: No restrictions
Deadline: March 31
Apply to: Maria Moors Cabot Prizes, above address

Ⓙ The *Knight-Bagehot Fellowship Program in Economics and Business Journalism* provides a nine-month course of study during the academic year to improve the quality of reporting by expanding participants' understanding of business, finance, and economics. Up to ten fellowships are awarded annually; fellows receive tuition plus a stipend of $28,000 to offset living expenses in New York City. Housing is available in a Columbia-affiliated facility. Applicants must have at least four years' professional experience, not necessarily in business and economics, and must have published work that has appeared regularly in the United States or Canada. Write for additional information and application.

Available to: See above
Deadline: March 1
Apply to: Director, Knight-Bagehot Fellowship Program, above address

Columbia University
Charles H. Revson Fellows
Program on the Future of the City of New York
New York, NY 10027

The *Revson Fellows Program* awards fellowships to those who have made a significant contribution to New York City or to another large metropolitan center and who can be expected to make even greater contributions in the future, after using Columbia University's instructional, research, and other resources for an academic year. Ten awards, consisting of a $18,000 stipend, four credit courses, and an unlimited number of audited courses, are given each year.

Available to: No restrictions
Deadline: February 1
Apply to: Above address

Common Wealth Awards
c/o PNC Bank, Delaware, Trustee
222 Delaware Avenue
PO Box 791
Wilmington, DE 19899-0791

[IN] The *Common Wealth Awards* are available in literature, the dramatic arts, mass communications, science and invention, government, public service, and sociology. Awards are given for a body of work, not for a specific project. Nominations are made by various bodies recognized as umbrella organizations in each category. *By Internal Nomination Only.*

The Commonwealth Club of California
595 Market Street
San Francisco, CA 94105
E-mail: cwc@sirius.com
Web site: http://www.commonwealthclub.org
Fax: 415-597-6729

Ⓜ The *California Book Awards* offer $2,000 for each gold medalist and $300 for silver medalists for the best work published by California writers during the calendar year. Up to ten medals are offered annually in the categories first work of fiction, fiction, nonfiction, poetry, juvenile literature, Californiana, and notable contributions to publishing. Authors must be legal residents of California when the manuscript is submitted for publication. Write, e-mail, or fax for additional information.

Available to: California authors
Deadline: January 31
Apply to: California Book Awards, above address

Community Writers Association
Box 312
Providence, RI 02901
E-mail: Mellis5910@aol.com
Web site: http://www.communitywriters.org/MEMBERSHIP/contest.htm

Ⓕ Ⓟ The *Community Writers Association International Writing Competition* offers a $500 prize in each of three categories: short story, novel, and poetry. The winning entries are included in *CWA Journal*, an international literary magazine. There is a $5 entry fee per poem or short story; $10 for novels. Write, e-mail, or visit the Web site for guidelines.

Available to: Writers 18 years or older
Deadline: June 1
Apply to: International Writing Competition, above address

Conference on Latin American History
University of Southern Florida
4202 East Fowler Avenue
SOC 107
Tampa, FL 33620
E-mail: clah@chuma.cas.usf.edu

Ⓝ The *Herbert Eugene Bolton Memorial Prize* offers $500 annually for the best book in English, published during the year before the award, on any significant aspect of Latin American history. The Conference awards several other prizes, with lesser monetary stipends, for articles on Latin American history. Publishers and CLAH members may nominate; for a book to be considered, each of three committee members must receive a copy. Inquire for further information and list of committee members.

Available to: No restrictions
Deadline: June 1
Apply to: CLAH Secretariat, above address

Connecticut Commission on the Arts
755 Main Street
1 Financial Plaza
Hartford, CT 06103
E-mail: ldente@ctarts.org
Web site: http://www.ctarts.org
Fax: 860-566-6462

Ⓜ *Artist Fellowships* in the amounts of $2,500 and $5,000 are offered to Connecticut residents. Grants are on a two-year cycle, with literary arts (poetry, fiction, drama) relevant in even-numbered years. Write for complete guidelines.

Available to: Writers who have lived and worked in Connecticut for at least one year
Deadline: September 2000 (inquire for exact date)
Apply to: Linda Dente, Program Director, Artist Fellowships, above address

Ⓜ The Commission on the Arts maintains a roster of performing artists in dance, music, and theater, as well as poets, writers, and storytellers, for public readings. Its *Arts Presentation Program* offers funding support (up to half the artist fee) to organizations for events featuring roster artists. New performing groups and writers are added to the roster every two years.

Available to: Connecticut residents and organizations
Deadline: Performing artists, October 2, 2000; master teaching artists, October 13, 2000
Apply to: Above address or sdocker@ctarts.org

Contemporary Arts Educational Project
6026 Wilshire Boulevard
Los Angeles, CA 90036

Ⓜ The *American Awards for Literature International Award* of $1,000 is given annually for a body of literary writing. The *American Awards for Literature,* given for fiction, poetry, drama, and belles lettres, currently carry no cash stipend. Publishers may submit four copies of a book published during the calendar year.

Available to: No restrictions for International Award; U.S. citizens for other awards
Deadline: December 31
Apply to: American Awards for Literature, above address

Converse College
Department of English
Spartanburg, SC 29302

Ⓕ Ⓟ The *Julia Peterkin Award* offers a cash prize of $750, along with payment of expenses for a reading, for poetry and fiction in alternating years. The award will be offered for poetry in 2000 and fiction in 2001. Fiction writers may submit a single short story or novel excerpt of no more than 20 pages; poets, four or five poems with a maximum of 15 pages total. Work may be published or unpublished. There is a $12 entry fee. Write for additional information and guidelines.

Available to: No restrictions
Deadline: February 15
Apply to: Julia Peterkin Award, above address

Cooperative Children's Book Center
4290 Helen C. White Hall
600 North Park Street
Madison, WI 53706
E-mail: khorning@facstaff.wisc.edu
Web site: http://www.soemadison.wisc.edu/ccbc/zolotow.htm

[IN] The *Charlotte Zolotow Award* of $1,000 is given annually for a picture book for young children (through age seven) published during the calendar year. The book may be fiction, nonfiction, poetry, or folklore. The recipient is chosen by a committee of children's literature experts. There is no application process. *By Internal Nomination Only.*

Copper Canyon Press
PO Box 271
Port Townsend, WA 98368
E-mail: info@ccpress.org
Web site: http://www.ccpress.org

Ⓟ The *Hayden Carruth Award for Emerging Poets* offers a cash prize of $1,000 and publication by Copper Canyon Press to writers who have published no more than two full-length books of poetry. Chapbooks of 32 pages or less are not considered full-length. There is a $15 handling fee. Send SASE for guidelines and entry form.

Available to: See above
Deadline: Submissions accepted in November
Apply to: Hayden Carruth Award, above address

Cornell University
Department of English
Goldwin Smith Hall
Ithaca, NY 14853

Ⓓ Ⓙ The *George Jean Nathan Award for Dramatic Criticism* is given for the best piece of drama criticism published in the United States during the theatrical year (July 1–June 30), whether article, essay, treatise, or book. Drama criticism that has been broadcast on television or radio is also eligible. One award, of $10,000, and a silver medallion are given annually. Send SASE for guidelines and selection committee list.

Available to: U.S. citizens
Deadline: September 30
Apply to: George Jean Nathan Award, above address

Council on Foreign Relations
Office of Membership and Fellowship Affairs
58 East 68th Street
New York, NY 10021
Fax: 212-861-2701
E-mail: membership@cfr.org
Web site: http://www.foreignrelations.org

Ⓙ The *Edward R. Murrow Fellowship,* for a nine-month residencce at the Council offices, is available yearly to an American foreign correspondent for "sustained analysis and research" and the opportunity to interact with foreign policy experts. The stipend equals the journalist's current salary up to $60,000. Write for additional information and application.

Available to: U.S. citizens serving abroad as journalists or those recently back from a foreign post who expect to go to one after the residence
Deadline: February 1
Apply to: Elise Lewis, Vice-President of Membership and Fellowship Affairs, above address

Council for International Exchange of Scholars
3007 Tilden Street, NW, Suite 5L
Washington, DC 20008-3009
E-mail: apprequest@cies.iie.org
Web site: http://www.cies.org
Fax: 202-362-3442

The Council administers the Department of State–sponsored *Fulbright Scholar Program* for advanced research and university lecturing in more than 130 countries around the world. Some 700 grants are awarded annually to faculty and professionals in virtually all academic disciplines, including creative writing. Grant benefits vary by country, but usually include international travel, a monthly stipend, and other allowances. Applications are available in March on-line and from the above address.

Available to: U.S. citizens
Deadline: August 1; other deadlines for special programs
Apply to: Box NEWS, above address

A similar program for scholars from abroad for university lecturing and advanced research in the United States is administered in this country by the Council. Interested non–U.S. citizens should inquire at the U.S. embassy or Fulbright agency in their home country.

Crab Orchard Review
Department of English
Southern Illinois University at Carbondale
Carbondale, IL 62901-4503
Web site: http://www.siu.edu/~crborchd

(P)   The *Crab Orchard Award Series in Poetry* offers a $2,000 first prize and a $1,000 honorarium for a reading at Southern Illinois U. for an unpublished original collection of poems, 50 to 70 pages long, written in English by a U.S. citizen or resident. The first runner-up will also receive a $1,000 honorarium for a reading, and both books will be published by Southern Illinois University Press. All submissions must be accompanied by a $20 entry fee, which covers a one-year subscription to *Crab Orchard Review*. Send SASE or visit the Web site for guidelines.

Available to: U.S. citizens or permanent residents
Deadline: Submissions accepted October 1–November 15
Apply to: John Tribble, Series Editor, Crab Orchard Award Series, above address

(F) (N)   The *Jack Dyer Fiction Prize* and the *John Guyon Literary Nonfiction Prize* each offer $1,000 and publication in *Crab Orchard Review*. Entries must be unpublished original work, not under consideration elsewhere. Writers may submit up to 6,000 words of fiction or up to 6,500 words of literary nonfiction. There is a $10 fee for each entry (one story/essay per entry), which covers a one-year subscription to the *Review*. Write for additional information and guidelines.

Available to: U.S. citizens or permanent residents
Deadline: Submissions accepted February 1–March 15
Apply to: Above address, with envelope marked "Fiction" or "Literary Nonfiction"

Crane-Rogers Foundation. *See* **Institute of Current World Affairs**

The Crescent Review
PO Box 15069
Chevy Chase, MD 20825
Web site: http://www.thecrescentreview.com

(F)   The *Chekhov Award for Short Fiction* offers $500 and publication in *The Crescent Review* for a short story of up to 7,000 words. A second prize of $200 and a third of $100 are also given. There is a $15 reading fee. Send SASE or, preferably, visit the Web site for guidelines.

Available to: No restrictions
Deadline: Submissions accepted August 15–October 1
Apply to: Chekhov Award for Short Fiction, above address

(F)   The *Renwick-Sumerwell Award for Short Fiction* offers $500 and publication in *The Crescent Review* for a short story of up to 7,000 words by a writer who has not published short fiction in any publication with a circulation of more than 300. A second prize of $200 and a third of $100 are also given. There is an $8 reading fee. Send SASE or, preferably, visit the Web site for guidelines.

Available to: See above
Deadline: Submissions accepted April 15–June 30
Apply to: Renwick-Sumerwell Award for Short Fiction, above address

Cultural Arts Council of Houston/Harris County
3201 Allen Parkway
Houston, TX 77019
E-mail: info@cachh.org
Web site: http://www.cachh.org

(M)   *Individual Artist Grants* are awarded annually by the Council to Houston or Harris Country artists and writers. These include *Artist Fellowship Awards* of $5,000 each and *Emerging Artist Fellowships* of $2,500 each. Write, e-mail, or visit the Web site for additional information and application.

Available to: Houston or Harris Country residents of at least two years
Deadline: Late fall (inquire for exact date)
Apply to: Individual Artist Grants, above address

Cumberland Poetry Review
PO Box 120128
Acklen Station
Nashville, TN 37212

Ⓟ The *Robert Penn Warren Poetry Prize* awards a $500 first place, a $300 second place, and a $200 third place for poems neither previously published nor submitted elsewhere. Prizewinners and honorable mentions will be published in *Cumberland Poetry Review*. Poets may enter as many as three poems of no more than 100 lines each. The $28 reading fee covers a one-year subscription to the *Review*. Write for required entry form.

Available to: No restrictions
Deadline: March 1
Apply to: Above address

Cushwa Center for the Study of American Catholicism
1135 Flanner Hall
University of Notre Dame
Notre Dame, IN 46556-5611
E-mail: cushwa.1@nd.edu

Ⓝ Two *Publication Awards* are offered by the Cushwa Center and the University of Notre Dame Press for manuscripts dealing with the American Catholic experience or the Irish in America. The award-winning manuscript will be published by the University of Notre Dame Press, and authors will receive a $500 advance on royalties. These awards are not limited to studies in any one discipline. Manuscripts from the humanities, history, and social studies will be considered; unrevised dissertations normally will not. Write for additional information and guidelines.

Available to: No restrictions
Deadline: December 31
Apply to: Publication Awards, above address

Cyclone Productions
Box 148849
Chicago, IL 60614
Web site: http://www.cyclone-entertainment.com
Fax: 773-665-7660

Ⓢ The *Cyclone Productions Screenwriters Project* annually awards grants of up to $5,000 and possible production to writers of diverse backgrounds and varied degrees of writing experience interested in a career in screenwriting. Work chosen for production will receive no less than the current minimums established by the Writers Guild of America. Applicants will be evaluated on the basis of a dramatic writing sample, which may be a completed screenplay, a treatment for a motion picture, or a synopsis for a motion picture, story, novel, or play. The submission should be adaptable to motion picture or television format. There is a $40 administration fee. Write or visit the Web site for application procedures.

Available to: No restrictions
Deadline: August 1
Apply to: Screenwriters Project, above address

Ⓢ The *Low-Budget Feature Project* selects one screenplay each year to be produced as a feature-length film. The completed work will likely be presented on the film festival circuit, with the intention of obtaining distribution. Financing for the film will come primarily from application fees for the project (90% of fees will finance the production; the remaining 10% will be used for administration). Additional financing may be provided by Cyclone Productions or other private contributors. Applicants should submit a feature-length screenplay with an ultra-low-budget in mind (very few locations; character- and dialogue-driven story line). There is a $50 entry fee. Write or visit the Web site for application procedures.

Available to: No restrictions
Deadline: April 1
Apply to: Low-Budget Feature Project, above address

Dana Awards
7207 Townsend Forest Court
Browns Summit, NC 27214
E-mail: danaawards@pipeline.com
Web site: http://danaawards.home.pipeline.com

Ⓕ Ⓟ The *Dana Awards* recognize work in four categories: the novel, poetry, literary/mainstream short fiction, and speculative short fiction (science fiction, fantasy, horror, and surrealism). A $1,000 prize is given for an unpublished novel, $500 for the best group of five unpublished poems, $500 for a literary/mainstream short story, and $500 for a speculative fiction short story. The awards are given by poet and novelist Mary Elizabeth Parker and her husband, Michael Dana, to encourage emerging writers. Novelists should submit the first 50 pages only of an unpublished novel, with a $20 entry fee; poets should submit up to five unpublished poems of any length, with a $10 entry fee; and short story writers in both categories should submit a story of up to 10,000 words (3,000 words or fewer preferred), with a $10 entry fee. E-mail, visit the Web site, or send SASE for guidelines. E-mail submissions are not accepted.

Available to: No restrictions
Deadline: October 31
Apply to: Above address

Shelby Cullom Davis Center for Historical Studies
Princeton University
Department of History
G-13 Dickinson Hall
Princeton, NJ 08544-1017
Web site: http://www.princeton.edu/~davisctr/

Visiting Davis Fellowships are available for one semester or a full academic year at the Davis Center at Princeton. Fellows are expected to pursue research related to the current theme of the Center and take part in its seminar program. The theme for 1999–2001 is "Conversion: Sacred and Profane." Emphasis is on interdisciplinary approaches and on topics that do not restrict participation to specialists in a single geographical area or period of time. Support for fellows varies according to the outside grants and sabbatical leave funds they bring with them; maximum support is $28,000 for a semester and $56,000 for the academic year. Write for additional information and application.

Available to: No restrictions
Deadline: December 1
Apply to: Manager, above address

Dayton Playhouse
1301 East Siebenthaler Avenue
Dayton, OH 45414
Fax: 937-277-9539

Ⓓ The *Dayton Playhouse FutureFest* will award $1,000 and production to previously unproduced and unpublished plays. Three full-scale selections, as well as three readers' theater selections, will be presented during FutureFest weekend in July. A $1,000 prize will be awarded to the winning playwright. Send SASE for guidelines before submitting.

Available to: No restrictions
Deadline: September 30 (no submissions accepted before August 1)
Apply to: Tom Warrick, Managing Director, above address

Delaware Division of the Arts
Carvel State Office Building
820 North French Street
Wilmington, DE 19801
Web site: http://www.artsdel.org
Fax: 302-577-6561

Ⓜ *Individual Artist Fellowships* are available in the literary arts to Delaware residents. Fellowships are $2,000 for emerging professionals, $5,000 for established professionals. Write for guidelines and application.

Available to: Delaware residents
Deadline: August 1
Apply to: Barbara King, Fellowship Coordinator, above address

Gladys Krieble Delmas Foundation
521 Fifth Avenue, Suite 1612
New York, NY 10175-1699
E-mail: delmasfdtn@aol.com
Web site: http://www.delmas.org
Fax: 212-687-8877

Predoctoral and postdoctoral grants for study in Venice and the Veneto region are awarded annually for historical research on Venice and the former Venetian empire, and for study of contemporary Venetian society and culture. Disciplines of the humanities and social sciences are eligible areas of study, including but not limited to archaeology, architecture, art, bibliography, economics, history, history of science, law, literature, music, political science, religion, and theater. Applicants must be U.S. citizens or permanent residents and have some experience in advanced research at the graduate level or above. Grants range from $500 to $14,500. Funds are for research in Venice and the Veneto only, and for transportation to, from, and within the Veneto. Write for additional information and application.

Available to: U.S. citizens or permanent residents
Deadline: December 15
Apply to: Above address

Delta Kappa Gamma Society International
PO Box 1589
Austin, TX 78767-1589
E-mail: societyexec@deltakappagamma.org
Fax: 512-478-3961

Ⓝ The *Educator's Award* of $1,500 is given annually in recognition of "outstanding educational research and writings of women authors whose book may influence the direction of thought and action necessary to meet the needs of today's complex society." The book must be written in English by one or two women and copyrighted during the calendar year prior to the year in which the award is given. Write for additional information and guidelines.

Available to: Women residents of the Society's member countries: Canada, Costa Rica, El Salvador, Finland, Germany, Guatemala, Iceland, Mexico, the Netherlands, Norway, Sweden, the United Kingdom, and the United States (including Puerto Rico)
Deadline: February 1
Apply to: Above address

Eben Demarest Trust
3 Mellon Bank Center, Room 4000
Pittsburgh, PA 15259-0001

The *Eben Demarest Fund* makes one annual grant of approximately $15,000 to a mature artist or archaeologist who wishes to concentrate for a time on a chosen field without having to depend entirely on the sale of work or outside employment. The beneficiary is chosen by the Eben Demarest Council. Unsolicited applications from individuals will not be accepted, but applications from organizations or institutions for unusually gifted people will be considered.

Available to: U.S. citizens preferred
Deadline: June 1 for the following calendar year
Apply to: Above address, attn: Laurie A. Moritz

DENMARK
Commission for Educational Exchange between Denmark and the U.S.A.
Fiolstraede 24. 3 sal
DK 1171 Copenhagen K
Denmark
E-mail: fulbdk@unidhp.uni-c.dk
Fax: 45-33-32-53-23

The *Binational Commission (Fulbright) Scholarships* for study and research in Denmark are available to university graduates with a specific research program. Grants cover maintenance and travel for graduate students and for postdoctoral or advanced research candidates.

Available to: U.S. citizens
Deadlines: October 25 for predoctoral applicants; August 1 for postdoctoral
Apply to: Predoctoral: Institute of International Education, 809 United Nations Plaza, New York, NY 10017; postdoctoral: Council for International Exchange of Scholars, 3007 Tilden Street, NW, Suite 5L, Washington, DC 20008-3009

Denver Center Theatre Company
1050 13th Street
Denver, CO 80204
Fax: 303-825-2117

Ⓓ The *U.S. West TheatreFest* annually sponsors a development program for new, unproduced full-length plays. Selected plays receive a week of rehearsal with professional actors and directors, culminating in a public reading. Plays chosen for the festival are optioned for Denver Center Theatre Company production.
Selected playwrights receive a $1,000 option fee, transportation to/from Denver, and housing for the festival, rehearsal, and performance period. Send SASE for additional information.

Available to: No restrictions
Deadline: December 31
Apply to: Bruce K. Sevy, Associate Artistic Director, U.S. West TheatreFest, above address

The *Francesca Primus Prize* of $3,000 is given annually for a previously unproduced full-length play by a woman. The winning play will receive a rehearsed public reading, with the playwright in residence, as part of the Denver Center Theatre Company U.S. West TheatreFest. The theatre retains the option to mount a full production of the work in its next subscription season. Send SASE for additional information and guidelines.

Available to: Women playwrights
Deadline: July 1
Apply to: Bruce K. Sevy, Associate Artistic Director, Francesca Primus Prize, above address

DePaul University
Theatre School
2135 North Kenmore
Chicago, IL 60614-4111
Web site: http://theatreschool.depaul.edu/programs/prize.htm

Ⓓ The *Cunningham Prize for Playwriting* awards $5,000 annually for an original full-length play, musical, or play for young audiences by a Chicago-area writer. Submissions should "affirm the centrality of religion, broadly defined, and the human quest for meaning, truth and community." Send SASE for guidelines.

Available to: Chicago-area playwrights (living within 100 miles of the Loop)
Deadline: December 1
Apply to: Cunningham Prize Selection Committee, above address

descant
Department of English
Texas Christian University
Box 297270
Fort Worth, TX 76129

Ⓕ Ⓟ The *Frank O'Connor Fiction Award* offers $500 to the best short fiction published in each volume of *descant*. The *Betsy Colquitt Award for Poetry* offers $500 to the best poem, or series of poems by a single author, published in each volume.

Available to: *descant* writers
Deadline: Ongoing
Apply to: Above address

Walt Disney Studios
500 South Buena Vista Street
Burbank, CA 91521-0750

Ⓢ The *Walt Disney Studios Fellowship Program* selects up to six writers annually to work full-time at developing their craft in the Disney Studio features or television division. The one-year fellowships, beginning in October, offer a salary of $33,000. Travel expenses and one month's housing will be paid for fellows from outside the Los Angeles area. Applications from minority writers are encouraged. No previous film or television writing experience is necessary. Send for guidelines and application.

Available to: No restrictions
Deadline: Inquire
Apply to: Fellowship Program, above address

District of Columbia Commission on the Arts and Humanities
410 8th Street, NW, Suite 500
Washington, DC 20004
Web site: http://www.capaccess.org/dccah
Fax: 202-727-4135

Ⓜ The *Artist Fellowship Program* offers fellowships of $2,500 to writers of poetry, fiction, and creative nonfiction who can significantly contribute to and promote the arts in the District of Columbia through artistic excellence. Send for guidelines and application.

Available to: D.C. residents
Deadline: Inquire
Apply to: Artist Fellowship Program, above address

Ⓜ The *Arts Education Projects Program* offers funds from $1,000 to $4,500 for programs that give training and exposure in the arts to young people in the District of Columbia, early childhood through twelfth grade, and that reinforce the importance of the arts in education. Programs providing in-service training and arts curriculum development for teachers and collaborative projects between schools and community facilities are also eligible. Activities may take place in traditional school settings or community facilities. The Commission encourages applicants to apply for projects in the schools. Send for guidelines and application.

Available to: D.C. residents
Deadline: Inquire
Apply to: Arts Education Projects Program, above address

Ⓜ The *City Arts Projects Program* offers grants of $1,000 to $4,500 to individuals and grants of $1,000 to $15,000 to organizations for projects that encourage the growth of quality arts activities throughout Washington and that make arts experiences accessible to D.C. residents. Projects must provide exposure to the arts and arts experiences to the broader community or persons traditionally underserved or separated from the mainstream because of location, economic constraints, or disability. Write for guidelines and application.

Available to: D.C. residents
Deadline: Inquire
Apply to: City Arts Projects Program, above address

Ⓜ The *Larry Neal Writers' Competition* awards prizes in poetry, fiction, dramatic writing, and the essay to District of Columbia writers.

Available to: D.C. residents
Deadline: Inquire
Apply to: Larry Neal Writers' Competition, above address

Djerassi Resident Artists Program
2325 Bear Gulch Road
Woodside, CA 94062-4405
E-mail: drap@djerassi.org
Web site: http://www.djerassi.org
Fax: 650-747-0105

Ⓡ The *Djerassi Resident Artists Program* offers one-month residences for writers and other creative artists on a 600-acre ranch south of San Francisco. Living space, studio space, and meals are provided without charge. There are seven thirty-day sessions between late March and mid-November. Send SASE or visit the Web site for guidelines and application.

Available to: Working writers
Deadline: February 15 for following year (e.g., 2/15/00 for 2001)
Apply to: Above address

Dobie–Paisano Fellowship Project
J. Frank Dobie House
702 East Dean Keeton Street
Austin, TX 78705
E-mail: aslate@mail.utexas.edu
Fax: 512-471-9997

Ⓡ The *Dobie–Paisano Writing Fellowships* provide a living allowance of $7,200 and free residence at Dobie's ranch, Paisano, fourteen miles west of Austin. Two six-month fellowships, the first beginning in September, the second in March, will be awarded. There is a $10 application fee. Write or e-mail for guidelines.

Available to: Native Texans, writers previously living in Texas for at least two years, or writers whose published work has Texas as its subject
Deadline: Late January (inquire for exact date)
Apply to: Audrey N. Slate, above address

DOMINICAN REPUBLIC
Altos de Chavon
La Romana
Dominican Republic
E-mail: altos@spacelab.net

Ⓡ This nonprofit center for the arts offers three fourteen-week residences beginning in September, February, and June. The majority of residents are visual artists; writers are welcome. Residents pay a $100 registration fee (to cover transportation between the airport and the colony) and a reduced residence rate of $350 a month; they contribute to the community by giving a reading, workshop, performance, or exhibit. Knowledge of Spanish is helpful.

Available to: Preference to creators of work influenced by or involved with Latin America and/or the Caribbean
Deadline: July 15
Apply to: Artists in Residence Program, Altos de Chavon, c/o Parsons School of Design, 66 Fifth Avenue, New York, NY 10011; fax 212-229-8988

Dorland Mountain Arts Colony
PO Box 6
Temecula, CA 92593
E-mail: dorland@ez2.net
Web site: http://www.ez2.net/dorland

® Residences of one to two months are available for writers as well as artists working in other disciplines. Six rustic cabins in a 300-acre nature preserve offer quiet and privacy for concentrated work. A donation of $300 a month is requested at the time of scheduling. Send #10 SASE for guidelines and application or print them out from the Web site.

Available to: No restrictions
Deadlines: September 1; March 1
Apply to: Above address

Dorset Colony
Box 519
Dorset, VT 05251

® *Dorset Colony House Residences* are available to writers for intensive work periods, from one week to two months. Up to eight writers are in residence at a time. Writers are accommodated in private rooms in a turn-of-the-century historic house located in Dorset village, southern Vermont. The requested fee is $120 per week. Send a letter of inquiry.

Available to: No restrictions
Deadline: Variable (fall and spring)
Apply to: John Nassivera, Director, above address

Dow Jones Newspaper Fund
PO Box 300
Princeton, NJ 08543-0300
E-mail: newsfund@wsj.dowjones.com
Web site: http://www.dj.com/newsfund
Fax: 609-520-5804

Ⓙ The *Dow Jones Newspaper Fund Business Reporting Program* offers up to twelve summer internships to minority college students. After a one-week training program, interns work as business reporters at a daily newspaper, where they are paid regular wages. Upon returning to school, they receive a scholarship of $1,000. Write for additional information and application.

Available to: Minority college sophomores and juniors
Deadline: November 1
Apply to: Business Reporting Program, above address

Ⓙ The *High School Journalism Teacher of the Year* program selects one teacher of the year and four distinguished advisors from candidates across the country. They may be nominated by newspapers, press associations, colleges, or high school principals for their outstanding abilities as journalism teachers. The teacher of the year then selects the best journalism student attending his or her high school, who will receive a $1,000 scholarship to study journalism in college. A $500 scholarship will be awarded to each of the students selected by the distinguished advisors.

Ⓙ Candidates for the *High School Workshop Writing Competition* must be nominated by directors of High School Journalism Workshops for Minorities. Up to eight scholarships, of $1,000 each, will be awarded for the freshman year in college; all are renewable for the sophomore year, pending continued interest in a journalism career, adequate grades, and financial need. Students do not apply for these scholarships.

Available to: Minority students slated to study journalism as college freshmen who attend above-mentioned workshop
Deadline: Teacher of the Year, July 1; High School Workshop Writing Competition, none
Apply to: Program Director, above address, for nomination forms for Teacher of the Year competition and information on workshops

Drama League of New York
165 West 46th Street, Suite 601
New York, NY 10036
E-mail: dlny@echonyc.com
Web site: http://www.dramaleague.org
Fax: 212-302-2254

Ⓓ   The Drama League's *New Directors/New Works* program is designed to foster artistic collaboration. Applications must be submitted by directors who are developing a project with a writer or artistic collaborator. The program offers selected teams the unique opportunity to workshop new material without the pressure of producers and critics. Each team is awarded a stipend of $1,000 for production expenses, and up to four weeks' use of a rehearsal space in New York City during the summer. Write or visit the Web site after December 1 for application and guidelines.

Available to: U.S. citizens or permanent residents at least twenty-one years old
Deadline: Usually February (projects accepted once a year; inquire for exact date)
Apply to: Artistic Director, above address

Dubuque Fine Arts Players
330 Clarke Drive
Dubuque, IA 52001
E-mail: snakelady@mwci.net

Ⓓ   The *National One-Act Playwriting Contest* awards a $600 first prize, a $300 second prize, and a $200 third prize for unproduced, unpublished one-acts. Musicals and children's plays are not eligible. The three winning plays may be produced. Writers should submit two copies, a $10 entry fee, and a completed entry form. Send SASE for guidelines and entry form.

Available to: No restrictions
Deadline: January 31
Apply to: Jennie Stabenow, Playwriting Contest Coordinator, above address

Dumbarton Oaks
1703 32nd Street, NW
Washington, DC 20007

Contact Dumbarton Oaks for application procedures for the following:

The *Bliss Prize Fellowship in Byzantine Studies* is intended to provide encouragement, assistance, and training to outstanding college seniors who plan to enter the field of Byzantine studies. The fellowship covers graduate school tuition and living expenses for two academic years, as estimated by the graduate school in which the successful candidate enrolls. It also covers summer travel (up to $5,000) for the intervening summer to/from areas important in Byzantine civilization and culture.

Fellowships are awarded to scholars who hold a doctorate (or appropriate final degree) or have established themselves in their field and wish to pursue research in Byzantine or pre-Columbian studies or landscape architecture. A stipend of $24,635 plus housing is available annually.

Junior Fellowships, with a stipend of $13,545 plus housing, are available to advanced graduate students who have completed course work for their doctorate and wish to pursue their dissertation or final project at Dumbarton Oaks.

Summer Fellowships, with a maintenance allowance of $185 per week plus housing, are available to scholars at any level.

Available to: No restrictions
Deadline: November 1
Apply to: Associate Director, above address

Dungannon Foundation
West Church Hill Road
Washington, CT 06794

[IN] The *Rea Award for the Short Story* offers $30,000 annually to "a writer who has made a significant contribution to the short story." Recipients are nominated and selected by a jury. *By Internal Nomination Only.*

Earhart Foundation
2200 Green Road, Suite H
Ann Arbor, MI 48105

Fellowship Research Grants are awarded to individuals who have established themselves professionally in such social science and humanities disciplines as economics, philosophy, international affairs, and government/politics. Applicants must be associated or affiliated with educational or research institutions and have their Ph.D. and several years' teaching experience; the effort supported should lead to the advancement of knowledge through teaching, lecturing, or publication. Eighty-five research grants were awarded in 1998, ranging from $500 to $25,000 (average $11,754). Write for additional information and guidelines.

Available to: See above
Deadline: Ongoing
Apply to: Fellowship Research Grants, above address

Early Childhood Resources and Information Center of the New York Public Library
66 Leroy Street
New York, NY 10014

© The *Ezra Jack Keats New Writer Award* of $1,000 is given annually to a promising new writer who has published no more than five children's books, work "that reflect the tradition of Ezra Jack Keats, a Caldecott Medal winner whose books often featured multicultural settings and portrayed strong family relationships." Honorees need not have illustrated the book(s); the book(s) must appeal to children ages nine and under. Publishers may submit books published during the calendar year. Established writers who have written for young adults or adults but have not previously published work for children are not eligible. Write for guidelines.

Available to: See above
Deadline: Inquire
Apply to: Ezra Jack Keats New Writer Award, above address

East-West Center
1601 East-West Road
Honolulu, HI 96848
E-mail: seminars@ewc.hawaii.edu
Web site: http://www.ewc.hawaii.edu
Fax: 808-944-7670

ⓙ The *Jefferson Fellowship Program* annually makes available, for six American and six Asian mid-career and senior-level print and broadcast journalists, awards for an immersion course on cultures and current issues in Asian Pacific countries. The program usually takes place in April/May, with fellows spending the first part of the program at the Center and the second part in the field (Asia/Pacific fellows visit the United States and American fellows go to Asia/Pacific destinations). Write, e-mail, or visit the Web site for additional information.

Available to: See above
Deadline: Early December (inquire for exact date)
Apply to: EWC Media Program, above address

East West Players
244 South San Pedro Street, Suite 301
Los Angeles, CA 90012
Fax: 213-625-7111

Ⓓ The *AT&T/East West Players New Voices Playwriting Competition* biannually awards a first prize of $1,000, plus a reading and possible workshop or production, for a full-length play that has not been professionally produced. Preference is given to Asian Pacific writers and works with Asian Pacific themes and cast. A second prize of $500 is awarded. There is a $15 entry fee. Send SASE for guidelines.

> Available to: See above
> Deadline: Inquire
> Apply to: AT&T/East West Players New Voices Playwriting Competition, above address

Eaton Literary Agency
PO Box 49795
Sarasota, FL 34230-6795
E-mail: info@eatonliterary.com
Web site: http://www.eatonliterary.com/award.htm
Fax: 941-365-4679

Ⓕ Ⓝ The *Eaton Literary Award* offers a $2,500 prize for a book-length work of fiction or nonfiction and a $500 prize for a short story or article. Write, e-mail, or visit the Web site for guidelines.

> Available to: No restrictions
> Deadline: August 31 for the book-length prize; March 31 for the short story/article prize
> Apply to: Above address

Eckerd College Review
4200 54th Avenue South
St. Petersburg, FL 33711
E-mail: siren@eckerd.edu

Ⓟ The *Eckerd College Review Poetry Contest* offers $500 and publication for a poem. Second- and third-place winners each receive $50 and publication; all contest entries will be considered for publication. There is a $7 entry fee for three poems; $3 for each additional poem. Send SASE or e-mail for guidelines.

> Available to: U.S. citizens
> Deadline: December 1
> Apply to: Poetry Contest, above address

Education Writers Association
1331 H Street, NW, Suite 307
Washington, DC 20005
E-mail: ewa@croslink.net
Web site: http://www.ewa.org
Fax: 202-637-9707

Ⓙ The *National Awards for Education Reporting* honor the best education reporting in the print and broadcast media during the calendar year. A $250 cash prize is awarded in each of twenty categories, and a $1,000 grand prize is given for the best of these. A $35 entry fee is required. Write to above address for rules and entry forms.

> Available to: Education journalists
> Deadline: Mid-January (inquire for exact date)
> Apply to: National Awards for Education Reporting, above address

Ⓙ The *National Fellowships in Education Reporting* offer an eight-week program of investigative study and travel for education journalists. The fellowships support up to twelve reporters for two months in pursuing special project in education. Fellows receive half-salary for the study period; travel expenses; access to expert sources; editing assistance, if desired; the opportunity to work with other reporters at EWA regional meetings and national seminar; and consultation with EWA staff about progress and problems during the project. Fellowships are open to full-time print or broadcast journalists who have been covering education at least two years, who have the endorsement of their employers, and who can show a likely outlet for the product of their study. Freelance writers may apply if they write about education a substantial portion of their time and have an agreement with a media organization to publish or air stories resulting from the fellowship. Write for guidelines.

Available to: See above
Deadline: Early May (inquire for exact date)
Apply to: National Fellowships in Education Reporting, above address

The Albert Einstein Institution
427 Newbury Street
Boston, MA 02115
E-mail: einstein@igc.org
Web site: http://www.aeinstein.org

The *Einstein Institution Fellows Program* supports research, writing, and systematic reflection on nonviolent action. The program offers support to scholars conducting research on the history, characteristics, and potential application of nonviolent action. Fellowships are available to Ph.D. candidates undertaking dissertation research or writing dissertations and to advanced scholars undertaking specific research projects on the history, characteristics, and potential applications of nonviolent action. Financial support includes a stipend, which takes into consideration such factors as the applicant's level of preparation, need, and prevailing academic salaries for comparable persons and projects. Awards are normally made for twelve-month periods, beginning on September 1. An exploratory letter of intent to the Program Director is encouraged and may be sent at any time. Write or e-mail for additional information and application procedures.

Available to: See above
Deadline: January 1
Apply to: Dr. Ronald McCarthy, Fellows Program Director, above address

Eisenhower Center for American Studies
923 Magazine Street
New Orleans, LA 70130
Fax: 504-539-9563

Ⓝ The *Forrest C. Pogue Prize,* of $1,500, is awarded annually to scholarly historical work in the field of the U.S. Army in World War II. Three copies of nominated work(s) published within the calendar year, along with a cover letter of introduction, should be sent to the Center. Write for additional information.

Available to: No restrictions
Deadline: February 15, 2000; inquire for 2001
Apply to: Annie Wedekind, Assistant Director, or Kevin Willey, Project Coordinator, above address

Ellipse Arts Center
4350 North Fairfax Drive
Arlington, VA 22203

Ⓟ The *Say the Word National Poetry Competition* offers $500 and publication as a hand-letter press broadside for an unpublished poem on a given theme. The winner will receive ten copies of the broadside. There is a $5 reading fee, payable to Treasurer, Arlington County, for up to five poems. Send SASE for guidelines.

Available to: U.S. citizens or permanent residents
Deadline: November 30
Apply to: Kim Roberts, above address

Emporia State University
English Department
Emporia, KS 66801-5087
Web site: http://www.emporia.edu/bluestem/index.htm
Fax: 316-341-5547

(P) The annual *Bluestem Award* offers $1,000 plus publication for a book-length collection of poems (at least 48 pages) by a U.S. author. Manuscripts may include poems published previously in periodicals or anthologies but not in full-length single-author volumes. There is a $15 reading fee.

Available to: U.S. citizens
Deadline: March 1
Apply to: Bluestem Award, above address

Maurice English Foundation for Poetry
c/o Helen W. Drutt English
2222 Rittenhouse Square
Philadelphia, PA 19103-5505

(P) The *Maurice English Poetry Award* of $3,000 is offered to an author in or beyond his or her sixth decade of life for a distinguished book of poems published during the preceding calendar year. The award honors Maurice English, whose work did not appear in book form until his fifty-fifth year. Contact the Foundation for information.

Available to: See above
Deadline: February 1, 2000; inquire for 2001
Apply to: Above address

The English-Speaking Union
16 East 69th Street
New York, NY 10021
Web site: http://www.english-speakingunion.org

(IN) The *Ambassador Book Awards* of $1,000 are given to writers who have made "an exceptional contribution to the interpretation of life and culture in the United States." The Union distributes books of winning authors throughout its libraries and facilities in Great Britain and forty other countries. There is no application process. *By Internal Nomination Only.*

The Ensemble Studio Theatre
549 West 52nd Street
New York, NY 10019
E-mail: estsloan@operamail.com
Fax: 212-664-0041

(D) The *Ensemble Studio Theatre/Alfred P. Sloan Foundation Science & Technology Project* is designed "to stimulate artists to create credible and compelling work exploring the worlds of science and technology and to challenge existing stereotypes of scientists and engineers in the popular imagination." Each season the Project commissions and develops new theater pieces and presents the results, at various levels of production, in its annual First Light Festival. Playwrights interested in receiving a commission should submit a one-page written proposal, consisting of a project description and simple outline or synopsis, and a résumé or biography. In the 1998–1999 season, a total of $50,000 in commissions was awarded. Write or e-mail for additional information.

Available to: No restrictions
Deadline: September 1
Apply to: Ross Peabody, Associate Program Director, EST/Sloan Science & Technology Project, above address

Willard R. Espy Literary Foundation
PO Box 614
Oysterville, WA 98641
Fax: 360-665-5151

® The Willard R. Espy Literary Foundation offers residences for the month of October in Oysterville, Washington, near the northern tip of Long Beach Peninsula on the state's southwest coast. Three chosen writers share accommodations in a bay-front cottage and receive a weekly stipend for food. Both emerging and established writers whose work reflects a Pacific Northwest background are eligible. Write for information.

Available to: See above
Deadline: July 31
Apply to: Above address

Ⓕ Ⓝ The *Willard R. Espy Award* of $1,000 is given annually to a writer of a work-in-progress set in the Pacific Northwest. The award is offered to emerging writers who have not yet published a book. For 2000, the award will be given for a novel or collection of short stories in progress. Write for additional information.

Available to: See above
Deadline: May 15, 2000; inquire for deadline and genre for 2001
Apply to: Above address

Evergreen Chronicles
PO Box 8939
Minneapolis, MN 55408-0939
E-mail: evgrnchron@aol.com

Ⓕ The *Evergreen Chronicles Novella Contest* offers $500 and publication in a special issue of *Evergreen Chronicles*, a journal of gay, lesbian, bisexual, and transgender art and culture. The contest is open to writers who have published no more than one novel or novella and whose work speaks of the gay, lesbian, bisexual, or transgender experience. Send SASE for guidelines.

Available to: See above
Deadline: September 30
Apply to: Evergreen Chronicles Novella Contest, above address

Experimental Television Center
109 Lower Fairfield Road
Newark Valley, NY 13811
E-mail: etc@servtech.com
Web site: http://www.experimentaltvcenter.org

The *Electronic Arts Grant Program* annually awards grants of up to $1,000 to New York State artists involved in the creation of audio, video, or computer-generated time-based works. Funds must be used for the completion of work currently in progress. Eligible forms include film; single- or multiple-channel audio and video; computer-based moving-imagery and sound works; installations and performances; and works for CD-ROM, multimedia technologies, and the Internet. Work must be innovative and creative, and must approach the various media as art forms; all genres are eligible, including experimental, narrative, and documentary. Write, e-mail, or visit the Web site for guidelines and application.

Available to: New York State residents
Deadline: March 15
Apply to: Electronic Arts Grant Program, above address

Fairmont State College
1201 Locust Avenue
Fairmont, WV 26554

Ⓕ Ⓟ The *Kestrel Writing Contest* offers $500 first prizes in poetry and fiction. Poets may submit three to six poems, totaling no more than 10 pages; fiction writers may submit one piece no longer than 25 double-spaced pages. Author's name should appear on cover letter only. The $15 entry fee per submission covers a one-year subscription to *Kestrel*. Send SASE for guidelines.

Available to: U.S. citizens or permanent residents
Deadline: June 1
Apply to: Kestrel Fiction Contest or Kestrel Poetry Contest, above address

Family Circle
375 Lexington Avenue
New York, NY 10017-5514

Ⓕ The *Mary Higgins Clark Mystery/Suspense Short Story Contest* annually awards a first prize of $1,000 and publication for a mystery/suspense short story of up to 3,500 words by a writer who has not been published in book form or in magazines with a circulation over 25,000. The next contest deadline and rules will be announced in the summer issue of *Mary Higgins Clark Mystery Magazine*.

Available to: No restrictions
Deadline: Consult *Mary Higgins Clark Mystery Magazine*
Apply to: Mary Higgins Clark Mystery/Suspense Short Story Contest, PO Box 4948, Grand Central Station, New York, NY 10163

Fellowship of Southern Writers
Arts & Education Council
PO Box 4203
Chattanooga, TN 37405

Ⓘ Ⓝ Eight biennial awards of $1,000 each are given in recognition of distinguished achievement in southern writing: the *Robert Penn Warren Prize for Fiction*, the *Hillsdale Prize for Fiction*, the *Hanes Prize for Poetry*, the *Cleanth Brooks Medal for Distinguished Achievement in Southern Letters*, the *Bryan Family Foundation Award for Drama*, the *Fellowship's Award for Nonfiction*, the *Fellowship's New Writing Award*, and the *James Still Award for Writing*. Eligible are writers who were born and brought up in the South, or who have resided there for a significant part of their lives, or whose works, in character or spirit, embody aspects of the southern experience. *By Internal Nomination Only*.

Final Draft
1600 Ventura Boulevard #800
Encino, CA 91436
E-mail: info@finaldraft.com
Web site: http://www.finaldraft.com
Fax: 818-995-4422

Ⓢ The first annual *Final Draft International Screenwriting Competition* was offered in 1999. A grand prize of $5,000 was awarded, plus literary agency representation and a trip to/from Los Angeles for meetings with studio executives, for a feature-length screenplay. Also awarded were a second prize of $3,000 and a third of $1,000. Write, e-mail, or visit the Web site for details on the 2000 and 2001 competitions.

Available to: No restrictions
Deadline: Inquire
Apply to: International Screenwriting Competition, above address

Fine Arts Work Center in Provincetown
24 Pearl Street
Provincetown, MA 02657

Ⓡ The Fine Arts Work Center in Provincetown "aims to help emerging artists and writers in the critical stage of their professional career by providing them with an opportunity to work independently in a congenial and stimulating environment." Fiction writers, poets, and visual artists are eligible; fellows are admitted on the basis of work submitted. Grants-in-aid are awarded. The program extends from October 1 through May 1. Send SASE for information and application.

   Available to: No restrictions
   Deadline: December 1
   Apply to: Director, above address

Ⓡ The *Senior Fellowship Program* annually awards $1,500 and an apartment at the Center to six accomplished poets and fiction writers at least fifty years old. Senior Fellowships target writers of particular originality and distinction recognized earlier in their careers and now "reemerging" with new work. The residence is for the month of September. Send SASE for guidelines and application.

   Available to: See above
   Deadline: July 1
   Apply to: Senior Fellowship Program, above address

FINLAND
Finnish Literature Information Center
Mariankatu 7 A 2
00170 Helsinki
Finland
E-mail: flic@finlit.fi
Web site: http://www.finlit.fi
Fax: 358-9-656-380

Ⓣ Translation grants are offered annually for translators and publishers, authors of critical works, and regular contributors to literary magazines published outside Finland. Applications should specify the amount of grant required, describe the project it will be used for and the expected duration, and the name of the prospective publisher. Projects should be concerned with the advancement of Finnish, Finnish-Swedish, and Sámi pro Lapp literature abroad. Applications for grants for scientific and scholarly translations (journals, dissertations, textbooks, technical literature) will not be considered.

   Available to: No restrictions
   Deadline: April 1 and November 1
   Apply to: Director, above address

F. Scott Fitzgerald Literary Conference
Rockville City Hall
111 Maryland Avenue
Rockville, MD 20560-2364

Ⓕ The *F. Scott Fitzgerald Literary Conference Short Story Contest* annually awards $500, and an invitation to read at the Conference, for an unpublished short story of 3,000 words or less by District of Columbia, Maryland, or Virginia writers. Three $100 runner-up prizes will also be awarded. Send SASE for guidelines.

   Available to: District of Columbia, Maryland, or Virginia residents
   Deadline: July (inquire for exact date)
   Apply to: Short Story Contest, above address

Five Points
Georgia State University
University Plaza
Atlanta, GA 30303-3083

Ⓕ The *Paul Bowles Prize for Short Fiction* awards $1,000 for the best short story of no more than 30 pages published in *Five Points*, a journal of poetry, fiction, creative nonfiction, and interviews. Send SASE for guidelines.

Available to: Fiction writers published in *Five Points*
Apply to: Paul Bowles Prize, above address

Ⓟ The *James Dickey Prize for Poetry* awards $1,000 and publication in *Five Points* for a previously unpublished collection of three to five poems, no more than 50 lines each. Poets may submit up to five poems. The $10 reading fee covers a one-year subscription to the journal. Send SASE for guidelines.

Available to: No restrictions
Deadline: November 30
Apply to: James Dickey Prize, above address

Florida Division of Cultural Affairs
Department of State
The Capitol
Tallahassee, FL 32399-0250
Web site: http://www.dos.state.fl.us
Fax: 904-922-5259

Ⓜ *Individual Fellowships* of $5,000 are given to Florida writers in poetry, fiction, children's literature (through the Literature Program), and playwriting (through the Theatre Program). Applicants must reside in the state at the time of application and for the duration of the fellowship period. Write for guidelines.

Available to: Florida residents
Deadline: Mid-January (inquire for exact date)
Apply to: Above address

Florida Playwrights' Process
PACT Institute for the Performing Arts
1111 McMullen-Booth Road
Clearwater, FL 33759
E-mail: ensignsp@gte.net
Web site: http://www.rutheckerdhall.net
Fax: 813-724-5976

Ⓓ The *Florida Playwrights' Process* offers $400 plus a travel stipend of $250 and production for an unproduced, unpublished full-length play with a cast limit of six, simple props and sets, and a maximum length of 2 hours. The selected Florida playwright must be available for workshops, readings, and performances as scheduled by the Program Director. The Florida Playwrights' Process offers a similar program for high school and middle school playwrights from Pinellas, Hillsborough, Polk, Hernando, and Pasco counties. Send SASE or e-mail for additional information and guidelines for either program.

Available to: Florida playwrights
Deadline: December 1
Apply to: Above address

The Florida Review
University of Central Florida
Department of English
Orlando, FL 32816

Ⓜ The *Florida Review Editors' Awards*, of $500 each, are offered in fiction, memoir, and poetry for previously unpublished work. Winning works will be published in the *Review*. Fiction and memoir submissions should be no longer than 10,000 words. Poets may submit three to five poems, each with a maximum of 40 lines. A reading fee of $10 for each submission covers a one-year subscription to the journal. Send SASE for guidelines.

Available to: No restrictions
Deadline: Submissions accepted January 1–March 15
Apply to: Editors' Awards, above address

Florida Studio Theatre
1241 North Palm Avenue
Sarasota, FL 34236
E-mail: Fstchris@aol.com
Fax: 941-955-4127

⒟ The *American Shorts Contest* offers $500 and production for the best very short play (5 pages or less) on a specified theme (announced each January). Up to twelve other entries will be selected for production as part of an evening of short works. Write for guidelines.

Available to: No restrictions
Deadline: Inquire for theme and deadline
Apply to: American Shorts Contest, above address

Folger Shakespeare Library
201 East Capitol Street, SE
Washington, DC 20003
E-mail: institute@folger.edu (for Folger Institute Programs);
brobeck@folger.edu (for Long-term and Short-term Fellowships)
Web site: http://www.folger.edu
Fax: 202-544-4623

The Folger Institute Programs offer *Consortium Funds* for participation in seminars to advanced graduate students and faculty from the Institute's affiliated universities: American, Amherst, Boston, Catholic, Columbia, CUNY Graduate School and University Center, Delaware, Duke, Emory, Fordham, George Mason, George Washington, Georgetown, Harvard, Howard, Johns Hopkins, Maryland–Baltimore County, Maryland–College Park, Massachusetts–Amherst, New York, North Carolina, North Carolina State, Notre Dame, Pennsylvania, Pennsylvania State, Princeton, Rochester, Rutgers, St. Andrews, South Carolina, SUNY at Buffalo, Syracuse, Vanderbilt, Virginia, West Virginia, William and Mary, and Yale.

Available to: See above
Deadlines: June 1 for fall-term seminars and year-long programs; September 1 for spring-term seminars
Apply to: Folger Institute, above address

The Folger Library offers a limited number of six-to-nine-month residential fellowships to advanced scholars who have made substantial contributions in their fields and whose research projects are appropriate to the collection of the Library. *Long-Term Fellowships* are supported by the Andrew W. Mellon Foundation, the National Endowment for the Humanities, and the Folger Library. The two *Mellon Postdoctoral Research Fellowships* carry stipends of $45,000 and $30,000. The three *National Endowment for the Humanities Fellowships* carry maximum stipends of $30,000. Mellon Fellowships and Folger Long-Term Fellowships are open to scholars from any country; NEH Fellowships are restricted to U.S. citizens or foreign nationals who have been living in the United States for at least three years.. *Short-Term Fellowships* offer up to $1,800 a month for one to three months to postdoctoral scholars, and are available from July to June yearly. Write, e-mail, or visit the Web site for further information and application.

Available to: See above
Deadlines: March 1 for short-term; November 1 for long-term
Apply to: Carol Brobeck, Fellowships Coordinator, above address

[IN] The *O. B. Hardison, Jr., Poetry Prize* of $2,000 is awarded annually by a panel of judges to an American poet whose art and teaching "exemplify great imagination and daring, and fine scholarship, in the spirit of the life and work of O. B. Hardison, Jr., former director of the Folger Shakespeare Library." *By Internal Nomination Only.*

Fontbonne College
6800 Wydown Boulevard
St. Louis, MO 63105

(P)   The *Hanks Chapbook Award* offers $500 and publication, with 100 copies reserved for the author, for a poetry manuscript, 24 to 30 pages long. Up to half of the manuscript may be poems previously published in magazines and journals. The winner also receives a week-long residence at the St. Louis Poetry Center, where he or she will give a public reading and conduct a workshop. There is a $12 entry fee.

Available to: No restrictions
Deadline: April 1
Apply to: Jason Sommer, Hanks Chapbook Award, above address

The Formalist
320 Hunter Drive
Evansville, IN 47711

(P)   The annual *Howard Nemerov Sonnet Award* offers $1,000 and publication in *The Formalist* for an original, unpublished sonnet. Writers may enter as many sonnets as they wish, with a $3 fee per sonnet. Eleven other finalists will be published. Send SASE for rules.

Available to: No restrictions
Deadline: June 15
Apply to: Howard Nemerov Sonnet Award, above address

Foundation for Contemporary Performance Arts
820 Greenwich Street
New York, NY 10014

[IN]   Individual artist grants, of $25,000 each, are awarded annually to artists in poetry, dance, music, theater/performance art, and visual arts. Grant recipients are selected on the basis of merit, innovative work, and the effect such recognition and support might have now in their careers. Grants are given to emerging as well as established artists. In 1998, thirteen grants were given. Unsolicited nominations are not accepted. *By Internal Nomination Only.*

The Foundation awards a limited number of discretionary grants to artists who need modest support for emergency situations related to their work. Requests should be made in the form of a letter to the Foundation.

Foundation for Iranian Studies
4343 Montgomery Avenue, Suite 200
Bethesda, MD 20814-4401
Fax: 301-657-4381

The Foundation offers an annual prize of $1,000 for the best Ph.D. dissertation in Iranian studies. Students completing their dissertations between July 1, 1999, and June 30, 2000, are eligible to apply for the 2000 prize; the 2001 prize is for work completed between July 1, 2000, and June 30, 2001. Dissertations must be nominated by the author's advisor and submitted with the dissertation committee's letter of acceptance.

Available to: Ph.D. candidates in Iranian studies
Deadline: August 1
Apply to: Above address

Four Way Books
PO Box 607
Marshfield, MA 02050
Web site: http://www.gypsyfish.com/fourway

(P) Four Way Books annually awards a cash prize and publication for a book-length collection of poems. Past prizes have included the *Four Way Award Series in Poetry*, of $1,500, and the *Levis Poetry Prize*, of $2,000. In 2000, the *Four Way Books Intro Prize in Poetry* will award a $1,500 honorarium and $500 in travel money to a U.S. poet who has not previously published a full-length collection. Guidelines for the 2001 contest will be available in November 2000. There is a $20 entry fee. Send SASE to the address below, or look for announcements in *Poets & Writers* and *American Poetry Review.*

Available to: U.S. poets
Deadline: Inquire (generally March 31)
Apply to: Four Way Books, PO Box 535, Village Station, New York, NY 10014

French-American Foundation
519 Madison Avenue, Suite 310
New York, NY 10022
E-mail: info@frenchamerican.org
Web site: http://www.frenchamerican.org
Fax: 212-829-8810

(J) The *French-American Foundation Journalism Fellowship Program* offers three American journalists and three French journalists a two-month program in one another's country. Applicants must be under thirty-five, bilingual, with a minimum of three years' print or broadcast reporting experience (international reporting preferred). Participants learn about and visit major institutions and media organizations in the respective countries and work at the office of an important newspaper or media organization. Fellows submit a complete report afterward to the French-American Foundation. A stipend covers lodging, meals, and travel. Write, e-mail, or visit the Web site for further information.

Available to: See above
Deadline: April 1
Apply to: Journalism Fellowship Program above, address

(T) The *French-American Foundation Translation Prize* of up to $7,500 is awarded annually for the best translation of a work from French into English published in the United States in the past year. All categories of prose are eligible, except for technical, scientific, and reference works and children's literature. Translations must be submitted by publishing houses, not individual translators.

Available to: No restrictions
Deadline: July 15
Apply to: Above address

Friends of American Writers
c/o Linda Milberg
2397 North Wayne
Chicago, IL 60614

(F) The *Friends of American Writers Literary Adult Awards* offer a first prize of $1,600 and a second prize of $1,000 for the best book published during the calendar year. Write for additional information.

(C) The *Friends of American Writers Young People's Literature Awards* annually offer two prizes of $900 each for the best books for young people from toddler to high school age published during the calendar year. Write for additional information.

Available to: U.S. writers
Deadline: December 15
Apply to: Above address for adult awards; Friends of American Writers, c/o Jane Larson, 400 East Randolph #2123, Chicago, IL 60601, for young people's awards

Friends of the Chicago Public Library*
400 South State Street, 10S-7
Chicago, IL 60605
Web site: www.cpl.lib.uic.edu/cpl.html

Ⓜ The *Carl Sandburg Literary Awards* offer four prizes of $1,000 each, in poetry, fiction, nonfiction, and children's literature to Chicago-area residents or native Chicago writers who have published a book between June 1 and May 31 of the award year. Publishers or authors must submit two copies of the book. There is a $25 entry fee. **PEN was unable to confirm the information for this edition but believes it is current. Inquire before applying*

Available to: Chicago-area residents or native Chicagoans
Deadline: August 1
Apply to: Chair, Carl Sandburg Literary Awards, above address

Friends of New Netherland
c/o New Netherland Project
New York State Library
CEC, 8th floor
Albany, NY 12230

Ⓝ The *Hendricks Manuscript Award* offers $1,000 for the best manuscript, published or unpublished, focusing on any aspect of the Dutch colonial experience in North America. The winning manuscript, if not otherwise obligated, will be considered for publication by Syracuse University Press. Write for additional information and guidelines.

Available to: No restrictions
Deadline: February 1
Apply to: Hendricks Manuscript Award Committee, above address

Robert Frost Foundation
90 Mount Vernon Street
Lawrence, MA 01843

Ⓟ The *Robert Frost Poetry Award* annually offers $1,000 to a poet from New England who has not yet published a full-length book of poetry. The award winner will be a featured reader at the Robert Frost Festival, held in Lawrence, Massachusetts. There is a $10 reading fee.

Available to: New England poets who have not published a full-length book of poetry
Deadline: Inquire
Apply to: Robert Frost Poetry Award, above address

The Fund for Investigative Journalism
5120 Kenwood Drive
Annandale, VA 22003
E-mail: Fundfij@aol.com
Web site: http://www.fij.org

Ⓙ The Fund for Investigative Journalism "makes grants to writers to enable them to probe abuses of authority or the malfunctioning of institutions and systems which harm the public." Reports supported by the Fund have appeared in newspapers and magazines, or as books, or have been broadcast. Some 850 grants totaling more than $1.4 million have been awarded, primarily to freelance investigative writers. There is no tuition support.

Available to: Anyone with a publisher's or producer's commitment
Deadline: February 1; June 1; October 1
Apply to: Peg Lotito, Executive Director, above address

The Fund annouces its *FIJ Prize*, of up to $10,000 for books and other investigative projects, at each of its triannual board meetings. At the final meeting of the year, the Fund awards either an additional $15,000 to a proposal already selected or a $25,000 prize for a new and compelling entry. The FIJ Prize is generally awarded only to an author who has found a publisher unwilling or unable to support a project as fully as it demands; the Fund will, however, consider proposals that might need its endorsement before a publisher agrees to an advance. Write or visit the Web site for guidelines and application.

Available to: See above
Deadline: Inquire
Apply to: Peg Lotito, Executive Director, above address

Fund for UFO Research
PO Box 277
Mount Rainier, MD 20712
Web site: http://www.fufor.org

Ⓙ The *Donald E. Keyhoe Journalism Award* of $1,000 is given for the best investigative reporting on UFO research by a professional mainstream journalist or freelance author in one or more of three categories: newspaper/magazine, radio broadcast, TV broadcast. Print entries must have appeared in a newsstand magazine or newspaper other than one devoted exclusively to reporting on UFOs. Write or visit the Web site for additional information.

Available to: No restrictions
Deadline: February 15
Apply to: Donald E. Keyhoe Journalism Award, above address

George Washington University
Department of English
Washington, DC 20052
Web site: http://www.gwu.edu/~english

Ⓕ Ⓟ The *Jenny McKean Moore Writers Program* at George Washington University engages a creative writer (a poet for 2000–2001; a fiction writer for 2001–2002) to teach two semesters at the university, at a salary of approximately $48,000. SASE with writing sample and résumé must accompany application. The visiting lecturer must live in Washington during the academic year.

Available to: No restrictions
Deadline: November 15
Apply to: Above address

Georgia State University Review
Georgia State University
Campus Box 1894
Atlanta, GA 30303-3083
E-mail: mnewcome@mindspring.com

Ⓕ Ⓟ The *Review's Writing Contest* offers a $1,000 prize and publication in the *Review* for an unpublished story and for an unpublished poem. Short story manuscripts should not exceed 7,500 words. Poets may submit up to three poems, each no longer than 2 pages. The reading fee is $10 for each story or group of three poems. Send SASE or e-mail for guidelines.

Available to: No restrictions
Deadline: January 15
Apply to: Writing Contest, above address

German Marshall Fund of the United States
11 Dupont Circle, NW, Suite 750
Washington, DC 20036
E-mail: info@gmfus.org
Web site: http://www.gmfus.org
Fax: 202-265-1662

Research Fellowships are available to established U.S. scholars for advanced research that seeks to improve the understanding of significant contemporary economic, political, and social developments relating to Europe, European integration, and relations between Europe and the United States. Projects should involve a comparative analysis of a topic in more than one country or the exploration of a topic in a single country in ways that will likely be relevant for other countries. Applicants must be graduate students, recent Ph.D. or LL.M. recipients, or more senior scholars. Awards of up to $40,000 will be made, with additional funds of up to $2,000 for travel. Write or e-mail for information and application.

Available to: U.S. citizens
Deadline: November 15
Apply to: Above address

GERMANY
Art Society (Künstlergilde)
Hafenmarkt 2
D-73728 Esslingen
Germany

Ⓜ The *Andreas Gryphius Prize* is given for the best essay, novel, or poem dealing with particular problems of German culture in Eastern Europe. One award of DM 25,000 and one of DM 7,000 are available annually.

Available to: No restrictions
Deadline: Inquire
Apply to: Andreas Gryphius Prize, above address

Ⓟ The *Nikolaus Lenau Prize,* established in 1985 in memory of Nikolaus Lenau (1802–1850), is given for the best poem dealing with particular problems of German culture in Eastern Europe. An award of DM 11,000 is given annually.

Available to: No restrictions
Deadline: Inquire
Apply to: Nikolaus Lenau Prize, above address

GERMANY
Stadt Buxtehude
Kulturabteilung
Stavenort 5
D-21614 Buxtehude
Germany

〔IN〕 The *Buxtehude Bulle* is awarded for the best young people's book (for ages twelve to eighteen) published in Germany during the preceding year. One prize of DM 10,000 is awarded annually. *By Internal Nomination Only.*

GERMANY
DAAD (German Academic Exchange Service)
Postfach 240
D-10106 Berlin
Germany
E-mail: BKP.berlin@daad.de (Berlin) or daadny@daad.org (New York)
Web site: http://www.daad.org

Ⓡ The *Artists-in-Berlin Program (Berliner Künstlerprogramm)* invites some fifteen to twenty internationally known artists, writers, composers, and filmmakers to spend twelve months in Berlin, where they have the opportunity to work undisturbed and to participate actively in the city's cultural life. Invited artists receive monthly grant installments for living costs and rent, travel expenses for the artist and any accompanying family members staying in Berlin for the duration of the invitation, and health and accident insurance. Write, e-mail or visit the Web site for guidelines and application. Forms may be obtained also by writing the Artists-in-Berlin Program, German Academic Exchange Service, 950 Third Avenue, New York, NY 10022.

Available to: No restrictions
Deadline: December 31
Apply to: Artists-in-Berlin Program, above address

DAAD awards short-term grants for study and research visits to Germany for scholars and Ph.D. candidates. For information, contact DAAD at the New York address listed above.

GERMANY
German Academy for Language and Literature
Alexandraweg 23
64287 Darmstadt
Germany
E-mail: DeutscheAkademie@T-Online.de
Fax: 49-06151-4092-99

[IN] The *Friedrich Gundolf Prize* is given to individuals who have distinguished themselves in disseminating German culture abroad. A brochure can be requested from the address above. One award of DM 20,000 is available annually. *By Internal Nomination Only.*

[IN] The *Johann Heinrich Voss Prize for Translation* recognizes an outstanding lifetime achievement in translation into German. One award of DM 20,000 is available annually. *By Internal Nomination Only.*

GERMANY
Goethe Prize of the City of Frankfurt
Römerberg 23
60311 Frankfurt am Main
Germany

[IN] The *Goethe Prize* is given to a writer whose creative work demonstrates a continuation of Goethe's ideals and thoughts. One award of DM 50,000 is available every three years. *By Internal Nomination Only.*

GERMANY
Institut für Europäische Geschichte
Alte Universitätsstrasse 19
D-55116 Mainz
Germany
E-mail: ieg2@inst-euro-history.uni-mainz.de
Web site: http://www.inst-euro-history.uni-mainz.de

Grants are offered for advanced study and research in Germany in modern and contemporary European history and the history of European religion with regard to the Reformation. Candidates must be university graduates. Write, e-mail, or visit the Web site for further information and application procedures.

Available to: No restrictions
Deadlines: Inquire
Apply to: For European history: Professor Heinz Duchhardt, Abteilung Universalgeschichte, above address; for history of European religion: Professor Gerhard May, Abteilung Religionsgeschichte, above address

Gerontological Society of America
1030 15th Street NW, Suite 250
Washington, DC 20005-1503
E-mail: geron@geron.org
Web site: http://www.geron.org

Ⓝ The *Age Studies Award* offers $1,000 and publication by the University Press of Virginia for an outstanding book-length manuscript in interdisciplinary scholarship on aging written for a humanities audience. Applicants should submit three copies of a description, along with table of contents, a sample chapter, and author vita. Finalists will be asked to submit five copies of the complete manuscript. Write or visit the Web site for additional information.

Available to: No restrictions

Deadline: Inquire
Apply to: Age Studies Award, University Press of Virginia, Box 3608 University Station, Charlottesville, VA 22903

Getty Grant Program
1200 Getty Center Drive, Suite 800
Los Angeles, CA 90049-1685
Web site: http://www.getty.edu/grant
Fax: 310-440-7703

Postdoctoral Fellowships provide support to scholars who have obtained their doctorates within the last six years to pursue interpretive research for projects that will contribute substantially and originally to the understanding of art and its history. A maximum of fifteen fellowships with stipends of $35,000 each are awarded for twelve-month periods.

Available to: For 2000, scholars whose doctorate (or the equivalent outside the United States) was conferred January 1, 1994–January 1, 2000; for 2001, scholars conferred a doctorate January 1, 1995–January 1, 2001
Deadline: November 1
Apply to: Above address

Collaborative Research Grants provide opportunities for teams of scholars to collaborate on interpretive research for projects that offer new explanations of art and its history. Teams may consist of two or more art historians, or of an art historian and one or more scholars from other disciplines. Funding is also available for researching and planning scholarly exhibitions; teams for these projects should include scholars from both museums and universities. Grant periods and stipends vary according to needs, but generally support research periods of one to two years.

Available to: See above
Deadline: November 1
Apply to: Above address

Curatorial Research Fellowships support the professional scholarly development of curators by providing them with time off from regular museum duties to undertake short-term research or study projects. Fellowships are reserved for full-time curators with at least three years' professional experience who are employed at museums with art collections. Fellowships provide stipends for research periods of one to three months.

Available to: See above
Deadline: November 1
Apply to: Above address

The Gilder Lehrman Center for the Study of Slavery, Resistance, and Abolition
34 Hillhouse Avenue
New Haven, CT 06520-8206
E-mail: gilder.lehrman.center@yale.edu
Web site: http://www.cis.yale.edu/glc/
Fax: 203-432-6943

Ⓝ The *Frederick Douglass Book Prize* awards $25,000 for the most outstanding book published in English during the calendar year on slavery and/or abolition and antislavery movements. The book may deal with any geographic area or time period; works related to the Civil War are eligible only if their primary focus relates to slavery or emancipation. Send SASE or e-mail for guidelines.

Available to: No restrictions
Deadline: February 1
Apply to: Frederick Douglass Book Prize, above address

Gilman School
5407 Roland Avenue
Baltimore, MD 21210

Ⓕ Ⓟ The *Reginald S. Tickner Writing Fellowship* is awarded annually to a serious poet or fiction
writer for an academic year. Responsibilities include teaching creative writing, directing
a speakers' series, advising a literary magazine, and working individually with students
on their writing. Fellows receive a competitive stipend ($16,000 in 1999) and assistance
from an intern. Gilman School is an independent boys' school that coordinates classes
with Bryn Mawr School and Roland Park Country School. Send SASE for guidelines.

Available to: No restrictions
Deadline: January (inquire for exact date)
Apply to: Meg Tipper, above address

Gival Press
PO Box 3812
Arlington, VA 22203
E-mail: givalpress@yahoo.com
Web site: http://www.givalpress.bizonthe.net

Ⓟ The *Gival Press Chapbook Competition* annually awards $500 and limited-edition publication
by this independent gay-owned publishing house for an unpublished collection of poems,
20 to 24 pages, on the theme of love. There is a $15 reading fee. Send SASE or e-mail for
guidelines.

Available to: No restrictions
Deadline: December 15
Apply to: Chapbook Competition, above address

Glimmer Train Press
710 SW Madison Street #504
Portland, OR 97205
Web site: http://www.glimmertrain.com
Fax: 503-221-0837

Ⓕ The *Fiction Open* offers a first prize of $2,000 and publication in *Glimmer Train,* a second prize
of $1,000, and third of $600 for previously unpublished fiction of any length and on any
theme. There is a $15 reading fee per story. Send SASE for guidelines.

Available to: No restrictions
Deadline: Submissions accepted May–June
Apply to: Fiction Open, above address

Ⓟ The *Poetry Open* offers a first prize of $500 and publication in *Glimmer Train,* a second prize of
$250, and a third of $100, for a poem of any length, form, and theme. There is a reading
fee of $10 for up to three previously unpublished poems. Send SASE for guidelines.

Available to: No restrictions
Deadline: Submissions accepted in April
Apply to: Poetry Open, above address

Ⓕ Twice yearly, the *Short Story Award for New Writers* offers $1,200 and publication in *Glimmer
Train* for a short story by a writer whose fiction has appeared in a nationally distributed
publication with a circulation above 5,000. The first runner-up will receive $500. All
applicants will receive the issue of *Glimmer Train* with the winning story. Word count
must not exceed 8,000. There is a $12 reading fee per story. Send SASE for guidelines and
further information.

Available to: See above
Deadline: Submissions accepted February–March for spring award; August–September
for fall
Apply to: Short Story Award for New Writers, above address

Ⓕ Also twice a year, the *Very Short Fiction Award* offers $1,200 and publication in *Glimmer Train* for a previously unpublished short short, not to exceed 2,000 words. The first runner-up will receive $500. There is a $10 reading fee per story. Send SASE for guidelines.

Available to: No restrictions
Deadline: Submissions accepted May–July for summer award; November–January for winter
Apply to: Very Short Fiction Award, above address

Dick Goldensohn Fund Projects
175 Fifth Avenue, Suite 2245
New York, NY 10010

Ⓙ The *Dick Goldensohn Fund* annually awards grants of up to $5,000 (with an average of $1,500) to reporters, editors, freelance writers, and others working on innovative journalistic projects. The Fund's goal is "to foster journalistic undertakings that investigate abuses of the public trust, spotlight overlooked aspects of contemporary life, or promote social, political, and economic justice." Send SASE for grant proposal procedure and details.

Available to: No restrictions
Deadline: February 15
Apply to: Above address

Goshen College
1700 South Main Street
Goshen, IN 46526
E-mail: douglc@goshen.edu

Ⓓ For its biennial competition, the *Goshen College Peace Playwriting Contest* seeks unproduced, unpublished one-acts exploring a contemporary peace theme. The winning playwright will be awarded $500, production, and room and board to attend rehearsals and/or production. Plays should be 20 to 50 minutes long. Include a one-paragraph synopsis and current résumé with script submission.

Available to: No restrictions
Deadline: December 31 of odd-numbered years
Apply to: Doug Caskey, Director of Theatre, above address

Great Lakes Colleges Association
535 West William, Suite 301
Ann Arbor, MI 48103
Web site: http://www.glca.org

Ⓕ Ⓟ The *New Writer Awards* recognize the best first books of poetry and fiction published during the previous year. Winning authors commit to visit GLCA colleges as soon as possible after publication; they participate in whatever promotional activities the colleges can arrange. Authors receive from each of the schools visited an honorarium of at least $300, room and board, and payment of transportation costs. Entries may be submitted by publishers only, who are limited to one entry each in poetry and in fiction.

Available to: No restrictions
Deadline: February 28
Apply to: Linda Krumholz, Director, GLCA New Writers Awards, English Department, Denison University, Granville, OH 43231

The Harry Frank Guggenheim Foundation
527 Madison Avenue
New York, NY 10022-4304
Web site: http://www.hfg.org
Fax: 212-644-5110

Research Grants, ranging from $15,000 to $35,000 a year for periods of one or two years, are available to postdoctoral scholars working on projects in any of the natural or social sciences or the humanities that "promise to increase understanding of the causes, manifestations, and control of violence, aggression, and dominance." Requests will be considered for salaries, employee benefits, research assistantships, computer time, supplies and equipment, field work, essential secretarial and technical help, and other items necessary to the successful completion of a project. Write or visit the Web site for additional information and application procedures.

Available to: No restrictions
Deadline: August 1
Apply to: Above address

The Foundation awards a small number of *Dissertation Fellowships* to individuals who will complete the writing of their dissertation within the award year. These fellowships, $10,000 each, are designed to assist doctoral candidates in completing their theses in a timely manner. Applications are evaluated in comparison with one another and not in competition with the postdoctoral research proposals. Applicants may be citizens of any country and studying at colleges or universities in any country.

Available to: No restrictions
Deadline: February 1
Apply to: Above address

John Simon Guggenheim Memorial Foundation
90 Park Avenue
New York, NY 10016
E-mail: fellowships@gf.org
Web site: http://www.gf.org
Fax: 212-697-3248

Ⓜ Fellowships are given annually to advanced professionals with a significant record of publication for research in any field of knowledge or creative work in any of the arts. Candidates should already have demonstrated exceptional capacity for productive scholarship or exceptional creative ability in the arts. The awards are given for a minimum of six months and a maximum of one year. In 1999, the average fellowship grant was $33,568. Write, e-mail, or visit the Web site for additional information and application.

Available to: U.S. and Canadian citizens or permanent residents
Deadline: October 1
Apply to: Above address

Guideposts
16 East 34th Street
New York, NY 10016
Web site: http://www.guideposts.org

The *Guideposts Young Writers Contest* offers to high school juniors or seniors a first prize of $8,000, a second of $7,000, a third of $5,000, and four honorable mentions of $1,000 each for true first-person stories about memorable or moving experiences. Prizes are awarded as scholarships to the accredited colleges or schools of the winners' choice. Submissions should not exceed 1,200 words. Write or visit the Web site for guidelines and additional information.

Available to: High school juniors and seniors
Deadline: November (inquire for exact date)
Apply to: Young Writers Contest, above address

Gulf Coast
University of Houston
English Department
Houston, TX 77204-3012

Ⓕ Ⓟ The *Gulf Coast Poetry and Short Story Prizes* award $500 and publication in *Gulf Coast* for a winning poem and short story. Fiction writers may submit one story, poets up to five poems totaling no more than 10 pages. The reading fee of $15 covers a one-year subscription to *Gulf Coast*. All submissions will be considered for publication. Send SASE for guidelines.

Available to: No restrictions
Deadline: February 15
Apply to: Poetry Prize or Short Story Prize, above address

Hadassah Magazine
50 West 58th Street
New York, NY 10019
Fax: 212-446-9521
E-mail: Hadamag@aol.com

Ⓕ The *Harold U. Ribalow Prize* is given annually for an outstanding work of fiction on a Jewish theme. Any book of fiction first published in English in the calendar year preceding the prize year is eligible (books published in 1999 are eligible for the 2000 prize). The prize consists of $1,000 and publication of an excerpt in *Hadassah*.

Available to: Published authors of fiction on a Jewish theme
Deadline: March 31
Apply to: Harold U. Ribalow Prize, above address

Hambidge Center
PO Box 339
Rabun Gap, GA 30568
E-mail: hambidge@rabun.net
Web site: http://www.rabun.net/~hambidge
Fax: 706-746-9933

Ⓡ Residency fellowships of two weeks to two months are available to artists in all fields. The Center awards some ninety fellowships annually, with eight artists in residence at any one time. Each fellow is provided with a private cottage and, for fellows in residence from May through October, a common evening meal; fellows in residence from November through April must prepare their own meals in the cottage kitchens. Send SASE for further information and application.

Available to: No restrictions
Deadline: November 1 for March–August residences; May 1 for September–December residences
Apply to: Residence Program, above address

The Harvard Review
Poetry Room
Harvard College Library
Cambridge, MA 02138

[IN] The *Daniel A. Pollack–Harvard Review Prize* awards $1,500 annually to the author of a book of poetry, fiction, or literary nonfiction that has been discussed in the *Review. By Internal Nomination Only.*

Harvard University Press
79 Garden Street
Cambridge, MA 02138

Ⓝ The *Robert Troup Paine Prize* of $3,000 is given every four years to the best manuscript on a designated subject that has been accepted for publication by Harvard University Press in the preceding four years. The subject for the period January 1, 1998–December 31, 2001, is science and the practical arts. Authors will be paid royalties as well as the $3,000 prize.

Available to: Authors with unpublished, original book-length manuscripts
Deadline: December 31, 2001
Apply to: Michael G. Fisher, Science Editor, Robert Troup Paine Prize, above address

Headlands Center for the Arts
944 Fort Barry
Sausalito, CA 94965
E-mail: staff@headlands.org
Web site: http://www.headlands.org
Fax: 415-331-3857

® The Headlands Center for the Arts is located in several restored historic military buildings in the Golden Gate National Recreation area. Live-in residences of three to five months are available to artists from the United States and abroad; live-out residences of eleven months are available to Bay Area artists only. Live-in residences entail studio, housing, stipend, and meals; live-out entail studio, stipend, and some meals. Residents are encouraged to interact with fellow residents, the environment, and the greater San Francisco community. Public programs include three open houses each year, interdisciplinary panels, and performances and informal presentations by residents and other artists.

Available to: California, Ohio, and North Carolina artists; residents of other states by invitation
Deadline: June for the following year (inquire for exact date)
Apply to: Above address

HEArt Quarterly
PO Box 81038
Pittsburgh, PA 15217
Web site: http://trfn.clpgh.org/heart
Fax: 412-244-0120

Ⓕ Ⓟ The *HEArt Quarterly Poetry and Short Fiction Contest* annually awards a $500 prize for a poem and for a short story. Submissions must be previously unpublished work that addresses social justice issues, including but not limited to racial, sexual, gender, and class discrimination. Poets may submit up to three poems, with a 5-page maximum total; fiction writers may submit one story up to 7,000 words. There is a $15 entry fee, which covers a one-year subscription to the *Quarterly*. Current subscribers' entry fees may be used to purchase gift subscriptions for others. Send SASE or visit the Web site for guidelines.

Available to: No restrictions
Deadline: February 28
Apply to: HEArt Quarterly Contest, above address

Hedgebrook
2197 East Millman Road
Langley, WA 98260

® Residences of one week to two months are available to women writers of diverse cultural backgrounds in six individual cottages on thirty wooded acres on Whidbey Island, near Seattle. Residence includes free room and board. Send SASE for the required application form; do not send submission before receiving an application.

Available to: Women writers
Deadline: October 1 for winter and spring; April 1 for summer and fall
Apply to: Above address

Heinz Family Foundation
3200 CNG Tower
Pittsburgh, PA 15222
E-mail: awards@heinz.org
Web site: http://www.awards.heinz.org

[IN] The *Heinz Awards*, $250,000 each, recognize significant and sustained contributions in five categories: arts and humanities; the environment; the human condition; public policy; and technology, the economy, and employment. There is no application process. *By Internal Nomination Only.*

Helicon Nine Editions
3607 Pennsylvania Avenue
Kansas City, MO 64111
Fax: 816-753-1090
Web site: http://www.heliconnine.com

(F)   The *Willa Cather Fiction Prize* offers a $1,000 award and publication by Helicon Nine for an original, unpublished manuscript of fiction (a novella or short story collection) between 150 and 300 double-spaced pages. Work that has appeared in magazines or anthologies is eligible. There is a $20 reading fee. Send SASE or visit the Web site for guidelines.

(P)   The *Marianne Moore Poetry Prize* offers a $1,000 award and publication by Helicon Nine for an original, unpublished poetry manuscript of at least 50 pages. Work that has appeared in magazines or anthologies is eligible. There is a $20 reading fee. Send SASE or visit the Web site for guidelines.

    Available to: No restrictions
    Deadline: Submissions accepted January 1–May 1
    Apply to: Literary Prizes, above address

Hemingway Days Festival
PO Box 993
Key West, FL 33041
Web site: http://www.hemingwaydays.com

[IN]   The *Conch Republic Prize for Literature* is awarded to an author whose life's work reflects the daring and creative spirit of Key West. The annual award includes $1,000 and paid transportation and lodging so that the recipient can accept the award during the Hemingway Days Festival, held the third week of July. *By Internal Nomination Only.*

(F)   The *Lorian Hemingway Short Story Competition* offers a $1,000 first prize, a $500 second prize, and a $500 third prize for short stories of any form or style, maximum 3,000 words. The competition is open to writers whose fiction has not appeared in a nationally distributed publication with circulation above 5,000. The reading fee for entries sent by June 1 is $10, and $15 for entries sent between June 1 and June 15. Send SASE for guidelines.

    Available to: No restrictions
    Deadline: June 15
    Apply to: Above address

Hemingway Western Studies Center
Boise State University
1910 University Drive
Boise, ID 83725
E-mail: ttrusky@boisestate.edu
Fax: 208-426-4373

The *Rocky Mountain Artists/Eccentric Book Competition* offers $500 and standard sales royalties for multiple-edition works (100 to 1,000 copies) relating to such public concerns as race, religion, gender, and the environment. The annual contest seeks to "encourage the creation of beautiful, terrifying, intriguing and ingenious, as well as inexpensive books." Works with special relevance to Rocky Mountain audiences are preferred. Authors and artists may submit sample copies, dummies, or publication proposals, with SASE for return of materials. Proposals specifying offset, copier, or silkscreen printing on commercial papers will be favored. Works may consist of text and/or visual content. Send SASE, fax, or e-mail for further information.

    Available to: U.S. writers
    Deadline: Inquire
    Apply to: Rocky Mountain Artists/Eccentric Book Competition, above address

The Heritage Foundation
214 Massachusetts Avenue, NE
Washington, DC 20002

Ⓙ The *Lawrence Wade Journalism Fellowship* is awarded annually to a journalism student or student journalist who best exemplifies the high ideals and standards of the late Lawrence Wade. The winning fellow receives a ten-week salaried internship at the Heritage Foundation and a $1,000 cash scholarship. Applicants must be enrolled full-time in an accredited college or university, and working toward an undergraduate or graduate degree, but need not be studying or majoring in journalism or a related communications field. Write for guidelines.

Available to: See above
Deadline: March 1
Apply to: Selection Committee, Lawrence Wade Journalism Fellowship, above address

Highlights for Children
803 Church Street
Honesdale, PA 18431
Fax: 717-251-7847

Ⓒ *Highlights for Children* sponsors an annual *Fiction Contest*. Previously unpublished short stories (for readers ages nine to twelve, a maximum of 900 words; for readers through age eight, a maximum of 500) will be judged for three cash prizes of $1,000 each. All entries will be considered for regular publication with payment at regular rates. Stories should not include violence. Send SASE for further information.

Available to: No restrictions
Deadline: Submissions accepted January 1–February 28
Apply to: Fiction Contest, above address

Ⓒ The *Highlights Foundation Scholarship Program* enables writers with a serious interest in writing for children to attend the Highlights Foundation Writers' Workshop at Chautauqua, New York. Awards vary in amount and requirements, and will be given at the discretion of the Highlights Foundation Scholarship Committee. Send SASE for guidelines.

Available to: Children's writers who have not attended the Writers' Workshop
Deadline: Applications accepted October 15–April 15
Apply to: Selection Committee, Highlights Foundation Scholarship Program, PO Box 686, Honesdale, PA 18431

Sidney Hillman Foundation
c/o UNITE!
1710 Broadway
New York, NY 10019-5299

Ⓙ Ⓝ The *Sidney Hillman Foundation Prize Awards* are given for outstanding contributions related in theme to the ideals of Sidney Hillman, including "the protection of individual civil liberties, improved race relations, a strengthened labor movement, the advancement of social welfare and economic security, greater world understanding." Contributions may be in nonfiction, daily or periodical journalism, or radio and television journalism, and must have been published or produced in the previous year. Several prizes of $2,000 each are awarded annually.

Available to: No restrictions
Deadline: Mid-January (inquire for exact date)
Apply to: Jo-Ann Mort, Executive Director, above address

Historic New Orleans Collection
533 Royal Street
New Orleans, LA 70130-2179
E-mail: WRC@hnoc.org
Web site: http://www.hnoc.org
Fax: 504-598-7108

Ⓝ The *Kemper and Leila Williams Prize in Louisiana History* is given annually for the best work of nonfiction dealing with Louisiana history or culture published during the calendar year. The prize consists of a cash award of $1,500 and an engraved plaque. All submissions must be made in quadruplicate. Write, e-mail, or visit the Web site for additional information and nomination form.

Available to: No restrictions
Deadline: January 15
Apply to: Chair, Kemper and Leila Williams Prize Committee, above address

History of Science Society
University of Washington
Box 351330
Seattle, WA 98195
E-mail: hssexec@u.washington.edu
Web site: http://depts.washington.edu/hssexec
Fax: 206-685-9544

Ⓝ The *Watson Davis and Helen Miles Davis Prize* of $500 is given annually to the best book on the history of science in English (original language or translation) directed to a wide readership and published during the preceding three years.

Available to: No restrictions
Deadline: April 1
Apply to: Robert J. Malone, Executive Director, above address

Ⓝ The *History of Women in Science Prize* of $500 is given annually to the best book (in odd-numbered years) or best article (in even-numbered years) on women and science published during the preceding four years.

Available to: No restrictions
Deadline: April 1
Apply to: Robert J. Malone, Executive Director, above address

Ⓝ The *Pfizer Award* of $2,500 and an inscribed medal is given annually for the best book on the history of science in English (original language or in translation) published during the preceding three years.

Available to: No restrictions
Deadline: April 1
Apply to: Robert J. Malone, Executive Director, above address

Ⓝ The *Henry and Ida Schuman Prize* awards $250 annually for an original essay by a graduate student on the history of science and its cultural influences.

Available to: Graduate students
Deadline: April 15
Apply to: Robert J. Malone, Executive Director, above address

Herbert Hoover Presidential Library Association
PO Box 696
West Branch, IA 52358-0696
E-mail: info@hooverassoc.org
Web site: http://www.hooverassoc.org
Fax: 319-643-2391

The *Herbert Hoover Presidential Travel & Grant Program* annually awards grants to researchers to cover the cost of trips to the Hoover Library. There is no specific dollar amount; grants

96

in recent years have ranged from $500 to $1,500. The Association will consider larger requests for extended graduate and postdoctoral research. All funds must be used for research at the Library. Applicants should consult with the archival staff about their topic before submitting a request. Write for additional information and application.

Available to: No restrictions
Deadline: March 1
Apply to: Chairman, Fellowship and Grant Committee, above address

The Horn Book
56 Roland Street
Boston, MA 02129
Web site: http://www.hbook.com

© The *Boston Globe–Horn Book Awards for Excellence in Children's Literature* are offered by the Boston Globe Newspaper Company and *The Horn Book* to foster and reward excellence in text and illustration of children's books. Three awards, of $500 each, are offered for fiction, nonfiction, and picture books; reprints and textbooks are not considered. Publishers may submit up to eight books per juvenile imprint divided into any of the three categories; submissions must be sent directly to the judges. Write or visit the Web site for names and addresses of current judges. Awards are made each autumn at the New England Library Association conference.

Available to: Authors of children's books published in the United States between June 1 and the following May 31
Deadline: May 15
Apply to: Boston Globe–Horn Book Awards, above address

George A. and Eliza Gardner Howard Foundation
Box 1867
Brown University
Providence, RI 02912
E-mail: Howard_Foundation@brown.edu
Web site: http://www.brown.edu/Divisions/Graduate_School/howard

The *George A. and Eliza Gardner Howard Foundation* seeks to support people in the middle stages of their careers whose work to date is evidence of their promise and achievement. Nominees normally should have the rank of assistant or associate professor or their nonacademic equivalents. Support is intended to augment paid sabbatical leaves.

The Foundation awards a limited number of fellowships each year, with stipends of $20,000 for one-year terms for independent projects. Awards are granted in a sequence, one year devoted to the arts, the next to the social sciences. In 2000–2001, awards will be made in sociology, anthropology, and philosophy; in 2001–2002, in painting, sculpture, and art history; in 2002–2003, in music and musicology; in 2003–2004, in history, including the history of science, and political science; in 2004–2005, in creative writing in English including novels, short stories, poetry, playwriting, essays, and creative nonfiction; and in 2005–2006, in literary criticism, film criticism, and translations. Fellowships are not available for work leading to an academic degree or for private study. Candidates must be nominated by a representative of an affiliated college or university, a professional critic or editor, or the director of a professional association. Write, e-mail, or visit the Web site for further information and application procedures.

Available to: See above
Deadlines: Mid-October for nominations; late November for applications with supporting materials
Apply to: Professor Henry F. Majewski, Administrative Director, above address

L. Ron Hubbard's Writers of the Future Contest
PO Box 1630
Los Angeles, CA 90078
E-mail: contests@authorservicesinc.com
Web site: http://www.writersofthefuture.com

Ⓕ The *Writers of the Future Contest* is an international search for new and amateur writers of science fiction or fantasy short stories or novelettes (under 17,000 words). A first prize of $1,000, a second of $750, and a third of $500 are offered quarterly. The quarterly winners compete for an annual grand prize of $4,000. Submissions must be unpublished; no entry fee is required. Entrants retain all rights. Send SASE, e-mail, or visit the Web site for guidelines.

Available to: Writers who have not professionally published a novel or short novel, more than three short stories, or more than one novelette
Deadlines: December 31, March 31, June 30, September 30
Apply to: Above address

Hudson River Classics
Box 940
Hudson, NY 12534
Fax: 518-828-1329

Ⓓ HRC's *Annual Playwriting Contest* offers $500, a staged reading, and room, board, and travel to attend performances for an unpublished evening-length work (a full-length play or a series of one-acts) by a New York State playwright. There is a $5 entry fee.

Available to: New York playwrights
Deadline: Submissions accepted March 1–June 1
Apply to: Annual Playwriting Contest, above address

Hudson Valley Writers' Center
300 Riverside Drive
Sleepy Hollow, NY 10591

Ⓟ The *Slapering Hol Press Chapbook Competition* offers $500, publication, and a reading at the Center for poets who have not published a book or a chapbook. Poets should submit a manuscript of 20 to 24 pages, on which their name does not appear; a separate cover sheet should give title, poet's name, address, phone number, brief bio and acknowledgments. There is a $10 reading fee. Send SASE for guidelines.

Available to: See above
Deadline: May 15
Apply to: Slapering Hol Press Chapbook Competition, above address

Humanitas Prize
17575 Pacific Coast Highway
Pacific Palisades, CA 90272
E-mail: humanitasp@aol.com
Web site: http://www.humanitasprize.org

Ⓢ The *Humanitas Prize* is given for excellence in writing for film and television with a focus on human values. Awards are made in eight categories: feature film, 90-minute-or-longer program on PBS or cable, 90-minute-or-longer program on network television, 60-minute television program, 30-minute television program, children's live-action program, children's animated program, and in cooperation with the Sundance Institute, independent feature film. The first three categories offer a $25,000 prize each; the remaining five offer $10,000 each. To be eligible, work must have been aired or screened between April 16 of the year preceding the deadline and April 15 of the award year. Write or e-mail for required application.

Available to: No restrictions
Deadline: April 15
Apply to: Above address

Humboldt State University
English Department
Arcata, CA 95521

(F) The *Raymond Carver Short Story Contest* annually awards $1,000 plus publication in *Toyon*, the HSU literary journal, for an unpublished short story of up to 6,000 words. Writers should submit two copies of their manuscript and a $10 reading fee. Send SASE for guidelines.

Available to: U.S. residents
Deadline: December 1
Apply to: Raymond Carver Short Story Contest, above address

Humboldt State University
Department of Theatre Arts
Arcata, CA 95521
E-mail: mtk3@axe.humboldt.edu
Web site: http://www.humboldt.edu/~mtk3
Fax: 707-826-5494

(D) The *National New Play Award* triennially offers $1,000, full production, and a two-week residence for the writer of an unproduced, unpublished full-length play. The next award will be given in 2002. Write, e-mail, or visit the Web site in 2001 for updated information.

Available to: No restrictions
Deadline: January 30, 2002
Apply to: National New Play Award, above address

Hurston/Wright Foundation
Virginia Commonwealth University
Department of English
PO Box 842005
Richmond, VA 23284-2005

(F) The *Hurston/Wright Award* of $1,000 is given annually to honor excellence in fiction writing by African-American students enrolled full-time in a U.S. college or graduate school. Writers may submit an unpublished short story or an excerpt from a novel, no longer than 25 pages. Send SASE for guidelines.

Available to: See above
Deadline: December (inquire for exact date)
Apply to: Hurston/Wright Award, above address

Icarus
Missouri Western State College
St. Joseph, MO 64507
Web site: http://www.mwsc.edu/~kocher/Gilgun.htm

(P) The *John Gilgun Poetry Award* offers $500 and publication in *Icarus*, an annual literary journal. Poets should submit two copies of up to five poems, no more than 100 lines each, and totaling no more than 10 pages. Send SASE or visit the Web site for guidelines.

Available to: No restrictions
Deadline: October 15
Apply to: Ruth Ellen Kocher, Editor, John Gilgun Poetry Award, above address

ICARUS
PO Box 1232
Kill Devil Hills , NC 27948
E-mail: gleneure@interpath.com

(P) The *ICARUS Poetry Competition* offers $500 for an unpublished poem or prose poem, with a 100-line limit, on a specific theme related to flight. The winning and finalist works will be published in a chapbook that will be given to all entrants. There is a $10 reading fee. Send SASE for guidelines and the current theme.

Available to: No restrictions
Deadline: July 1
Apply to: Poetry Competition, above address

ICELAND
Ministry of Education, Science and Culture
Solvholsgata 4
IS-150 Reykjavik
Iceland
E-mail: postur@mrn.stjr.is
Web site: http://www.mrn.stjr.is
Fax: 354-1-562-3068

Several scholarships are offered for advanced study and research in the language, literature, and history of Iceland at the University of Iceland. Grants are for a period of eight months, and cover tuition plus a cash stipend (currently $900 a month).

Available to: U.S. citizens
Deadline: October 31
Apply to: Institute of International Education, U.S. Student Programs Division, 809 United Nations Plaza, New York, NY 10017

ICELAND
Sigurdur Nordal Institute
PO Box 1220
122 Reykjavik
Iceland
E-mail: ulfarb@rhi.hi.is
Web site: http://www.nordals.hi.is
Fax: 354-1-562-6263

Ⓣ The *Snorri Sturluson Icelandic Fellowships* are granted to writers, translators, and scholars in the humanities to enable them to stay in Iceland for at least three months, to improve their knowledge of the language, culture, and society. The amount of each fellowship is based on travel expenses to/from Iceland, plus living expenses while in the country. Applicants should submit a brief but thorough account of the purpose of their stay, specifying the anticipated duration, as well as a curriculum vitae.

Available to: No restrictions
Deadline: October 31
Apply to: Snorri Sturluson Icelandic Fellowships, above address

Idaho Commission on the Arts
Box 83720
Boise, ID 83720-0008
E-mail: cconley@ica.state.id.us
Web site: http://www.state.id.us/arts/
Fax: 208-334-2488

Ⓜ The Idaho Commission on the Arts offers three grant programs for writers. *Fellowships* of $3,500 are awarded for artistic excellence (one per lifetime), with disciplines rotating on a three-year cycle. *Writer-in-Residence* awards of $8,000 are given for highest artistic excellence (one per lifetime); during a three-year term, the writer gives twelve community readings in the state, with travel and other expenses covered. The literature fellowship and writer residence awards will be given next in 2001. *QuickArt$* funds are awarded quarterly for specific projects and professional development. The maximum for QuickArt$ projects is $1,000; the maximum for professional development is $400. These grants are available only to Idaho residents of at least one year before application. Write, e-mail, or visit the Web site for guidelines and further requirements.

Available to: Idaho residents
Deadline: Inquire for 2001 deadline for literature fellowships and writer residences;

upcoming deadlines for QuickArt$ are May 1, August 7, and November 6, 2000; and February 5, 2001

Apply to: Literature Director, above address

Illinois Arts Council
James R. Thompson Center
100 West Randolph, Suite 10-500
Chicago, IL 60601
E-mail: info@arts.state.il.us
Web site: http://www.state.il.us/agency/iac
Fax: 312-814-1471

Ⓜ *Artists' Fellowships* of $5,000 and $10,000 are offered annually to Illinois writers of poetry and prose, and playwriting/screenwriting. A limited number of $500 *Finalist Awards* are also given yearly. Write, e-mail, or visit the Web site for guidelines before submitting.

Available to: Illinois writers
Deadline: September 1 for playwriting/screenwriting; December 1 for poetry and prose
Apply to: Above address

Ⓡ *Arts-in-Education* residences provide support for Illinois artist residences in schools and communities statewide, ranging from one week to six months. Primary and secondary educational institutions, community colleges, and local arts and community organizations are eligible, as well as four-year colleges and universities if the residence involves the local K–12 student population. To be considered for the program, writers must apply for inclusion in the Artists Roster. Applications for inclusion are reviewed every two years (the next round will be in 2001). Roster artists are paid a stipend of $800 per week. Write, e-mail, or visit the Web site for additional information.

Available to: Illinois writers
Deadline: June 1, 2001 for roster inclusion; February 15 for residency
Apply to: Arts-in-Education Program, above address

The *Illinois Artstour Program* links Illinois performing artists, including writers who have done public readings, with Illinois presenters. Writers may present their work and conduct workshops, master classes, residences, and lecture/demonstrations sponsored by Illinois presenters. To be considered, writers must apply for inclusion in the Illinois Artstour Roster. Write for additional information.

Available to: Illinois writers
Deadline: Inquire
Apply to: Illinois Artstour Program, above address

Ⓜ *Literary Awards* are given annually to Illinois writers publishing new work in Illinois nonprofit literary magazines with editorial offices in the state whose primary mission is to publish contemporary poetry, fiction, and creative nonfiction. Creative nonfiction, distinguished by a strong narrative, literary quality found in personal essays or memoirs, does not include primarily analytical, scholarly, or journalistic works. Interviews and reviews are ineligible. Companion awards of $1,000 each are given to thirteen other writers publishing new work in similar literary magazines.

Available to: Previously unpublished Illinois writers with work appearing in Illinois nonprofit literary magazines
Deadline: March 1
Apply to: Above address

The *Short-Term Artist Residencies (STAR) Program* provides funding for Illinois nonprofit organizations to work with Illinois professional artists to develop and implement residence programs that bring arts activities into the community. Each residence lasts from one to five days. The Arts Council will support half of the artist's fee; the local sponsor must provide the remaining half and cover other expenses. Writers are encouraged to seek sponsors to initiate programs. Write, e-mail, or visit the Web site for additional information.

Available to: Illinois nonprofit organizations

Deadline: Ongoing
Apply to: STAR Program, above address

Ⓜ *Special Assistance Grants* are available to Illinois writers as the budget allows. They aim to support artists in promoting professional growth, gaining access to artistic venues, or resolving specific artistic problems. Write, e-mail, or visit the Web site for additional information.

Available to: Illinois writers
Deadline: Ongoing
Apply to: Above address

Illinois State University
English Department
Stevenson Hall
Campus Box 4240
Normal, IL 61790-4240
E-mail: rccruz@ilstu.edu
Web site: http://www.its.ilstu.edu/cjohnson

Ⓕ Ⓟ The *Charles Johnson Awards for Fiction and Poetry* offer $500 in each genre to U.S. ethnic minority college students and to college students "whose work freshly explores the experience/identity of a minority or marginalized culture." Eligible writers may submit one short story of up to 25 pages, or three to five poems totaling up to 6 pages. Manuscripts are not returned. Send SASE or e-mail for further information.

Available to: See above
Deadline: January 28
Apply to: Ricardo Cortez Cruz, above address

Indiana Review
Ballantine Hall 465
1020 E. Kirkwood Avenue
Bloomington, IN 47405-7103
Web site: http://www.indiana.edu/~inreview/ir.html

Ⓕ The *Indiana Review Fiction Prize* offers $500 and publication for a short story in any style and on any subject, up to 15,000 words. Contestants may enter multiple times under separate cover. Author's name, address, and phone number should appear on a cover letter only. The fee is $10 per entry, and all entrants receive a copy of the prize issue. Send SASE for notification with submission. Manuscripts will not be returned.

Available to: No restrictions
Deadline: November 15
Apply to: Fiction Prize, above address

Indiana University–Purdue University at Indianapolis
National Youth Theatre Playwriting Competition
425 University Boulevard #309
Indianapolis, IN 46202
E-mail: dwebb@iupui.edu
Web site: http://www.iupui.edu/~comstudy/playsym/symwork.html
Fax: 317-278-1025

Ⓓ The *National Youth Theatre Playwriting Competition* biennially awards ten finalists for professionally unproduced plays for youth. Cash awards of $1,000 each are given to the top four playwrights, whose scripts are showcased in polished readings at the National Youth Theatre Symposium held on the Indianapolis campus. Send SASE for guidelines. Submissions must be accompanied by an official entry form.

Available to: No restrictions
Deadline: September 1, 2000, and 2002
Apply to: Dorothy Webb, National Youth Theatre Playwriting Competition, above address

The Ingersoll Prizes
The Ingersoll Foundation
934 Main Street
Rockford, IL 61103

Ⓘ⃞ⁿ The *T. S. Eliot Award for Creative Writing* and the *Richard M. Weaver Award for Scholarly Letters* honor "authors of abiding importance" and call attention to their works. Authors "of international eminence in literature and humanities whose works affirm the moral principles of Western Civilization" are considered for the $25,000 awards. *By Internal Nomination Only.*

Inkwell Magazine
Manhattanville College
Box 1379
2900 Purchase Street
Purchase, NY 10577

Ⓟ The *Inkwell Poetry Competition* annually offers a grand prize of $1,000 and three honorable mentions of $50 each for an unpublished poem no longer than 40 lines. Winning entries and ten finalists will be published in *Inkwell*. The entry fee is $10 for the first poem and $5 for each additional poem, up to five. Send SASE for guidelines.

Available to: No restrictions
Deadline: August 31
Apply to: Poetry Competition, above address

Ⓕ The *Inkwell Short Fiction Contest* annually offers a grand prize of $1,500 for a previously unpublished short story of up to 2,500 words. The winning entry and three other finalists will be published in *Inkwell*. The entry fee is $15 per story. Send SASE for guidelines.

Available to: No restrictions
Deadline: December 31
Apply to: Short Fiction Contest, above address

Institute on the Arts & Civic Dialogue
Harvard University
69 Dunster Street
Cambridge, MA 02138-5908
E-mail: dialogue@arts-civic.org
Web site: http://www.arts-civic.org
Fax: 617-495-9121

Ⓡ In order "to support the creation of artistic works that address the issues of our time and enhance discourse by citizens in our democracy, and to explore how those works can attract and engage audiences whose members cross boundaries created by economic, social, and intellectual and cultural difference," the Institute offers residences to professional artists working in all disciplines for a six-week summer program. Of special interest are artists whose work deals with food and hunger, the environment, and reproductive rights and genetics. Selected artists are provided with funds, facilities, travel, and accommodations to allow them to engage with collaborators on the development of new work. Write, e-mail, or visit the Web site for additional information.

Available to: No restrictions
Deadline: February 1
Apply to: Above address

Institute of Current World Affairs
Crane-Rogers Foundation
4 West Wheelock Street
Hanover, NH 03755
E-mail: icwa@valley.net
Web site: http://www.icwa.org
Fax: 603-643-9599

One or two fellowships are awarded per year to provide talented individuals an opportunity to develop a deep understanding of a topic, country or region outside the United States and to share that understanding with interested segments of the English-speaking public. Candidates should be men and women under thirty-six who demonstrate initiative, character, communications skills, seriousness of purpose, and enthusiasm for their chosen fields. Full support, including living and traveling expenses, is provided for the duration of the fellowship, which is normally two years. Awards are not made to support work toward academic degrees or to underwrite specific programs of research as such, but are aimed at providing the opportunity to acquire a thorough knowledge and understanding of the forces at work in the chosen area. Interested candidates should writer a letter of intent to the Executive Director before submitting a formal application. Write, e-mail or visit the Web site for further information.

Available to: See above
Deadline: April 1 and September 1
Apply to: Peter B. Martin, Executive Director, above address

Institute for Humane Studies
George Mason University
3401 North Fairfax Drive, Suite 440
Fairfax, VA 22201-4432
E-mail: ihs@gmu.edu
Web site: http://www.theihs.org
Fax: 703-993-4890

The *Hayek Fund for Scholars* awards up to $1,000 to students and untenured faculty who would like to participate in professional activities. Applicants must explain how participation will advance their careers and their understanding of the classical liberal tradition. Write, e-mail, or visit the Web site for additional information.

Available to: Students and untenured faculty members
Deadline: Ongoing
Apply to: Hayek Fund for Scholars, above address

The *Humane Studies Fellowships* offer up to $12,000 in tuition and stipend for an academic year to approximately eighty graduate and undergraduate students who have a clearly demonstrated interest in the classical liberal/libertarian tradition of individual rights and market economies, and are interested in applying the principles of this tradition in their work. Write, e-mail, or visit the Web site for additional information and application.

Available to: Full-time graduate students, and junior or senior undergraduates
Deadline: December 31
Apply to: Humane Studies Fellowships, above address

Ⓓ Ⓕ *IHS Film & Fiction Scholarships* offer up to $10,000 in tuition and stipend to talented graduate
Ⓢ   students pursuing an MFA in film, fiction writing, or playwriting who have demonstrated an interest in classical liberal ideas and their application in contemporary society. Write, e-mail, or visit the Web site for additional information and application.

Available to: Graduate students in the creative arts
Deadline: January 15
Apply to: Film & Fiction Scholarships, above address

Ⓜ   The *IHS Young Communicators Fellowships* assist appropriate candidates in taking advantage of strategic short-term opportunities that can enhance their abilities and credentials to pursue careers involving the communication of ideas. Each fellowship consists of a stipend of up to $2,500 for a twelve-week period, and housing and travel assistance up to $2,500 if required. Fellowships cannot be used for tuition or living expenses associated with pursuing a degree. Eligible are college juniors or seniors, graduate students, or recent graduates who have a clearly demonstrated interest in the classical liberal tradition of individual rights and market economies who are intent on pursuing a career in journalism, film, writing (fiction or nonfiction), publishing, or market-oriented public policy; they must also have arranged or applied for an internship, training program, or other short-term opportunity related to their intended career. Write, e-mail, or visit the Web site for additional information.

Available to: See above
Deadline: March 15 for summer positions; at least ten weeks in advance for other positions
Apply to: Young Communicators Fellowships, above address

③ The *Felix Morley Journalism Competition* awards a first prize of $2,500 to an outstanding young writer whose work demonstrates an appreciation of classical liberal principles. These include inalienable individual rights; their protection through private property, contract, and rule of law; voluntarism in human relations; and the self-ordering market, free trade, free migration, and peace. Applicants must be full-time students (college, university, or high school), or be twenty-five or younger, and must submit a clipping or legible copy of three to five separate examples of their work—editorials, op-eds, articles, essays, and reviews—along with an entry form. Write, e-mail, or visit the Web site for additional information and application.

Available to: See above
Deadline: December 1
Apply to: Morley Competition, above address

Institute of International Education
U.S. Student Programs Division
809 United Nations Plaza
New York, NY 10017

The *USIA Fulbright* and other grants for graduate study abroad are available in academic fields and the creative and performing arts. Among the requirements is proficiency in the language of the country to be visited. Grants cover the costs of international travel, tuition, living, and health insurance.

Available to: U.S. citizens
Deadline: October 25
Apply to: USIA Fulbright, above address

Institute for the Study of Diplomacy
1316 36th Street, NW
Washington, DC 20007
Web site: http://data.georgetown.edu/sfs/programs/isd/
Fax: 202-965-5811

③ The *Edward Weintal Prize for Diplomatic Reporting* offers a cash award to recognize initiative, hard digging, and bold thinking in the coverage of American diplomacy and foreign policy. The competition is open to print and broadcast media. There is no standard entry form. A nomination for the most recent calendar year should include clippings (print media) or cassettes and transcript (broadcast media), a cover letter, and biographical material on the nominee.

Available to: No restrictions
Deadline: Mid-January (inquire for exact date)
Apply to: Weintal Prize, above address

Inter American Press Association Scholarship Fund
2911 NW 39th Street
Miami, FL 33142
E-mail: zulaydominguez@aol.com
Web site: http://www.sipiapa.org
Fax: 305-635-2272

③ Five scholarships of $13,000 each are available annually to U.S. and Canadian print journalists, ages twenty-one through thirty-five, for advanced study and research for nine months in Latin America. Candidates must be fluent in Spanish or Portuguese and have a well-defined program that will enable them to return to promote freedom of the press and understanding among the Americas. The program also brings Latin American journalists to study in Canada or the United States.

Available to: Natives of the Western Hemisphere
Deadline: December 31
Apply to: Above address

Intermedia Arts
2822 Lyndale Avenue South
Minneapolis, MN 55408
E-mail: allstaff@intermediaarts.org
Web site: http://www.intermediaarts.org

The *Minnesota McKnight Fellowship for Interdisciplinary Artists* annually awards four fellowships, of $12,000 each, to artists working in interdisciplinary forms who "exhibit a sustained commitment to exploring the changing relationships among artistic disciplines, diverse cultural forms and/or traditional expressions. Interdisciplinary work . . . fuses, integrates or explores the boundaries between at least two distinct art disciplines"; writing may be one of those disciplines. Applicants must reside in Minnesota. An additional $2,000 is available for travel and/or presentation of work during the two-year period. Send SASE or visit the Web site for guidelines and application.

Available to: Residents of Minnesota working in interdisciplinary art forms
Deadline: Late January (inquire for exact date)
Apply to: Minnesota McKnight Fellowship for Interdisciplinary Artists, above address

® The *National McKnight Artist Fellowship for Interdisciplinary Artists* awards $10,000 to an artist for a four-week residence at Intermedia Arts, which may be in consecutive or nonconsecutive weeks. Up to $4,000 is available for travel, lodging, and daily expenses related to the residence; a maximum of $2,000 in organizational support and/or materials will be available for creating or presenting artwork and/or leading an educational activity during the residence. The fellowship seeks to support outstanding work by interdisciplinary artists who "exhibit a sustained commitment to exploring the changing relationships between artistic disciplines, diverse cultural forms, and/or traditional modes of expression," and to foster broader understanding of interdisciplinary art forms. Applicants must demonstrate an accomplished body of interdisciplinary work and have teaching and/or mentoring experience. Judges will pay close attention to the impact on the local artistic community. Send SASE for guidelines.

Available to: No restrictions
Deadline: Mid-April for letter of interest; mid-June for applications from invited candidates (inquire for exact dates)
Apply to: National McKnight Fellowship for Interdisciplinary Artists, above address

INTERNATIONAL
Arvon Foundation
11 Westbourne Crescent
London W2 3DB
England
E-mail: london@arvonfoundation.org

℗ The Arvon Foundation plans to sponsor an *International Poetry Competition* in 2000; details were unavailable at press time. Past competitions have awarded a first prize of £5,000, five prizes of £500 each, and ten prizes of £250. Winning entries are published in an anthology. Contact the Foundation for further information and guidelines.

Available to: No restrictions
Deadline: Inquire
Apply to: International Poetry Competition, above address

INTERNATIONAL
Simone and Cino del Duca Foundation
10, rue Alfred de Vigny
75008 Paris
France

IN The *Cino del Duca World Prize*, of 200,000 French francs, is awarded yearly in October to encourage a writer of any nationality whose work constitutes a message of modern humanism. The author's work should be of a scientific or literary nature. *By Internal Nomination Only.*

INTERNATIONAL
Fédération Internationale des Traducteurs
Secretary General
Peter Krawutschke
3711 Winding Way
Kalamazoo, MI 49004
E-mail: info@fit-ift.org
Web site: http://www.fit-ift.org

(T) The Pierre-François Caillé-FIT Foundation offers grants to affiliated translators to enable them to spend time in a country in which their target language is the national language and to establish contact with translators or interpreter circles in that country.

Available to: Translators affiliated with a member society of FIT
Deadline: Ongoing
Apply to: Above address

The following international translation prizes are awarded by FIT. American translators must apply through the American Translators Association.

(T) The *Aurora Borealis Prize for Outstanding Translation of Fiction Literature* and the *Aurora Borealis Prize of Outstanding Translation of Nonfiction Literature*, sponsored by the Norwegian Association of Nonfiction Writers and Translators (NFF), are given either for a single translation of outstanding quality or for the entire body of a translator's fiction and nonfiction work. Applicants must be members of an FIT member society; in the United States, this is the American Translators Association.

(T) The *Pierre-François Caillé Memorial Medal* is awarded once every three years, during FIT congresses, for "promoting the standing and reputation of the translating profession on an international level." The recipient must be a member of an FIT member society; in the United States, this is the American Translators Association.

(T) The *Karel Capek Medal* is awarded once every three years, during FIT congresses, to "promote the translation of literary works written in languages of limited diffusion." The recipient must be a member of an FIT member society; in the United States, this is the American Translators Association.

(T) The *Astrid Lindgren Translation Prize* is awarded once every three years, during FIT congresses, for "promoting the translation of works written for children."

Available to: Translators sponsored by a member society of FIT
Deadline: Six months before an FIT congress (query American Translators Association for date)
Apply to: American Translators Association, 225 Reinekers Lane #590, Alexandria, VA 22314, attn: Walter Bacak; or e-mail ata@atanet.org

INTERNATIONAL
Premio Feltrinelli
c/o Accademia Nazionale dei Lincei
Palazzo Corsini
Via Lungara 10
00165 Rome
Italy

(IN) The *Antonio Feltrinelli International Prize*, of 100 million Italian lire, is awarded to persons distinguishing themselves in the arts and sciences. The prize is given annually to citizens of any country, in alternating fields: moral and historical sciences; physical, mathematical, and natural sciences; medicine; fine arts; and literature. *By Internal Nomination Only.*

INTERNATIONAL
Fundación Cultural Lya y Luis Cardoza y Aragón
Callejón de las Flores núm. 1
Barrio del Niño Jesús, Coyoacán
0400 Mexico, D.F.
Mexico
E-mail: elrio@mail.internet.com.mx
Fax: 52-55-54-40-10

(N) The *Premio Anual de Ensayo Literario Hispanoamericano Lya Kostakowsky*, of $25,000, is given
annually for an unpublished essay written in Spanish on a given theme. Entries must be
no longer than 50 pages. Write, fax, or e-mail for guidelines and current theme.

Available: Writers writing in Spanish
Deadline: October 15
Apply to: Above address

INTERNATIONAL
Impac
37 Dame Street
Dublin 2
Ireland
E-mail: dub.award@iol.ie
Web site: www.impac-systems.com or http://www.impacdublinaward.ie
Fax: 353-1-671-5385

(F) The *International Impac Dublin Literary Awards* annually offer 100,000 Irish pounds for "a work
of fiction that makes a lasting contribution to world literature." This, the world's richest
prize for a single work of fiction, is sponsored by Impac, a management-productivity
engineering company, and the Dublin municipal government. The award is given to a
work of fiction written and published in English, or written in another language and
published in English translation, during the calendar year. If the winning book is originally
in English, the prize is awarded solely to the author; if the winning work is a translation,
the author receives 75,000 pounds and the translator 25,000. The Dublin City Public
Libraries invite libraries around the world to nominate any number of titles, which must
then be submitted by the publishers. Individual authors may not submit work directly.
Write for additional information.

Available to: No restrictions
Deadline: Mid-November for library nominations
Apply to: International Impac Dublin Literary Contest, Awards Office, above address

INTERNATIONAL
International Academy of Poetry and Poetics
Frauenhoferstrasse 3
97076 Würzburg
Germany

(IN) The *International Rainer Maria Rilke Prize for Poetry* of $20,000 is given every five years to
honor the lifetime work of a writer who has published poetry in more than one European
language. There is no application process. *By Internal Nomination Only.*

INTERNATIONAL
International League of Antiquarian Booksellers
Bibliographical Prize Secretary
Konrad Meuschel
Hauptstrasse 19A
D-53604 Bad Honnef am Rhein
Germany
Fax: 49-2224-5642

(N) The *International League of Antiquarian Booksellers Bibliography Prize* is awarded to the author
of the best work, published or unpublished, of learned bibliography or research into the

history of the book or of typography, and books of general interest on the subject. One prize of $10,000 is given every four years. Entries must be submitted in a language that is commonly understood around the world. The next award will be given in 2002.

Available to: No restrictions
Deadline: December 31, 2000
Apply to: Above address

INTERNATIONAL
The Irish Times
10–15 D'Olier Street
Dublin 2
Ireland
Web site: http://www.ireland.com

[IN] The *Irish Times International Fiction Prize* awards 7,500 Irish pounds biennially to the author of a work of fiction written in English and published in Ireland, the United Kingdom, or the United States. There is no application process; nominations are submitted by a screening panel, consisting of literary editors and critics based in Ireland, Europe, and North America. The next prizes will be awarded in 2001. *By Internal Nomination Only.*

[IN] The *Irish Times Irish Literature Prizes*, of 5,000 Irish pounds each, are awarded biennially in four categories: fiction, nonfiction prose, poetry, and work in the Irish language. Candidates must have been born in Ireland or be Irish citizens, although they may live in anywhere. *By Internal Nomination Only.*

INTERNATIONAL
Jerusalem International Book Fair
PO Box 775
Jerusalem 91007
Israel
E-mail: jer_fair@netvision.net.il
Web site: http://www.jerusalembookfair.com
Fax: 972-2-624-3144

[IN] The *Jerusalem Prize* of $5,000 is awarded annually to a writer whose work expresses the theme of the freedom of the individual in society. The prize is presented each year at the Jerusalem International Book Fair. Recipients are chosen by the Book Fair jury. There is no application process. *By Internal Nomination Only.*

INTERNATIONAL
The Journalists in Europe Fund
4, rue du Faubourg Montmartre
75009 Paris
France
E-mail: europemag@europemag.com
Web site: http://euromag.com/journalistes_en_europe
Fax: 33-1-48-24-40-02

Ⓙ Ⓡ The *Journalists in Europe* program gives journalists the opportunity to acquire firsthand experience of European countries, to explore the ties among them and between Europe and the rest of the world, and to see how the European Union and its institutions work. The program lasts from early October to the end of May. Candidates must be between twenty-five and thirty-five years of age, must be currently employed journalists with at least four years' full-time experience, and should have a working knowledge of English and French. Write for complete information.

Available to: See above
Deadline: January 15
Apply to: Above address

INTERNATIONAL
Maison Internationale de la Poésie
Chaussée de Wavre, 150
1050 Brussels
Belgium
Web site: http://www.maison-int-poesie.cfwb.be
Fax: 32-2-511-52-83

(IN) The *Grand Prix des Biennales* of 150,000 Belgian francs biennially awarded by an international jury to a poet chosen for the worldwide significance of his or her work. The next award is to be given in September 2000. *By Internal Nomination Only.*

INTERNATIONAL
The Mitchell Prizes
The Burlington Magazine
14–16 Duke's Road
London WC1H 9AD
England
Fax: 44-171-388-1230

(N) The *Eric Mitchell Prize* annually awards $5,000 for an outstanding first book of art history by a promising scholar. Publications are assessed in terms of their scholarly, literary, and critical merit. Books must be published within the calendar year preceding the deadline. Publishers are asked to send titles of books they wish to nominate.

(N) The *Mitchell Prize for the History of Art* annually awards $15,000 to the author(s) of books in English that have made outstanding and original contributions to the study and understanding of the visual arts. Criteria and requirements are the same as for the Eric Mitchell Prize.

Available to: No restrictions
Deadline: April 30
Apply to: Caroline Elam, above address

INTERNATIONAL
Alexander S. Onassis Public Benefit Foundation
56, Amalias Avenue
GR-105 58 Athens
Greece
E-mail: pubrel@onassis.gr
Web site: http://www.onassis.gr
Fax: 30-1-32-36-044

(D) The *Onassis International Prize* (its most recent submission deadline was December 31, 1999), will be given in 2001 for a new and original theatrical play written in English, French, German, Greek, Italian, or Spanish. A first prize of $150,000, a second of $100,000, and a third of $75,000 will be awarded. For information about future competitions, contact the Foundation or visit the Web site.

Available to: No restrictions
Deadline: Inquire
Apply to: Above address

INTERNATIONAL
Juan Rulfo Award
Comisión de Premiación
Avenida Alemania 1370
Guadalajara, Jalisco 44190
Mexico
E-mail: Msierra@udgserv.cencar.udg.mx
Fax: 52-3-810-0379

(M) The *Juan Rulfo Award for Latin American and Caribbean Literature* awards $100,000 for lifetime achievement to a native of Latin America or the Caribbean who writes in Spanish, Portuguese, or English; or a native of Spain or Portugal who writes in Spanish or Portuguese. Any writer who has produced noteworthy work in poetry, drama, the novel, the short story, or the essay is eligible. The prize is funded by a group of Mexican government agencies, universities, and businesses. Nominations may be made by cultural or educational institutions, associations, or groups interested in literature. Nominators should send the writer's vita and supporting documents.

Available to: See above
Deadline: June 17, 2000; inquire for 2001
Apply to: Awards Committee, above address, or David Unger, U.S. Coordinator, Guadalajara International Book Fair, Division of Humanities NAC 6293, City College of New York, New York, NY 10031

INTERNATIONAL
Singapore Repertory Theatre
Telok Ayer Performing Arts Centre
182 Cecil Street
Singapore 069547
E-mail: singrep@cyberway.com.sg
Web site: http://www.singrep.com.sg

Ⓓ The *International Herald Tribune/Singapore Repertory Theatre International Playwriting Competition* annually offers a playwright $15,000 plus full production and transportation, lodging, and per diem to attend rehearsals and performances for a full-length, professionally unproduced English-language play dealing with some aspect of modern Pan-Asian identity. Write, e-mail, or visit the Web site for guidelines.

Available to: No restrictions
Deadline: March 1, 2000; inquire for 2001
Apply to: IHT/SRT International Playwriting Competition, above address

INTERNATIONAL
Amaury Talbot Fund
Barclays Bank Trust Company Ltd
Osborne Court
Gadbrook Park, Northwich
Cheshire CW9 7UE
England

Ⓝ The *Amaury Talbot Fund Annual Prize*, of approximately £600, is given for the most valuable work of anthropological research relating to Africa published in the calendar year for which the prize is being awarded. First preference is given to works relating to Nigeria, second to works relating to West Africa as a whole, and then to works relating to the rest of Africa. Two copies of the work in question must be submitted; these will not be returned.

Available to: No restrictions
Deadline: March 31, for work published in the previous calendar year
Apply to: Above address, reference WO844

INTERNATIONAL
UNESCO
Division of Creativity, Cultural Industries and Copyright
1, rue Miollis
75732 Paris
France
E-mail: m.bulos@unesco.org
Web site: http://www.unesco.org/culture/toleranceliterature
Fax: 33-1-45-68-55-95

Ⓒ The *UNESCO Prize for Children's and Young People's Literature in the Service of Tolerance* awards $8,000 biennially for works for the young that best embody the concepts and ideals of tolerance and peace and promote mutual understanding based on respect for other people and cultures. The works may be novels, collections of short stories, or picture books, in two categories: books for children up to age twelve and those for young people thirteen to eighteen. Entries must have been published in the two years before the award deadline (2000 and 2001 for the 2003 prize). All submissions should be accompanied by a summary in English or French. Publishers should send three copies of each book, with a limit of one title per age category, to their respective countries' National Commission for UNESCO. Write for additional information.

Available to: No restrictions
Deadline: January 31, 2002
Apply to: Ms. Maha Bulos, above address

INTERNATIONAL
UNESCO
International Fund for the Promotion of Culture (IFPC)
1, rue Miollis
75732 Paris Cedex 15
France
E-mail: s.berriche@unesco.org
Fax: 33-1-45-68-55-99

®   The *UNESCO–Aschberg Bursaries for Artists Program* covers round-trip travel expenses and provides residences at host and partner institutions around the world for artists in various disciplines. In 1999–2000 the host institution open to U.S. writers was Sanskriti Kendra in New Delhi. Eligibility and application procedures vary according to the host institution; for most bursaries, applicants must be under age thirty-five. Contact the IFPC for current information and application.

Available to: No restrictions
Deadline: Inquire (generally April 30)
Apply to: UNESCO-Aschberg Bursaries for Artists, above address

INTERNATIONAL
UNESCO/Françoise Gallimard Prize
c/o Béatrice Mennechet
5, rue de Lille
Paris 75007
France
Web site: http://www.unesco.org/culture/creativity/literature/html_eng/gallimard1.htm
Fax: 33-1-42-60-61-52

Ⓕ   The *UNESCO/Françoise Gallimard Prize* is given to writers under forty "striving to express the tensions and hopes of our time and to reflect them in a literary work, thus helping to build a better world."
Two awards, one of $20,000 for a work written in French and one of $10,000 for a work written in another language but translated into French, are given for novels or short story collections published in the two years preceding the award year. The competition will be reserved for candidates from a different group of countries every year. Write or fax for additional information.

Available to: Contact for list of eligible countries
Deadline: Inquire
Apply to: Above address

International Center for Journalists
1616 H Street, NW, 3rd floor
Washington, DC 20006-4999
E-mail: editor@icfj.org
Web site: http://www.icfj.org
Fax: 202-737-0530

Ⓙ   The *Worth Bingham Prize* of $10,000 honors newspaper or magazine investigative reporting of stories of national significance about circumstances in which the public interest is being ill served. Entries may include a single story, a series of related stories, or up to three unrelated stories. Columns and editorials are eligible. Individual stories must have been published during the calendar year preceding the deadline; in the case of a series, at least half the individual stories must have been published during the contest year. Write or e-mail susan@icfj.org for guidelines and entry form.

Available to: No restrictions
Deadline: February 15
Apply to: Worth Bingham Prize, above address

☺ The *Arthur F. Burns Fellowship* offers young print and broadcast journalists from the United States and Germany the opportunity to work and report from abroad. Ten journalists from each country are selected annually to work at counterpart news organizations in the foreign country. Travel expenses and a stipend are provided for. Applicants must be working journalists in any news media, under age thirty-five, with demonstrated journalistic talent and an interest in U.S.–European affairs. Proficiency in German for U.S. journalists is not required but will be regarded favorably in the selection process. Write, e-mail, or visit the Web site for application requirements.

Available to: See above
Deadline: March 1
Apply to: Burns Fellowship, above address

☺ The *Ford Environmental Journalism Fellowships* annually send two U.S. environmental reporters overseas to train journalists and report on environmental matters. Fellows are posted for up to three months in their country of choice; preference is given to countries or regions in the developing world or with new democracies. On assignment, fellows work closely with host organizations, conducting workshops, seminars, and lectures, and consulting with local media organizations. Travel expenses and a stipend are provided. Write, e-mail, or visit the Web site for further information.

Available to: Environmental journalists
Deadline: November 1
Apply to: Ford Environmental Journalism Fellowships, above address

☺ The *Senator John Heinz Fellowship in Environmental Reporting* combines the training of overseas journalists with reporting on international environmental matters. One fellow per year is posted for up to three months in the country of his or her choice; preference is given to countries or regions in the developing world or in new democracies. While on assignment, the fellow works closely with a host organization, conducting workshops, seminars, and lectures, and consulting with local media organizations. Travel expenses and a stipend are provided for. Write, e-mail, or visit the Web site for further information.

Available to: U.S. journalists
Deadline: November 1
Apply to: Senator John Heinz Fellowship, above address

☺ The *ICFJ-KKC Journalism Fellowship in Japan*, sponsored by the Keizai Koho Center (Japan Institute for Social and Economic Affairs) allows for five American journalists to travel to Japan for a two-week working program in the fall that includes visits to Japanese news media, business leaders, and government officials. The second week of the program is devoted to independent research and reporting projects designed by each participant. Applicants should have at least five years of media experience and no substantial previous travel to Japan. Write, e-mail, or visit the Web site for application requirements and forms.

Available to: U.S. journalists
Deadline: August 1
Apply to: ICFJ-KKC Fellowship, above address

☺ The *Knight International Press Fellowships*, sponsored by the John S. and James L. Knight Foundation, annually support some twenty-two American journalists and news executives. Fellows spend from two to nine months abroad in a variety of teaching, training, consulting, and assistance roles, usually working in conjunction with an overseas media center. Travel expenses and a stipend are provided for. Write for guidelines and application.

Available to: U.S. journalists

Deadline: January 15 and July 15
Apply to: Knight Fellowships, above address

The International Consortium of Investigative Journalists
The Center for Public Integrity
910 17th Street NW, 7th floor
Washington, DC 20006
E-mail: info@icij.org
Web site: http://www.icij.org
Fax: 202-466-1102

Ⓙ The *ICIJ Award for Outstanding International Investigative Reporting* offers $20,000 for an individual investigative piece of work or single-subject series on a transnational topic of world significance. The investigative work must involve reporting in at least two countries. The award is open to any professional journalist or team of journalists of any nationality. Send SASE, e-mail, or visit the Web site for guidelines.

Available to: No restrictions
Deadline: July 1
Apply to: ICIJ Award, above address

International Quarterly
PO Box 10521
Tallahassee, FL 32303-0521
E-mail: IQ@english.fsu.edu
Web site: http://mailer.fsu.edu/~vbrock
Fax: 904-224-5127

Ⓜ The *Crossing Boundaries Writing Awards* consist of two prizes of $1,000 each, with publication in *International Quarterly*, for poetry, fiction, nonfiction, and "crossing boundaries," a category that includes "atypical work and innovative or experimental writing." Translations into English are accepted. There are no length requirements for poetry; the reading fee for poetry is $15 for a maximum of five poems. Writers in other categories should submit a manuscript of no more than 5,000 words with a $15 entry fee. The judges reserve the right not to award a prize in a given category if no entry is deemed worthy of merit. Send SASE for guidelines.

Available to: No restrictions
Deadline: March 1
Apply to: Crossing Boundaries Writing Awards, above address

International Reading Association
PO Box 8139
Newark, DE 19714
Fax: 302-731-1057

Ⓒ The *International Reading Association Children's Book Awards* are given to authors whose early work shows unusual promise for a career in children's literature. The awards are given for a first or second book published during the calendar year, in any country and any language. Selection focuses on books of fiction or nonfiction of high literary quality. Three prizes, of $500 each, are awarded annually: one for literature for younger children (ages four to ten), one for literature for older children (ages ten to seventeen), and one for informational work.

Available to: Beginning authors of any nationality
Deadline: November 1
Apply to: Children's Bok Awards, Executive Offices, above address

Ⓒ Ⓟ The *IRA Lee Bennett Hopkins Promising Poet Award* offers $500 every three years to a promising new writer of children's poetry (for children and young adults up to twelfth grade) who has published no more than two books. Write for guidelines.

Available to: No restrictions
Deadline: December 1
Apply to: Hopkins Award, Executive Offices, above address

The *Outstanding Dissertation of the Year Award* of $1,000 is given annually for dissertations in reading or related fields. Studies using any research approach (ethnographic, experimental, historical, survey, etc.) are encouraged. Each study will be assessed in the light of its particular approach, the scholarly qualification of its results, and its significant contribution to knowledge within the reading field.

Available to: Doctoral candidates
Deadline: October 15
Apply to: Outstanding Dissertation Award, Research Division, above address

The *Helen M. Robinson Award* of $500 is given annually to assist doctoral students at the early stages of their dissertation research. Applicants must be members of the International Reading Association.

Available to: IRA members
Deadline: June 15
Apply to: Robinson Award, Research Division, above address

© The *Paul A. Witty Short Story Award* offers $1,000 to an author of an original short story published for the first time during the calendar year in a periodical for children. The story should serve as a literary standard that encourages young readers to read periodicals.

Available to: No restrictions
Deadline: December 1
Apply to: Witty Award, Executive Offices, above address

International Research and Exchanges Board
1616 H Street, NW
Washington, DC 20006
E-mail: irex@irex.org
Web site: http://www.irex.org
Fax: 202-628-8189

Individual advanced research grants are available in all disciplines, with an emphasis on projects in the humanities and social sciences. Grants are awarded to predoctoral and postdoctoral scholars for a period of one to twelve months for research in Central and Eastern Europe and Eurasia. U.S. scholars in policy research and development and in cross-disciplinary studies are strongly urged to apply. Fellowships are also awarded for U.S. specialists, doctoral candidates, and senior scholars to conduct advanced social sciences and humanities research in Mongolia for periods of one to four months. Normally candidates must be U.S. citizens or permanent residents, have advanced graduate student status or a Ph.D., and possess sufficient command of the host-country language for advanced research. Grants and stipends vary according to the country of study and academic level. Write, e-mail, or visit the Web site for additional information.

Available to: See above
Deadline: November 1
Apply to: Above address

International Women's Media Foundation
1726 M Street, NW, Suite 1002
Washington, DC 20036
E-mail: IWMF@aol.com
Web site: http://www.IWMF.org
Fax: 202-496-1977

ⓙ The *Courage in Journalism Award* recognizes women journalists who have demonstrated extraordinary qualities pursuing their work under difficult or dangerous circumstances. The award consists of $2,000 and a crystal eagle, presented at ceremonies in New York City, Los Angeles, and Washington, D.C.

Available to: Women journalists
Deadline: Inquire
Apply to: Sherry Rockey, Executive Director, above address

Intersection for the Arts
446 Valencia Street
San Francisco, CA 94103
E-mail: intrsect@wenet.net
Fax: 415-626-1636

Ⓜ The *Joseph Henry Jackson Award* is given to the author of an unpublished work-in-progress of fiction, nonfiction, short fiction, or poetry. One award, of $2,000, is given annually. Send SASE for guidelines and application.

Available to: Northern California or Nevada residents for three consecutive years before deadline date, twenty to thirty-five years old
Deadline: January 31
Apply to: Above address

Ⓜ The *James D. Phelan Award* is given for an unpublished work-in-progress of fiction (novel or short stories), nonfiction, poetry, or drama. One award, of $2,000, is given annually. Send SASE for guidelines and application.

Available to: Native Californians twenty to thirty-five years old
Deadline: January 31
Apply to: Above address

Ⓝ A *Special Award for Nonfiction* of $1,000 is given to nonfiction writers who apply for the Jackson or the Phelan award but are not selected as winners. No separate application is required.

The Iowa Review
308EPB
University of Iowa
Iowa City, IA 52242
Web site: http://www.uiowa.edu/~iareview

The *Iowa Award* and the *Tim McGinnis Memorial Award*, in the amounts of $1,000 and $500, respectively, are given annually by *The Iowa Review*. The Iowa Award honors the best work of the year in any genre; the Tim McGinnis Award is for work with a light touch and a distinctive comic vision. There is no separate application process; all work published in the *Review* during the previous year is considered for each award.

Available to: Contributors to *The Iowa Review*

Iowa State University
Department of English
203 Ross Hall
Ames, IA 50011-1201
E-mail: englgrad@iastate.edu
Fax: 515-294-6814

The *Pearl Hogrefe Fellowship* is granted once each year to support beginning graduate study in creative writing. The fellowship, for a nine-month academic year, covers the cost of tuition and includes a stipend of $950 a month. Write for application guidelines.

Available to: No restrictions
Deadline: January 31
Apply to: Above address

IRELAND
Fish Publishing
Durrus, Bantry
County Cork
Ireland
E-mail: fishpublishing@tinet.ie
Web site: http://www.sleeping-giant.ie/fishpublishing

Ⓕ The *Fish Short Story Prize* annually awards $1,500, or 1,000 Irish pounds, for an unpublished short story not exceeding 5,000 words. Two second prizes of a one-week residence at the

Anam Cara Writers and Artists Retreat in Eyeries, West Cork, and a weekend residential workshop at Dingle Writing Courses in Ventry, County Kerry, are also offered. The top fifteen stories will be published in a yearly anthology. There is a $12 (£8) entry fee for the first or only story, with an additional $8 (£5) for another story submitted in the same envelope. Write, e-mail, or see the Web site for additional information.

Available to: No restrictions
Deadline: November 30
Apply to: Fish Short Story Prize, above address

IRELAND
Tyrone Guthrie Centre
Annaghmakerrig
Newbliss
County Monaghan
Ireland
E-mail: thetgc@indigo.ie
Fax: 353-47-54380

®   The Tyrone Guthrie Centre offers one-week to three-month residences throughout the year to writers who have shown "evidence of sustained dedication and a significant level of achievement." Overseas writers are expected to pay the cost of residence; the Center does offer assistance in obtaining grants from cultural institutions in the writer's home country. Write, e-mail, or fax for guidelines.

Available to: Established writers
Deadline: None
Apply to: Above address

Irish American Cultural Institute
One Lackawanna Place
Morristown, NJ 07960
E-mail: irishwaynj@aol.com
Web site: http://www.irishaci.org
Fax: 973-605-8875

[IN]   The *Irish American Cultural Institute Literary Awards* are given to encourage excellence among Irish writers in Irish or English. Any writer resident in Ireland with published works of fiction, poetry, or drama is eligible. Prizes are awarded annually, a total of $15,000 a year, on the basis of work. *By Internal Nomination Only.*

The *Irish Research Fund* offers grants up to a maximum of $5,000 for research on the Irish experience in America. Applications are accepted from all disciplines. Write, e-mail, or fax for additional information.

Available to: No restrictions
Deadline: October 1
Apply to: Irish Research Fund, above address

Isle Royale National Park
800 East Lakeshore Drive
Houghton, MI 49931-1895
Fax: 906-482-8753

®   The Isle Royale *Artist-in-Residence Program* offers two-to-three-week residences from early June to mid-September to writers, journalists, and artists. Isle Royale is an island wilderness on Lake Superior; a rustic cabin with basic cooking equipment, fuel, pit toilet, and no electricity or running water is provided, as is a canoe for transportation. Artists are asked to contribute a piece of work representative of their stay and to share their experience with the public through demonstrations, talks, readings, or other means. Send SASE for guidelines and application.

Available to: No restrictions
Deadline: February 15
Apply to: Artist-in-Residence Program, above address

Italian Americana
University of Rhode Island
College of Continuing Education
80 Washington Street
Providence, RI 02903

(P) The *John Ciardi Lifetime Achievement Award in Poetry* annually offers $1,000 and publication for an original poem in *Italian Americana,* a biannual journal of poetry, fiction, historical articles, book reviews, and memoirs of the Italian-American experience. Poets who have published at least one book of poetry, not including chapbooks, are eligible. Submit a list of published books. Two awards totaling $500 are also offered for the best fiction published in *Italian Americana* each year.

Available to: See above
Deadline: Inquire
Apply to: John Ciardi Lifetime Achievement Award in Poetry, above address

ITALY
Harvard University Center for Italian Renaissance Studies
Villa I Tatti
Via di Vincigliata 26
50135 Firenze (FI)
Italy
E-mail: Vitatti@tin.it
Web site: http://www.vit.firenze.it

The Harvard University Center for Italian Renaissance Studies offers up to fifteen fellowships each academic year, available to postdoctoral scholars doing advanced research in any aspect of the Italian Renaissance. Normally fellowships are reserved for scholars in the early stages of their careers, and for those whose projects require their presence in Florence. The maximum grant will be no higher than $30,000; most grants will be considerably less.

Available to: No restrictions
Deadline: October 15
Apply to: Villa I Tatti, Harvard University, University Place, 124 Mount Auburn Street, Cambridge, MA 02138-5762. Send original letter of application to the address in Italy above, and a duplicate to the Villa I Tatti office in Cambridge.

ITALY
Italian Cultural Institute
686 Park Avenue
New York, NY 10021-4009
Web site: http://www.italcultny.org/transgrants.htm
Fax: 212-861-4018

(T) In order to encourage the circulation of Italian works abroad, *Italian Government Translation Prizes and Grants* are awarded for the translation of Italian literary and scientific works into English. Prizes are awarded only to previously translated and published works. Grants are available for translation projects, though monies are remitted only after the publication of the translated work and upon receipt of one copy of the published book. Write or visit the Web site for further information.

Available to: No restrictions
Deadline: March 31 and September 30
Apply to: Above address

Ivri-NASAWI (New Association of Sephardi and Mizrahi Artists and Writers International)
1033 North Orlando Avenue
Los Angeles, CA 90069
E-mail: sephardi@ivri-nasawi.org
Web site: http://www.ivri-nasawi.org

(M) The *National Sephardi Literary Contest* offers more than $5,000 in prize money for fiction, poetry, and nonfiction by Jewish writers. Writers may enter only one unpublished submission per category, up to 3,000 words. There are no restrictions on subject matter, but an affinity for Sephardi, Mizrahi, or Anusi (Crypto-Jewish) experience is encouraged. There is a $7 entry fee per submission. Send SASE, e-mail, or visit the Web site for details and guidelines.

Available to: Jewish writers
Deadline: Inquire
Apply to: NSLC Jury, above address

Jacksonville State University
Department of English
700 Pelham Road North
Jacksonville, AL 36265-1602
E-mail: swhitton@jsucc.jsu.edu
Fax: 256-782-5441

Ⓓ The *Southern Playwrights Competition* annually awards $1,000 and production for a full-length play or solo piece by a resident or native of Alabama, Arkansas, Florida, Georgia, Kentucky, Louisiana, Mississippi, North Carolina, South Carolina, Tennessee, Texas, Virginia, or West Virginia. Plays must be unpublished, original works that deal with the southern experience and that have not received Equity production. Send SASE for guidelines and entry form.

Available to: See above
Deadline: February 15
Apply to: Southern Playwrights Competition, above address

Rona Jaffe Foundation
c/o Beth McCabe
97 Governor Mattocks Road
Barnet, VT 05821

Ⓘ The *Rona Jaffe Foundation Writers' Awards* offer several grants, up to a maximum of $8,500, to emerging women writers of fiction, poetry, and creative nonfiction. The Foundation does not accept unsolicited nominations or applications. *By Internal Nomination Only.*

Alice James Books
University of Maine at Farmington
98 Main Street
Farmington, ME 04938
Web site: http://www.umf.maine.edu/~ajb

Ⓟ The *Beatrice Hawley Award* annually offers $1,000 and publication by Alice James Books for a book of poetry. A runner-up receives $500 plus publication and joins the cooperative for three years. This commitment consists of attending four meetings per year, helping judge the press's future book contests, and "buddying" a new member through the publishing process. There is a $20 entry fee. Send SASE or visit the Web site for guidelines.

Available to: No restrictions
Deadline: December 1
Apply to: Beatrice Hawley Award, above address

Ⓟ The *Jane Kenyon Chapbook Award*, established in 1997 in memory of poet and cooperative member Jane Kenyon, biennially offers $300, publication, and 25 copies for a chapbook manuscript. There is a $12 reading fee. Send SASE or visit the Web site for guidelines.

Available to: U.S. residents
Deadline: June 15, 2001
Apply to: Jane Kenyon Chapbook Award, above address

Ⓟ The *New England/New York Award* annually offers publication by Alice James to two books of poetry. Additionally, the winner receives $1,000 and the runner-up $500. The award carries a three-year work commitment with the cooperative, which consists of attending four meetings per year, helping judge the press's future book contests, and "buddying" a new member through the publication process. There is a $20 entry fee, which will cover the cost of one title or cassette ordered from the Alice James backlist. Send SASE or visit the Web site for guidelines.

Available to: Poets living in New England or New York State
Deadline: September 1
Apply to: New England/New York Award, above address

JAPAN
Association of International Education
Information Center
4-5-29 Komaba
Meguro-ku
Tokyo 153
Japan
Web site: http://www.aiej.or.jp

The *Monbusho Scholarships*, tenable in Japan, are given to university graduates, with preference to candidates in the fields of Japanese culture and science, or those for whom study in Japan will enhance the value of their specific program. Grants for up to two years, covering tuition, transportation costs, and a stipend of 185,500 yen per month, are available annually.

Available to: U.S. citizens
Deadline: Varies; contact Japanese embassy or nearest consulate
Apply to: Nearest Consulate General of Japan. Information can be obtained from Japan Information Center, Consulate General of Japan, 299 Park Avenue, 18th floor, New York, NY 10171.

JAPAN
The Japan Foundation
152 West 57th Street, 39th floor
New York, NY 10019
Web site: http://www.jfny.org/jfny/
Fax: 212-489-0409

Fellowships are offered to writers and other artists who wish to pursue creative projects in Japan with their Japanese counterparts. Fellowships are tenable in Japan for periods of two to six months during the Japanese fiscal year (April 1–March 31) and are not renewable. Fellows receive stipends and are paid living expenses. Tuition and fees may also be paid. Airfare to and from Tokyo will be provided for the fellow only. The Japan Foundation also offers research and doctoral fellowships. Research fellows receive stipends of 370,000 to 430,000 yen per month during their stay in Japan, doctoral fellows 310,000 yen per month; additional allowances are made for accompanying dependents, health insurance, and academic fees for a maximum of 140,000 yen per month. Write for further information and application procedures.

Available to: U.S. citizens and permanent residents.
Deadline: December 1 for artist fellowships; November 1 for research and doctoral fellowships
Apply to: Above address (New York) or nearest Consulate General of Japan for artist fellowships

JAPAN
Japan–U.S. Friendship Commission
1120 Vermont Avenue, NW, Suite 925
Washington, DC 20005
E-mail: artist@jusfc.gov
Web site: http://www.jusfc.gov
Fax: 202-418-9802

The *United States/Japan Creative Artists' Program* provides six-month residences in Japan for individual creative artists in any discipline. While in Japan, artists work on a project that may include the creation of new work or pursuit of individual artistic goals. When planning their stay abroad, prospective fellows should consider how exposure to Japan's contemporary or traditional cultures can influence their creative work. Each selected artist receives a monthly stipend of 400,000 yen for living expenses, 100,000 yen a month as a housing supplement, and up to 100,000 yen a month for professional support services. Artists also are provided with up to $6,000 for round-trip transportation for the artist, domestic partner, and/or unmarried children (up to age eighteen), a baggage/storage allowance; and a stipend for pre-departure Japanese-language study in the United States. Write, e-mail, or visit the Web site for additional information and application.

Available to: U.S. citizens or permanent residents
Deadline: June 26, 2000; inquire for 2001
Apply to: Above address

The Jerome Foundation
125 Park Square Court
400 Sibley
St. Paul, MN 55101
Web site: http://www.jeromefdn.org
E-mail: info@jeromefdn.org

The *Jerome Foundation Travel and Study Grant Program,* cofunded by the Dayton-Hudson Foundation and the General Mills Foundation, annually offers up to $4,000 for travel in the United States and up to $5,000 for foreign travel to Minnesota artists and art administrators in any discipline (including literary and dramatic arts), for a period of significant professional development through travel and study.

Available to: Minnesota residents
Deadline: February (inquire for exact date)
Apply to: Above address

Jewel Box Theatre
3700 North Walker
Oklahoma City, OK 73118

Ⓓ The *Jewel Box Theatre Playwriting Award* offers $500 and possible production to an unproduced full-length play of "strong ensemble nature with an emphasis on character rather than spectacle." Send SASE in October for guidelines and entry form.

Available to: No restrictions
Deadline: January 15
Apply to: Playwriting Award, above address

Jewish Book Council
15 East 26th Street
New York, NY 10010
E-mail: jbc@jewishbooks.org

Ⓜ The *National Jewish Book Awards* are given annually for published books, widely distributed in the United States, that are of literary merit and of Jewish interest. Monetary awards are in the following categories: Jewish history, Jewish thought, Sephardic and Ashkenazic customs and culture, Israel, the Holocaust, Eastern European studies, other nonfiction, scholarship, reference books, autobiography/memoir, fiction, children's literature, and illustrated children's books.

Available to: No restrictions
Deadline: November 30
Apply to: Above address

Jewish Community Center of Cleveland
3505 Mayfield Road
Cleveland Heights, OH 44118
E-mail: MaxKJ@aol.com

Ⓓ The *Dorothy Silver Playwriting Competition* offers an award of $1,000 plus a staged reading of the winning play at the JCC Theatre in Cleveland; $500 is awarded on announcement, and $500 on or around the date of the reading, to help cover travel and "in-residence" expenses for the playwright. Submissions must be original, unproduced works, suitable for full-length presentation, that provide fresh, significant perspectives on the range of Jewish experience. The theater will have permission to perform the first fully staged production of the winning script after the staged reading, without payment of royalties. No submissions returned without SASE.

Available to: No restrictions
Deadline: December 15
Apply to: Lisa Kollins, Managing Director, JCC Theatre, above address

The Lyndon Baines Johnson Foundation
2313 Red River Street
Austin, TX 78705
Fax: 512-478-9104

A limited number of *Grants-in-Aid of Research*, ranging from $500 to $2,000, are available semiannually for research at the Lyndon B. Johnson Library. The grant periods are September 1 through February 28, and March 1 through August 31. The funds are for the purpose of helping defray living, travel, and related expenses incurred while conducting research at the Library. Applicants should write to the chief archivist of the library at the above address to obtain information about the availability of relevant materials before submitting a grant-in-aid proposal.

Available to: Scholars and graduate students
Deadlines: July 31 for September–February; January 31 for March–August
Apply to: Executive Director, above address

Johnson Publishing Company
820 South Michigan Avenue
Chicago, IL 60605

(F) The *Gertrude Johnson Williams Writing Contest* annually awards $5,000 for a short story of up to 2,500 words that best depicts the African-American spirit to confront adversity. The contest is open to all Americans of African descent who have not previously received money or other financial consideration for writing short stories, novels, plays, or television or movie scripts. The winning entry is announced in *Ebony*. Five runners-up will receive $1,000 each. Look for guidelines in *Ebony*, or send SASE to above address.

Available to: African-American writers
Deadline: Varies; consult *Ebony* for current deadline
Apply to: Gertrude Johnson Williams Writing Contest, above address

Chester H. Jones Foundation
PO Box 498
Chardon, OH 44024

(P) The *National Poetry Competition* offers prizes of $1,000, $750, $500, $250, $100, and $50, plus publication in the Foundation anthology. Competitors may submit no more than ten poems, written in English, that have not been previously published or broadcast. Send SASE for brochure and entry form.

Available to: U.S. and Canadian citizens and residents
Deadline: March 31
Apply to: National Poetry Competition, above address

James Jones Society
Wilkes University
Wilkes-Barre, PA 18766
E-mail: english@wilkes.edu
Web site: http://wilkes1.wilkes.edu/~english/jones.html

(F) The *James Jones First Novel Fellowship* annually awards $5,000 for an unpublished novel, novella, or collection of related short stories by an American writer who has not published a book-length work of fiction. Writers should submit 50 opening pages, a 2-page thematic outline, and a $15 application fee. Send SASE for guidelines.

Available to: U.S. citizens
Deadline: March 1
Apply to: James Jones First Novel Fellowship, above address

Journal of the History of Ideas
Rutgers University
88 College Avenue
New Brunswick, NJ 08903-5059
E-mail: dkelley@rci.rutgers.edu
Fax: 732-932-8708

Ⓝ The *Morris D. Forkosch Prize* awards $2,000 for a first book on intellectual history published during the calendar year. Books must be in English (no translations) and must pertain to one or more of the major disciplines associated with "intellectual history": history (including the history of various arts and sciences), philosophy (including the philosophy of science, aesthetics, and other fields), political thought (including economics, social science, and anthropology), and literature (including literary criticism and theory). Publishers should limit nominations to two books. Write for additional information and submission procedures.

Available to: First-book authors
Deadline: December 31
Apply to: Morris D. Forkosch Prize, above address

The Henry J. Kaiser Family Foundation
2400 Sand Hill Road
Menlo Park, CA 94025
Web site: http://www.kff.org
Fax: 650-854-4800

Ⓙ The *Kaiser Media Fellowships in Health* fund up to six print, television and radio journalists interested in health policy, health financing and public health. The program aims to provide fellows with diverse opportunities to pursue individual projects combined with group briefings and site visits on a range of health and social policy matters. Fellows receive an annual stipend of $45,000 (prorated for the length of the fellowship); travel funds for research are also available. Applicants must be U.S. citizens working for an accredited U.S. media organization, with at least five years' journalistic experience. Write, e-mail, or visit the Web site for application procedures.

Available to: U.S. citizens working for an accredited U.S. media organization
Deadline: March (inquire for exact date)
Apply to: Penny Duckham, Executive Director, Kaiser Media Fellowship Program, above address

Ⓙ The *Kaiser/National Press Foundation Media Mini-Fellowships* offer up to fifteen print, television, and radio journalists the opportunity to research and report on a health policy, health financing, or public health topic of their choice. Typically, grants are $5,000 each (up to $10,000 for broadcast projects). Priority is given to projects otherwise unlikely to be undertaken or completed, focusing on matters that are underreported or have not been covered, and that have a high likelihood of being published/aired and reaching a mass audience. Write, e-mail, or visit the Web site for application procedures.

Available to: Working journalists
Deadline: October 15
Apply to: Penny Duckham, Executive Director, Kaiser Media Fellowship Program above address

Ⓙ The *Kaiser Media Internships* are available to young minority journalists interested in specializing in urban public health reporting. The program provides an initial week-long briefing on urban public health issues and health reporting at the National Press Club in

Washington, D.C. Interns then are based for ten weeks at a host newspaper or television station, typically under the direction of the health or metro editor/news director, where they report on health matters. The program ends with a three-day meeting and site visits in Boston. Interns receive a twelve-week stipend and paid travel expenses. Write, e-mail, or visit the Web site for application procedures.

Available to: Young minority journalists
Deadline: Inquire
Apply to: Penny Duckham, Executive Director, Kaiser Media Fellowship Program, above address

Kalliope, a journal of women's art
Florida Community College at Jacksonville
3939 Roosevelt Boulevard
Jacksonville, FL 32205
Web site: http://www.fccj.org/kalliope

(P) The *Sue Saniel Elkind Poetry Contest* offers $1,000 plus publication in *Kalliope* for the best unpublished poem of up to 40 lines written by a woman. The entry fee is $4 per poem, or $10 for three. Send SASE for guidelines.

Available to: Women
Deadline: November 1
Apply to: Sue Saniel Elkind Poetry Contest, above address

Kansas Arts Commission
700 Southwest Jackson Street, Suite 1004
Topeka, KS 66603-3761
E-mail: KAC@arts.state.ks.us
Fax: 785-296-4989

(M) *Kansas Artist Fellowships* of $5,000 each are given annually to Kansas residents who have been living in the state for at least one year. Fellowship disciplines rotate in a two-year cycle, with fiction and poetry in even-numbered years and playwriting in odd-numbered. Additionally, up to twelve *Mini-Fellowships* of $500 each are available annually. Write or e-mail for guidelines and application.

Available to: Kansas residents
Deadline: October (inquire for exact date)
Apply to: Kansas Artist Fellowships, above address

Kappa Tau Alpha
University of Missouri
School of Journalism
120 Neff Hall
Columbia, MO 65211
E-mail: ktahq@showme.missouri.edu
Fax: 573-884-1720

(J) (N) The *Frank Luther Mott–Kappa Tau Alpha Journalism and Mass Communications Research Award* of $1,000 is given annually for the best research-based book about journalism or mass communications published during the year. Applicants should submit six copies of the book. Edited volumes, textbooks, and revised editions of previously entered books are not eligible. Write or e-mail for additional information.

Available to: No restrictions
Deadline: Early December (inquire for exact date)
Apply to: Dr. Keith Sanders, Executive Director, above address

The Donald Keene Center of Japanese Culture
507 Kent Hall
Columbia University
New York, NY 10027
Fax: 212-854-4019

(T) The *Japan–U.S. Friendship Commission Prize for the Translation of Japanese Literature* is awarded annually to two book-length translations of Japanese literature into English by a U.S. translator in the categories of modern and classical literature. The prize is intended for translators who are not widely recognized for their work, though they may have published. Submissions may include unpublished manuscripts, works in press, and translations published after January 1, 1996. Send SASE for additional information and application.

Available to: U.S. translators
Deadline: March 1
Apply to: Above address

The Kennedy Center
American College Theater Festival
Washington, DC 20566-0001
E-mail: skshaffer@mail.kennedy-center.org
Fax: 202-416-8802

The Kennedy Center American College Theater Festival (KC/ACTF) holds several regional festivals with workshops each year. All college and university theaters are eligible and encouraged to participate. Regional finalists are invited to Washington for an eight-day noncompetitive festival at the Kennedy Center, with transportation, lodging, and daily expenses provided for. The following awards, which make up the *Michael Kanin Playwriting Awards Program*, are available to student playwrights whose plays are produced in the festival.

(D) The *Anchorage Press Theatre for Youth Playwriting Award* is given for a play by a festival student with a theme appealing to young people from kindergarten through twelfth grade. The award consists of a cash prize of $1,000 and a fellowship to, in alternating years, the New Visions/New Voices festival at the Kennedy Center and the Bonderman/IUPUI festival in Indianapolis. Anchorage Press will publish the winning play, lease it for production, and pay the author royalties.

(D) The *Jane Chambers Playwriting Award*, co-sponsored by the Women and Theatre Program of the Association for Theatre in Higher Education, offers $1,000 for a full-length play or a performance-art text by a woman. The winner will also receive free registration at the Women and Theatre Conference in late July, when the winning play will receive a rehearsed reading. Submitted work should "reflect a feminist perspective and contain a majority of roles for women performers." Send SASE for guidelines and application form.

Available to: Women playwrights
Deadline: February 15
Apply to: Jane Chambers Playwriting Award, c/o Mary A. Donahoe, Department of Theatre Arts, Wright State University, Dayton, OH 45435-0001

(D) The *David Mark Cohen National Playwriting Award* is given to any working playwright whose play is produced by a college or university theater program and entered as an Associate or Participating entry within KC/ACTF. All rules regulating entries into KC/ACTF apply except those related to the definition of student playwrights. The winning playwright will receive a cash award of $1,000, possible publication by Dramatic Publishing, Inc., and up to $500 toward travel and expenses to attend a script-in-hand reading at the annual August meeting of the Association for Theatre in Higher Education.

(D) The *Fourth Freedom Forum Playwriting Award* is given for the best plays on the themes of world peace and international disarmament. First place wins a $5,000 cash prize, a fellowship to the Sundance Theatre Laboratory, and an offer from Palmetto Play Service to publish, license, and market the play. A second-place award of $2,500 is also given. Grants of $1,500 and $1,000 will be made to the theater departments of the colleges/universities producing the first- and second-place winners, respectively.

Ⓓ The *Lorraine Hansberry Award* is given for the best play by a student on the subject of the black experience. The first place wins a $2,500 cash prize, a fellowship at the National Playwrights Conference at the Eugene O'Neill Theatre Center, and publication of the play by Dramatic Play Service. Second prize is $1,000. Grants of $750 and $500 will be made to the theater departments of the colleges/universities producing the first- and second-place winners, respectively.

Ⓓ The *KC/ACTF College Musical Theater Award* is given for outstanding achievement in the creation of a work for the musical theater by college and university students. First prize is $1,000 each for lyrics, music, book, and producing institution. The musical must be produced by a college or university participating in the ACTF, and half of the creative team must be students.

Ⓓ The *KC/ACTF Sí TV Playwriting Award* is given for the best play by a Latino student playwright participating in KC/ACTF. The award consists of a cash prize of $2,500 and an internship at a prestigious playwriting retreat program. The playwright will also receive an offer of a contract with Dramatic Publishing, Inc., to publish, license, and market the script. A grant of $500 will be made to the theater department of the college or university producing the winning play.

Ⓓ The *National AIDS Fund CFDA–Vogue Initiative Award for Playwriting* is given for the best new collegiate writing about the personal and social implications of HIV/AIDS. The winner will receive a cash award of $2,500 and a fellowship to attend the Bay Area Playwrights Festival in San Francisco.

Ⓓ The *National Student Playwriting Award* is given for the best production of a play written by a full-time graduate or undergraduate student participating in regional festivals. The award consists of a cash prize of $2,500, membership in the Dramatists Guild, production at the Kennedy Center, a publication contract with royalties through Samuel French, and a nine-day fellowship at the Sundance Theatre Laboratory.

Ⓓ The *Short Play Awards Program* recognizes two or three outstanding productions of short plays in U.S. colleges each year, with consideration for presentation at the national festival at the Kennedy Center. The award consists of a cash prize of $1,000, publication and catalogue listing by Samuel French, and membership in the Dramatists Guild. (A short play is defined as a one-act without intermission that within itself does not constitute a full evening of theater.)

Ⓓ The *Jean Kennedy Smith Playwriting Award for the Best Play Written on the Theme of Disability* is given for the best student-written script that explores the human experience of living with a disability. The play must be produced and entered in KC/ACTF. The winning playwright will receive a cash award of $2,500, active membership in the Dramatists Guild, and a fellowship to attend a prestigious playwriting program, with transportation, housing, and a per diem included.

Ⓓ The *Mark Twain Comedy Playwriting Award* is given for the best student-written full-length comedy play produced by a college or university and entered in KC/ACTF. The first-place award consists of a cash prize of $2,500, a fellowship to attend a prestigious second-step playwriting retreat, and an offer of a contract with Dramatic Publishing, Inc., to publish, license, and market the play. The second-place award consists of $1,500. Grants of $750 and $500 will be made to the producing organizations of the first- and second-place winner, respectively.

Available to: College and university students, except the David Mark Cohen Award
Deadline: December 1
Apply to: Above address for application procedures

Ⓓ The Kennedy Center American College Theater Festival also sponsors an annual *Ten-Minute Play Festival*. A first-place award of $1,000 is given to the playwright selected from the national festival finalists; another $1,000 award is given for the best comic monologue selected from the finalist 10-minute plays presented at the Kennedy Center. Contact the regional chair for information and submission procedures.

Available to: College and university students
Deadline: Inquire
Apply to: Above address for list of regional chairs

John F. Kennedy Library Foundation
John F. Kennedy Library
Columbia Point
Boston, MA 02125-3313
E-mail: library@kennedy.nara.gov
Web site: http://www.cs.umb.edu/jfklibrary/index.htm
Fax: 617-929-4599

The *Hemingway Research Grants*, ranging from $200 to $1,000, are offered to between five and ten scholars and writers, to help defray living, travel, and related costs incurred while doing research in the Hemingway Collection. Applications are evaluated on the basis of expected use of the Collection, the degree to which projects address research needs in Hemingway or related studies, and qualifications of applicants.

> Available to: No restrictions; preference given to Ph.D. candidates doing dissertation research
> Deadline: March 15
> Apply to: Hemingway Research Grants, above address

The *Kennedy Library Research Grants*, ranging from $500 to $1,500, are offered to between fifteen and twenty scholars and students, to help defray living, travel, and related costs incurred while doing research in the textual and nontextual holdings of the library. Applications are evaluated on the basis of expected use of available library holdings, the degree to which projects address research needs in Kennedy-period studies, and qualifications of applicants.

> Available to: No restrictions; preference given to Ph.D. candidates doing dissertation research
> Deadlines: March 15 for spring grants; August 15 for fall
> Apply to: William Johnson, Chief Archivist, above address

The *Marjorie Kovler Research Fellowship* of $2,500 is intended to support a scholar in the preparation of a substantial work in the area of foreign intelligence and the presidency, or a related topic.

> Available to: No restrictions
> Deadline: March 15
> Apply to: William Johnson, Chief Archivist, above address

The *Arthur M. Schlesinger Jr. Research Fellowship*, carrying a stipend of up to $7,000, is intended to support scholars in the preparation of substantial works on the foreign policy of the Kennedy years, especially with regard to the Western Hemisphere, or on Kennedy domestic policy, especially with regard to racial justice and to the conservation of natural resources. The fellowship may be awarded to a single individual or divided between two recipients.

> Available to: No restrictions
> Deadline: August 15
> Apply to: William Johnson, Chief Archivist, above address

The *Abba P. Schwartz Research Fellowship*, carrying a stipend of up to $3,100, is intended to support a scholar in preparing a substantial work on immigration, naturalization, or refugee policy.

> Available to: No restrictions
> Deadline: March 15
> Apply to: William Johnson, Chief Archivist, above address

The *Theodore C. Sorensen Research Fellowship* of $3,600 is intended to support a scholar in preparing a substantial work on domestic policy, political journalism, polling, or press relations.

Available to: No restrictions
Deadline: March 15
Apply to: William Johnson, Chief Archivist, above address

Robert F. Kennedy Memorial Book & Journalism Awards
1367 Connecticut Avenue, NW, Suite 300
Washington, DC 20036
E-mail: info@rfkmemorial.org
Web site: www.rfkmemorial.org

Ⓕ Ⓝ The *Robert F. Kennedy Annual Book Award*, of $2,500, is given for the best book of fiction or nonfiction published during the previous year. Four copies of each book should be submitted with a letter of introduction or press release, and an entry form. There is a $25 handling fee per entry.

Available to: Published authors of fiction or nonfiction
Deadline: January (inquire for exact date)
Apply to: Director, RFK Book Awards, above address

Ⓙ Nine *Robert F. Kennedy Journalism Awards for Outstanding Coverage of the Problems of the Disadvantaged*, of $1,000 each, are available annually in the categories of print (newspaper, magazine), cartoon, television, radio, photojournalism, international print, international broadcast, international radio, and international photojournalism. At the discretion of the awards committee, an additional grand prize of $2,000 may be granted to the outstanding winner. The competition is open to both professional and student journalists (college undergraduates), whose entries will be judged separately. Write for guidelines.

Available to: See above
Deadline: Last Friday in January
Apply to: Director, RFK Journalism Awards, above address

Kent State University
Department of English
PO Box 5190
Kent, OH 44242-0001
Web site: http://www.kent.edu:80/english/wick/WickPoetry.htm

Ⓟ The *Stan and Tom Wick Poetry Prize* of $2,000 is given for a first book of poems in English by a writer who has not published a book of poetry. The winning collection will be published by Kent State University Press. Manuscripts should be between 48 and 68 pages; the poet's name must not appear within. Submissions should include a cover sheet with the applicant's name, address, and telephone number, and title of the manuscript. There is a $15 reading fee for each submission. Send SASE or visit the Web site for additional information.

Available to: No restrictions
Deadline: May 1
Apply to: Stan and Tom Wick Poetry Prize, above address

Kentucky Arts Council
Old Capital Annex
300 West Broadway
Frankfort, KY 40601-1950
E-mail: lori.meadows@mail.state.ky.us
Fax: 502-564-2839

Ⓜ Kentucky artists' fellowships of $5,000 are available every other year in poetry, fiction, and playwriting. Write for application.

Available to: Kentucky residents
Deadline: September 15 in even-numbered years
Apply to: Lori Meadows, Individual Artist Program Director

Kentucky Foundation for Women
332 West Broadway, Suite 1215
Louisville, KY 40202
E-mail: kfw@kfw.org
Web site: http://www.kfw.org
Fax: 502-561-0420

Grants are available biennially to women writers in Kentucky whose work "focuses on a feminist, not feminine, consciousness." The Foundation seeks to support writers "who describe the realities of women's lives, who experiment in style and substance, analyze language, or who are working to enlarge the feminist literary and historical heritage." *Project Grants* of $3,000 and $5,000 are awarded for specific projects; *Process Grants* of $3,000 and $5,000 are awarded for ongoing creativity of people with a track record of producing work in line with Foundation goals; *Encouragement Grants* of $1,000 are awarded to applicants who have not received full grants. Write for further information and guidelines.

Available to: Feminist writers who live or work in Kentucky or whose work powerfully and directly affects the lives of women in Kentucky
Deadline: October 1 of even-numbered years
Apply to: Above address

Kentucky Writers' Coalition
851 South Fourth Street #207
Louisville, KY 40203

Ⓟ The *Jim Wayne Miller Prize in Poetry* awards $500 and publication in a regional journal, for a single poem. A reading in Louisville honors the winning poet. Poems may be of any length or style. The entry fee is $5 per poem; Coalition members may enter one poem at no charge and additional poems at $3 each. Write for guidelines.

Available to: U.S. citizens
Deadline: January 30
Apply to: Jim Wayne Miller Prize in Poetry, above address

Kiplinger Reporting Program
Ohio State University
School of Journalism
242 West 18th Avenue
Columbus, OH 43210

Ⓙ The Kiplinger Reporting Program annually offers fellowships to eight print and broadcast journalists to do aggressive reporting in the public interest. Each fellowship consists of a $20,000 stipend and a tuition waiver for a four-quarter master's degree at the Ohio State University School of Journalism. The application fee is $30. Write for additional information and application materials.

Available to: Journalists with at least five years' professional experience
Deadline: January 1
Apply to: Above address

Knight-Ridder Internships for Native American Journalists
c/o St. Paul Pioneer Press
345 Cedar Street
St. Paul, MN 55101-1057

Ⓙ The *Knight-Ridder Internships for Native American Journalists* offer a twelve-week summer apprenticeship for five selected applicants. Interns will receive paid positions at Knight-Ridder newspapers in the Midwest. Successful interns may be invited to return to a Knight-Ridder newspaper for a second or third internship. Write for additional information and application procedures.

Available to: Promising Native American journalists
Deadline: Inquire
Apply to: Rubén Rosario, Coordinator, above address

Knoxville Writers' Guild
PO Box 10326
Knoxville, TN 37939
Web site: http://www.korrnet.org/writers or http://www.sunsite.utk.edu/utpress

Ⓕ The *Peter Taylor Prize for the Novel* offers $1,000 and publication with a standard royalty contract from the University of Tennessee Press, co-sponsor of the prize, and for an unpublished novel. There is a $20 reading fee. Send SASE or visit one of the Web sites for guidelines.

Available to: U.S. residents
Deadline: Submissions accepted February 1–April 30
Apply to: Tennessee Book Award–Peter Taylor Prize, above address

KOREA
Korean Culture and Arts Foundation
Literature & Visual Arts Team
1-130, Dongsoong-dong, Chongro-ku
Seoul 110-510
Korea
E-mail: sgkang@caibs.kcaf.or.kr
Web site: http://www.kcaf.or.kr
Fax: 82-2-760-4701

Ⓣ The *Korean Literature Translation Award* biennially offers a $50,000 grand prize for the best published translation from Korean into another language. Two work-of-merit prizewinners will receive $10,000 each. If no work is deemed of sufficient merit for the grand prize, the finest entry will be awarded $30,000. A publisher who has made an outstanding contribution to promoting Korean literature abroad will receive $10,000. Submissions may be in any literary genre (poetry, short story, play, literary criticism, novel; collections and anthologies accepted). Write, e-mail, or visit the Web site for additional information and guidelines.

Available to: No restrictions
Deadline: 2001 (inquire for exact date)
Apply to: Korean Literature Translation Award, above address

The Koret Foundation
33 New Montgomery, Suite 1090
San Francisco, CA 94105
Web site: http://www.koretfoundation.org

ⓘⓝ The *Koret Jewish Book Awards*, co-sponsored by the National Foundation for Jewish Culture, offers $10,000 for the best book or books published in the calendar year that "underline the centrality of books in Jewish culture and encourage serious readers to seek the best of Jewish books published throughout the year." Awards are given in three categories: fiction, history, and thought and philosophy. There is no application process. *By Internal Nomination Only.*

Kosciuszko Foundation
15 East 65th Street
New York, NY 10021-6595
E-mail: thekf@aol.com
Web site: www.kosciuszkofoundation.org
Fax: 212-628-4552

In addition to the award listed below, the Kosciuszko Foundation offers tuition scholarships and research grants for U.S. citizens of Polish descent and American scholars pursuing research on Polish subjects. Funds may be used at American colleges and universities or at academic institutions in Poland. Write, e-mail, or visit the Web site for additional information.

The *Metchie J. E. Budka Award* of $1,000 is given for outstanding scholarly work in Polish literature from the fourteenth century to 1939, Polish history from 962 to 1939, and Polish–

American relations. The award recognizes outstanding work in one of these fields by American graduate students or recent doctoral degree recipients. Write, e-mail, or visit the Web site for guidelines.

Available to: See above
Deadline: July (inquire for exact date)
Apply to: The Metchie J. E. Budka Award, above address

Lake Forest College
Religion Department
555 North Sheridan Road
Lake Forest, IL 60045

(N)   The *Bross Prize* is given every ten years to the best book-length manuscript on the relation between any discipline or topic of investigation and the Christian religion. The next award will be presented in 2000. At least $20,000 will be given, in one to three prizes. Three typewritten copies of each manuscript must be submitted, or the author will be asked to assume copying costs incurred by the prize committee.

Available to: No restrictions
Deadline: Summer 2000 (inquire for exact date)
Apply to: Bross Prize, above address

Laughing Stork Press
PO Box 860700
Shawnee Mission, KS 66286
Web site: http://www.bellylaughs.com

(N)   In 1999, *Stork Search* offered a $1,000 first prize, plus publication in the anthology *Belly Laughs and Babies*, for a heartwarming, humorous, true short story, up to 750 words, about pregnancy, childbirth, adoption, or new parenthood. The prize amount may change in 2000. Send SASE or visit the Web site for guidelines and updated information.

Available to: No restrictions
Deadline: December 30
Apply to: Stork Search, above address

The Ledge
78-44 80th Street
Glendale, NY 11385

(P)   The *Ledge Poetry Award* offers $1,000 plus publication for an unpublished poem. Poets may submit poems of any length, with a $9 entry fee for the first one to three poems, and $3 for each additional. A second prize of $200 and a third of $100 are also offered. All poems submitted will be considered for publication in *The Ledge*. Send SASE for guidelines.

Available to: No restrictions
Deadline: April 30
Apply to: Poetry Award, above address

(P)   The *Ledge Poetry Chapbook Competition* annually awards $1,000 and 50 copies of a typeset, professionally printed chapbook for a poetry manuscript of 16 to 28 pages. The $12 entry fee covers a copy of the winning chapbook. Send SASE for guidelines.

Available to: No restrictions
Deadline: October 31
Apply to: Poetry Chapbook Competition, above address

Ledig House International Writers' Colony
59 Letter S Road
Ghent, NY 12075

(R)   Residences of one week to two months are available to writers in all fields during two sessions: April through June and mid-August through October. Applications, accepted at any time, should include a letter of recommendation, a brief biography, a copy of recent published work, or if unpublished, a 10-page sample (work will not be returned), and a one-page description of work to be undertaken. Write for further details.

Available to: English-speaking writers
Deadline: Ongoing
Apply to: Executive Director, above address

Leeway Foundation
123 South Broad Street, Suite 2040
Philadelphia, PA 19109
E-mail: info@leeway.org
Web site: http://www.leeway.org
Fax: 215-545-4021

The Leeway Foundation supports women artists in the greater Philadelphia area and promotes their increased recognition and representation in the community. Grants of $15,000 to $50,000 are made in a selected visual or literary discipline each year. In 2001, the Foundation will offer awards for excellence and achievement in poetry. Applications will be available in September 2000. Write or e-mail for more information.

Available to: Philadelphia-area women artists
Deadline: Inquire
Apply to: Above address

Lifebridge Foundation
PO Box 793
Times Square Station
New York, NY 10108
E-mail: LB457@aol.com
Web site: http://www.lifebridge.org
Fax: 212-757-9711

Project grants are offered to individuals who, "through cultural, educational, and/or scientific means, are dedicated to creating bridges of understanding among all people by bringing to realization the concepts of one humanity and the interconnectedness of all life." Although the Foundation generally nominates, it does accept introductory letters, of no more than three pages, specifying how a project reflects the Foundation's purposes and aims. Write, e-mail, or visit the Web site for additional information. (E-mail is for information requests only; no e-mailed introductory letters or proposals will be accepted.)

Available to: No restrictions
Deadline: Inquire
Apply to: Above address

Lindbergh Foundation
2150 Third Avenue North, Suite 310
Anoka, MN 55303-2296
E-mail: lindbergh@isd.net
Web site: http://www.isd.net/lindbergh
Fax: 612-576-1664

© The *Anne Spencer Lindbergh Prize in Children's Literature* awards $5,000 biennially to the children's fantasy novel judged the best published in English during the two year-period. Writers should submit four copies of each book and a $25 application fee for each title. Write, fax, or e-mail for further information.

Available to: No restrictions
Deadline: November 1
Apply to: Anne Spencer Lindbergh Prize, above address

Literal Latte
61 East 8th Street, Suite 240
New York, NY 10003
E-mail: LitLatte@aol.com
Web site: http://www.literal-latte.com

Ⓕ Ⓟ The *Literal Latte Fiction and Poetry Awards* and the *Literal Latte Roy T. Ames Essay Awards* annually
Ⓝ offer a $1,000 first prize, a $300 second prize, and a $200 third prize in each genre for an unpublished short story, essay, and poem. Winning entries appear in *Literal Latte*, a journal of prose, poetry, and art published six times a year. A $10 reading fee applies to each story, essay, or group of six or fewer poems; a $15 fee covers, in addition, a one-year subscription to the journal. The journal also sponsors the *Literal Latte Food Verse Contest*, which offers a first prize of $500. Send SASE, e-mail, or visit the Web site for guidelines.

Available to: No restrictions
Deadline: January for Fiction Award; July for Poetry Award; September for Essay Award
(inquire for exact dates and Food Verse Contest)
Apply to: Above address (specify genre)

Literary Arts
720 SW Washington, Suite 700
Portland, OR 97205
E-mail: la@literary-arts.org
Web site: http://www.literary-arts.org

Ⓜ The *Oregon Book Awards* are given to outstanding Oregon authors for works published during the twelve months ending March 31. Nominations are accepted for poetry, fiction, literary nonfiction, drama, and books for young readers. The winner in each category receives a cash prize of $1,000. Publishers, authors, and friends may nominate books. Write, e-mail, or visit the Web site for guidelines.

Available to: Oregon residents
Deadline: Late May (inquire for exact date)
Apply to: Oregon Book Awards, above address

Ⓜ *Oregon Literary Fellowships* and the *Women Writers Fellowship* are awarded to Oregon writers in two categories: emerging and published. The fellowships help those in need of funds initiate, develop, or complete a literary project in poetry, drama, fiction, literary nonfiction, or young readers' literature. Of special interest for the Women Writers Fellowship are writers whose work explores experiences of race, class, physical disability, or sexual orientation. The fellowships range from $500 to $3,000. Write, e-mail, or visit the Web site for guidelines.

Available to: Oregon writers
Deadline: June 30
Apply to: Oregon Literary Fellowships or Women Writers Fellowship, above address

Gerald Loeb Awards
The Anderson School at UCLA
110 Westwood Plaza, B307
Box 951481
Los Angeles, CA 90095-1481
E-mail: loeb@anderson.ucla.edu
Web site: http://www.anderson.ucla.edu/media/loeb
Fax: 310-825-7977

Ⓙ The *Gerald Loeb Awards for Distinguished Business and Financial Journalism* recognize journalists nationwide who have made significant contributions to the understanding of business, finance, and economic matters. The awards rank among the profession's highest honors. The competition is open to business reporting over the calendar year in eight media categories: large, medium, and small newspapers; magazines; commentary; deadline/ beat writing; television; and radio. Winners, who in each category receive $2,000, are announced in late spring.

Available to: Writers for U.S. commercial publications

Deadline: Early February (inquire for exact date)
Apply to: Above address

The Loft Literary Center
1011 Washington Avenue, South
Minneapolis, MN 55415
E-mail: loft@loft.org
Web site: http://www.loft.org

Ⓜ The *McKnight Artist Fellowships for Writers* annually offer five $10,000 and two $20,000 awards to Minnesota poets and creative prose writers. The $10,000 *Loft Awards in Poetry* are awarded to Minnesota poets; the $10,000 *Loft Awards in Creative Prose* are awarded to three writers of fiction and/or creative nonfiction. The $20,000 *Loft Awards of Distinction* are offered in poetry and creative prose in alternating years to Minnesota writers with significant publication credits. Send SASE or visit the Web site for additional information and guidelines.

Available to: Minnesota residents
Deadline: Mid-November (inquire for exact date)
Apply to: McKnight Artist Fellowships for Writers, above address

Ⓕ Ⓟ The Loft *Mentor Series Contest* provides eight Minnesota poets and fiction writers the opportunity for intensive study with nationally known visiting writers, in addition to a small stipend. Winners participate in seminars, individual critiques, and public forums and readings with local and visiting mentors. The application fee is waived for Loft members; $10 for nonmembers. Send SASE or visit the Web site for additional information and guidelines.

Available to: Minnesota poets and fiction writers
Deadline: Mid-May (inquire for exact date)
Apply to: Loft Mentor Series, above address

The *Minnesota Literature Live Grants* offer up to $800 to Minnesota organizations outside the seven-county Minneapolis/St. Paul metropolitan area to present events that promote literature by a Minnesota author. Eligible events include readings, writing workshops, storytelling, oral history activities, and in-school residences.

Available to: See above
Deadline: On-going
Apply to: Minnesota Literature Live Grants, above address

Ⓜ The *Minnesota Writers' Career Initiative Program* provides financial support and professional assistance to advanced writers of poetry, fiction, creative nonfiction, or children's literature to develop and implement serious, multifaceted plans for the next phase of their career. This phase might involve, but is not limited to, greater recognition, increase in book sales, significant expansion of audience, or publication by a major press. As many as four winners will receive grants of up to $8,000 and up to $1,500 in honoraria.

Available to: Minnesota residents
Deadline: Inquire
Apply to: Career Initiative Program, above address

Longwood College
Department of English
Farmville, VA 23901

[IN] The *John Dos Passos Prize for Literature* is given annually to a writer with a substantial publication record. The award is intended primarily for American creative writers in mid-career, particularly those whose work shares with that of Dos Passos an intense and original exploration of American themes. A medal for literary achievement and a cash prize of $1,000 are awarded each year. *By Internal Nomination Only.*

Los Angeles Public Library
630 West Fifth Street
Los Angeles, CA 90071

IN   The *Los Angeles Public Library Literary Award* of $10,000 is given annually for an outstanding body of work. There is no application process. *By Internal Nomination Only.*

Los Angeles Times Book Prizes
Times Mirror Square
Los Angeles, CA 90053

IN   The *Los Angeles Times Book Prizes* are given in the following categories: fiction, first fiction (*Art Seidenbaum Award*), poetry, history, biography, current interest, science and technology, and body of work by a writer living in or writing on the American West (*Robert Kirsch Award*). Eligible books must have been published in English in the United States between January 1 and December 31 of the award year. The winner in each category receives $1,000 and a citation. *By Internal Nomination Only*.

Lotus Press
PO Box 21607
Detroit, MI 48221
Fax: 313-861-4740

M   The *Naomi Long Madgett Poetry Award*, formerly sponsored by the Hilton-Long Poetry Foundation, offers a cash prize of $500 and publication by Lotus Press of a volume of poems by an African-American. Send SASE for guidelines.

Available to: African-American poets
Deadline: Submissions accepted February 1–April 1
Apply to: Constance Withers, above address

Louisiana Division of the Arts
PO Box 44247
Baton Rouge, LA 70804
E-mail: arts@crt.state.la.us
Web site: http://www.crt.state.la.us/arts
Fax: 504-342-8173

M   Two fellowships of up to $5,000 are given annually to Louisiana writers of poetry, fiction, and nonfiction. Applicants must have been Louisiana residents for at least two years before the application date. Write for guidelines and the required application.

Available to: Louisiana residents
Deadline: Applications must be ostmarked by September 1
Apply to: Above address

Love Creek Productions
c/o Cynthia Granville
162 Nesbit Street
Weehawken, NJ 07087-6817

D   The *Short Play Festival* selects at least fifty-two finalists yearly to receive a mini-showcase production in New York City. The best in competition receives a cash prize. Entries should have at least two characters, be under 40 minutes long, unpublished, and unproduced in New York City in the past year. Authors must enclose a permission letter for Love Creek to produce their play if it is chosen, and should state whether an Equity showcase is acceptable. Several times a year, Love Creek awards cash prizes in mini-festivals with specified themes. Send SASE for schedules, themes, and deadlines.

Available to: No restrictions
Deadline: Ongoing for Short Play Festival; inquire for mini-festivals
Apply to: Short Play Festival or Mini-Festivals, above address

Amy Lowell Poetry Travelling Scholarship
Choate, Hall & Stewart
Exchange Place
53 State Street
Boston, MA 02109-2891

(P)   The *Amy Lowell Poetry Travelling Scholarship* awards approximately $32,000 annually to an American-born poet to spend one year outside North America, in whatever place the recipient feels will most advance his/her work in poetry. Although it is not a requirement, recipients in recent years have been published poets with professional standing. Write for application form and guidelines.

Available to: U.S. native citizens
Deadline: October 1 for application requests; October 15 for application submissions
Apply to: F. Davis Dassori, above address

Lukas Prize Project
Columbia University
Graduate School of Journalism
2950 Broadway
New York, NY 10027
E-mail: yk287@columbia.edu
Web site: http://www.jrn.columbia.edu/lukas

(N)   The *J. Anthony Lukas Prize* annually awards $10,000 for a published book-length work "of narrative nonfiction on an American topic that exemplifies the literary grace, the commitment to serious research, and the social concern that characterized the distinguished work of the award's namesake." Send SASE, e-mail, or visit the Web site for guidelines and entry form.

Available to: No restrictions
Deadline: October 15 for books published January 1–September 30; December 31 for books published October 1–December 31
Apply to: J. Anthony Lukas Prize, above address

(N)   The *J. Anthony Lukas Work-in-Progress Award* annually offers $45,000 to aid in the completion of a significant work of nonfiction. Applicants must already have a contract with a publisher to write the book. They should send a copy of their original book proposal, a sample chapter, evidence of a contract with a publisher, and an explanation of how the award will advance the book's progress. Send SASE, e-mail, or visit the Web site for guidelines and entry form.

Available to: No restrictions
Deadline: January (inquire for exact date)
Apply to: J. Anthony Lukas Work-in-Progress Award, above address

(N)   The *Mark Lynton History Prize* annually awards $10,000 to the published book-length work of history, on any subject, that "best combines intellectual or scholarly distinction with felicity of expression." Send SASE, e-mail, or visit the Web site for guidelines and entry form.

Available to: No restrictions
Deadline: October 15 for books published January 1–September 30; December 31 for books published October 1–December 31
Apply to: Mark Lynton History Prize, above address

Lullwater Review
Emory University
Box 22036
Atlanta, GA 30322

(P)   The *Lullwater Prize for Poetry* awards $500 and publication in *Lullwater Review*. Poets may submit no more than six poems; all submissions will be considered for publication. There is an $8 reading fee; sample issues are available for $5 each. Send SASE for guidelines.

Available to: No restrictions
Deadline: Early March (inquire for exact date)
Apply to: Lullwater Prize for Poetry, above address

Lynchburg College
Department of English
Lynchburg, VA 24501
E-mail: allen@hopwood.lynchburg.edu

®   Each semester, the *Richard H. Thornton Writer-in-Residence Program* selects a fiction writer, playwright, or poet to spend eight weeks at Lynchburg College in Virginia. The resident writer receives a stipend of $8,000 and is provided with housing and meals. Although considerable time is reserved for personal work, the resident must also teach a weekly seminar to advanced-level undergraduate writers, give one public reading on campus, and visit classes as a guest speaker.

     Available to: Writers with at least one published book and evidence for effective teaching
Deadlines: March 1 for fall term; September 1 for spring
Apply to: Send résumé and cover letter outlining qualifications to Tom Allen, Thornton Chair, Richard H. Thornton Writer-in-Residence, above address.

Lyndhurst Foundation
517 East Fifth Street
Chattanooga, TN 37403-1826

[IN]   The *Lyndhurst Prize* is awarded to select individuals who have made significant and distinctive contributions in the arts, particularly writing and photography, and in community service and leadership. The prize carries a three-year stipend and is intended to enable prizewinners to pursue interests over an extended period of time without financial pressure. The prize is given solely at the initiative of the board of trustees, never in response to applications, requests, or nominations. *By Internal Nomination Only.*

Lynx House Press
c/o Creative Writing Program
Eastern Washington University
705 West First
Spokane, WA 99201
E-mail: cnhowell@mail.ewu.edu

℗   The *Blue Lynx Poetry Prize* offers $1,500 and publication of a book-length manuscript of poems by a U.S. poet. Applicants should submit a manuscript of at least 48 pages, the $18 entry fee, and SASE for notification.

     Available to: U.S. residents
Deadline: Early April (inquire for exact date)
Apply to: Blue Lynx Poetry Prize, above address

John D. and Catherine T. MacArthur Foundation
140 South Dearborn Street
Chicago, IL 60603
E-mail: 4answers@macfound.org
Web site: http://www.macfdn.org

[IN]   The *MacArthur Fellows Program* provides unrestricted fellowships to exceptionally talented and promising individuals who have given evidence of originality, dedication to creative pursuits, and capacity for self-direction. MacArthur Fellows receive an income, ranging from $30,000 to $75,000 annually for five years, so that they may devote themselves to their own endeavors at their own pace. The Foundation hopes that freedom from financial constraints will lead to significant contributions to society that otherwise might not be made. There is no application process. *By Internal Nomination Only.*

     Research and Writing Grants are awarded annually through the Program on Global Security and Sustainability of the Foundation. Grants are given to support research and writing projects that "promise to illuminate the dynamics of international security, sustainability and cooperation." Projects to be carried out by individuals or two-person teams are eligible; projects related to research or writing of doctoral dissertations are not. Grants are awarded for periods of up to eighteen months. Applicants may request up to $75,000 for individual projects, and up to $100,000 for two-person collaborations. Write for further information and guidelines.

Available to: No restrictions
Deadlines: February 1
Apply to: Program on Global Security and Sustainability, above address

John J. McCloy Fund
American Council on Germany
14 East 60th Street
New York, NY 10022
E-mail: acgrd@aol.com
Fax: 212-758-3445

Ⓙ The *John J. McCloy Fund* offers fellowships for American journalists to spend approximately a month in Germany. Fellowships cover the cost of transatlantic airfare, local ground transportation, and daily expenses.

Available to: American journalists
Deadline: Ongoing
Apply to: Above address for information; for applications, Robert Petretti, Graduate School of Journalism, Columbia University, New York, NY 10027

MacDowell Colony
100 High Street
Peterborough, NH 03458
Web site: http://www.macdowellcolony.org

Ⓡ *MacDowell Colony Fellowships* support residences at the colony in Peterborough, for writers and other artists to concentrate on creative work without interruption. Studios and room and board are provided; residences are for up to eight weeks. Write for further information and application.

Available to: Writers, visual artists, composers, filmmakers, architects, and interdisciplinary artists
Deadlines: January 15 for May–August; April 15 for September–December; September 15 for January–April
Apply to: Above address

The Madison Review
Department of English
University of Wisconsin
600 North Park Street
Madison, WI 53706

Ⓕ Ⓟ The *Madison Review/Phyllis Smart Young Prize in Poetry* and the *Madison Review/Chris O'Malley Fiction Award* are given annually for the best group of three poems and the best short story, respectively, submitted during the month of September. Each award carries a cash prize of $500 and publication in *The Madison Review*. Multiple or previously published submissions are ineligible. There is a $3 entry fee. Send SASE for guidelines.

Available to: No restrictions
Deadline: Submissions accepted in September only
Apply to: Phyllis Smart Young Prize in Poetry or Chris O'Malley Fiction Award, above address

Maine Community Foundation
245 Main Street
Ellsworth, ME 04605
E-mail: grants@mainecf.org
Web site: http//www.mainecf.org

The *Martin Dibner Memorial Fellowship for Maine Writers Fund* offers one or two grants from

$500 to $1,000 for the professional development of Maine writers, particularly those just becoming established in their craft. Grants may be used for writing workshops, for example, or for living expenses while a writer completes a manuscript. Write or e-mail for further information and guidelines.

Available to: Maine residents
Deadline: September 1
Apply to: Martin Dibner Memorial Fellowship, above address

MAMMOTH press
7 South Juniata Street
DuBois, PA 15801
E-mail: mammothbooks@hotmail.com
Web site: http://cac.psu.edu/~dwm7/mammoth.htm

Ⓜ MAMMOTH press sponsors an annual contest for book-length prose and poetry. The winner receives $750 as an advance against royalties, a standard royalty contract, and publication in a first edition of at least 500 copies in trade paperback. All finalists are considered for publication. There is a $20 entry fee for each manuscript. Send SASE or e-mail for guidelines; e-mail submissions are not accepted.

Available to: No restrictions
Deadline: Submissions accepted January 1–April 30 for creative nonfiction; May 1–August 31 for fiction; and September 1–December 31 for poetry
Apply to: Antonio Vallone, Editor, above address

Manhattan Theatre Club
311 West 43rd Street, 8th floor
New York, NY 10036
Web site: http://www.mtc-nyc.org
Fax: 212-399-4329

Ⓓ *Playwriting Fellowships* are offered annually to emerging New York City–based playwrights from all backgrounds who have completed their formal education and can demonstrate financial need. The fellowship includes a commission of $5,000 for a new play; a production assistantship, with a stipend of $1,500, during which the writer will observe rehearsals for one of eight plays presented at MTC each season; and financial assistance of $3,500 for living and other expenses. Send SASE for deadlines and eligibility requirements before applying.

Available to: New York City–based playwrights, age thirty-five or younger
Deadline: Inquire
Apply to: Maggie Malone, Literary Assistant, above address

Marin Arts Council
251 North San Pedro Road
San Rafael, CA 94903
E-mail: alison@marinarts.org
Fax: 415-499-8537

Ⓜ The *Individual Artist Grants Program* offers grants to Marin County writers in poetry, fiction, and other creative prose. Send SASE for guidelines and application.

Available to: Marin County residents
Deadline: Inquire in fall 2000
Apply to: Alison DeJung, Grants Coordinator, above address

Marlboro Review
PO Box 243
Marlboro, VT 05344
E-mail: marlboro@stratos.net
Web site: http://www.marlbororeview.com

Ⓟ The *Marlboro Review Poetry Prize* annually offers $1,000 and publication in *Marlboro Review*, a biannual journal of poetry, fiction, essays, translations, and reviews, for the best poem or group of poems. Poets may send up to five poems of any length or style, with a $10 reading fee. All entries will be considered for publication. Send SASE or visit the Web site for guidelines.

Available to: No restrictions
Deadline: December 31
Apply to: Poetry Prize, above address

Maryland Library Association
400 Cathedral Street
Baltimore, MD 21201-4401
E-mail: mla@mail.pratt.lib.md.us
Fax: 410-625-9594

[IN] The *Maryland Author Award* of $2,000 is given annually for a body of work by a writer who was born or lives in, or has close ties to, Maryland. Awards are given on a rotating basis according to genre. The 2000 award will be for adult fiction; the 2001 award for children's literature. There is no application process; nominations are made by the members of the Maryland Library Association. *By Internal Nomination Only.*

Maryland State Arts Council
601 North Howard Street
Baltimore, MD 21201
E-mail: pdunne@mdbusiness.state.md.us
Web site: http://www.msac.org
Fax: 410-333-1062

Ⓜ *Individual Artist Awards* are given to Maryland artists, through an anonymous, competitive process, to encourage and sustain their pursuit of artistic excellence. A limited number of awards of $1,000, $3,000, and $6,000 are offered each year in various disciplines on a rotating basis.

Available to: Maryland residents at least eighteen years old, excluding students
Deadline: Inquire for exact date and disciplines
Apply to: Above address

Massachusetts Cultural Council
120 Boylston Street, 2nd floor
Boston, MA 02116-4600
E-mail: claudia.heiman@art.state.ma.us
Web site: http://www.massculturalcouncil.org
Fax: 617-727-0044

Ⓜ *Artist Grants Fellowships* of $7,500 are given to Massachusetts writers in fiction, poetry, and playwriting. Finalists in each category receive $1,000. Applicants must be at least eighteen years old, legal residents of Massachusetts for the last two years, and not enrolled in a related degree-granting program. Fellowship disciplines rotate on a two-year cycle, with fiction and poetry fellowships offered in even-numbered years and playwriting/new-theater-work fellowships offered in odd-numbered years. Write, e-mail, or visit the Web site for guidelines and application.

Available to: Massachusetts writers
Deadline: December (inquire for exact date)
Apply to: Artist Grants Program, above address

Ⓜ *Professional Development Grants* up to $500 are offered to working artists and not-for-profit administrators in the arts, humanities, and interpretive sciences to help cover costs associated with attending professional conferences, workshops, seminars, residences or master classes. Grants are not designed to support touring, exhibition, and/or presentation opportunities. Funds can be used only to reimburse registration fees, tuition, and transportation costs; expenses such as supplies and materials are not covered. Write, e-mail, or visit the Web site for additional information and application.

Available to: Massachusetts residents at least eighteen years of age
Deadline: 15th of every month except June
Apply to: Professional Development Grants, above address

Massachusetts Institute of Technology
Knight Science Journalism Fellowships
E-32-300, 77 Massachusetts Avenue
Cambridge, MA 02139-4307
E-mail: www-ksjf@mit.edu
Web site: http://web.mit.edu/knight-science/
Fax: 617-258-8100

Ⓙ Six *Knight Science Journalism Fellowships* are awarded annually to U.S. print and broadcast journalists whose primary work is to inform broad audiences about recent developments in technology and science and their wider social effects. The fellowships, open to freelance journalists and employees of news-gathering organizations, involve full-time residence at MIT for the academic year; fellows receive a stipend of $35,000. Write for further information and application.

Available to: See above
Deadline: March 1
Apply to: Above address

Maui Writers Conference
2118 Wilshire Boulevard, Suite 726
Santa Monica, CA 90403-5784
E-mail: mauiscript@aol.com
Web site: http://www.maui.net/~writers

Ⓢ The Maui Writers Conference *National Screenwriting Competition* offers a first prize of $3,000 and fully paid admission to the Maui Writers Retreat and the Maui Writers Conference for a feature-length screenplay. A second prize of $1,000 and a third of $500 are also offered; each includes fully paid admission to the Conference. There is a $45 entry fee. Write, e-mail, or visit the Web site for guidelines and entry form.

Available to: No restrictions
Deadline: July 1
Apply to: National Screenwriting Competition, above address

Medieval Academy of America
1430 Massachusetts Avenue
Cambridge, MA 02138
E-mail: maa@fas.harvard.edu
Web site: http://www.georgetown.edu/MedievalAcademy/
Fax: 617-492-3303

Ⓝ The *John Nicholas Brown Prize* awards $1,000 annually for a first-published book in the field of medieval studies. Books published three years before the submission date are eligible. Three copies of the book should be sent to the Academy office, accompanied by copies of published reviews and by an author's statement that it is his or her first book in the medieval field.

Available to: North American residents
Deadline: November 1
Apply to: John Nicholas Brown Prize, above address

Ⓝ The *Van Courtlandt Elliott Prize* awards $500 annually for a first article on a medieval topic, published in any journal, of not less than 5 pages. Articles published one year before the submission date are eligible. Three copies of the article should be submitted, together with an author's statement that it is his or her first article in the medieval field.

Available to: North American residents
Deadline: November 1

Apply to: Van Courtlandt Elliott Prize, above address

Ⓝ The *Haskins Medal* is presented annually to the author of a book in medieval studies judged to be of outstanding importance and distinction. Books published within five years before the submission date are eligible. Three copies of the book should be sent to the Academy office, accompanied by copies of published reviews.

Available to: North American residents
Deadline: November 1
Apply to: Haskins Medal, above address

MEXICO
U.S.–Mexico Fund for Culture
Londres 16 P.B.
Col. Juarez 06600
Mexico, D.F.
Mexico
E-mail: usmexcult@fidemexusa.org.mx
Web site: http://www.fidemexusa.org.mx
Fax: 52-5-566-80-71

The U.S.–Mexico Fund for Culture provides economic support, ranging from $2,000 to $25,000, for projects of excellence that reflect the artistic and cultural diversity of Mexico and the United States and that can lead to close, lasting collaboration and exchange among artists, researchers and scholars, independent groups, and related institutions of the two countries. In particular, the Fund seeks to promote editions of prose and poetry that help disseminate literature from one country in the other. Special consideration will be given to translation and anthology projects that entail close collaboration between author and translator or editor. Support will be given also to residences, conferences, symposia, workshops, and so on that unite authors, translators, editors, publishers, and interested audiences, in order to encourage dialogue about literature in both countries. Write, enclosing SASE with adequate return postage, to the above address, or consult the Web site for guidelines and application.

Available to: U.S. and Mexican citizens
Deadline: April 28, 2000 (inquire for 2001)
Apply to: Above address

Michener Center for Writers
University of Texas at Austin
J. Frank Dobie House
702 East Dean Keeton Street
Austin, TX 78705

Ⓜ The *James A. Michener Fellowship* of $15,000 per year, plus remission of tuition, is offered to candidates accepted for the University of Texas MFA program designed for students who wish to work in at least two fields among fiction, poetry, screenwriting, and playwriting. Write for application procedures.

Available to: See above
Deadline: January 15
Apply to: Above address

[IN] The *James A. Michener Memorial Prize* offers $10,000 a year to writers who have published a first book at age forty or later. A group of nominators will submit names of deserving writers to a panel chosen by the Michener Center. There is no application process. *By Internal Nomination Only.*

Michigan Council for Arts and Cultural Affairs. *See* **ArtServe Michigan**

Michigan Library Association
6810 South Cedar, Suite 6
Lansing, MI 48911

Ⓜ The *Michigan Author Award* of $1,000 is given for an outstanding body of work by a Michigan resident, a longtime Michigan resident who has recently relocated, or an author whose works are identified in subject with Michigan. The award is given in conjunction with the Library Association's annual conference, which the winner must attend. Writers are cited for a published body of fiction, nonfiction, and/or poetry, consisting of three or more titles, adult or juvenile. Nominations may be made by librarians, publishers, or individuals. Write for required application.

Available to: See above
Deadline: June 30
Apply to: Michigan Author Award, above address

Michigan Quarterly Review
University of Michigan
3032 Rackham Building
Ann Arbor, MI 48109-1070
E-mail: mgr@umich.edu
Web site: http://www.umich.edu/~mqr/

Ⓕ The *Lawrence Foundation Prize* annually awards $1,000 for the best short story published in *Michigan Quarterly Review* during the previous calendar year. The magazine's editorial board chooses the winner.

Available to: *Michigan Quarterly Review* contributors

Michigan State University
Victims and the Media Program
School of Journalism–Dept. W
East Lansing, MI 48824-1212
Web site: http://www.journalism.msu.edu/victmed/dart.html
Fax: 517-355-7710

Ⓙ The *Dart Award* offers a $10,000 prize for the U.S. newspaper entry that "best illustrates the effects of violence on victims and how they cope with emotional trauma," and that treats victims and their experiences with accuracy, insight, and respect. The award is given as a team prize, with entries judged as a total package, including headlines, cutlines, graphics, artwork, and layout. The winning organization is responsible for dividing the prize money among staff members in proportion to individual contributions. Write or visit the Web site for guidelines.

Available to: U.S. newspapers
Deadline: March 1
Apply to: Dart Award, above address

Middle East Report
1500 Massachusetts Avenue, Suite 119
Washington, DC 20005
E-mail: merip@igc.org
Web site: http://www.merip.org

Ⓙ The *Philip Shehadi New Writers Award*, established in memory of a contributing editor of *Middle East Report* who was killed in Algiers in 1991, offers $500 and publication for an article, 3,000 to 5,000 words, that focuses on the Middle East or contemporary relations of states and societies in the region. All entrants receive a one-year subscription to the *Report*. Send SASE, e-mail, or visit the Web site for guidelines.

Available to: No restrictions
Deadline: Inquire
Apply to: Philip Shehadi Award, above address

Midland Community Theatre
2000 West Wadley
Midland, TX 79705
Web site: http://www.mct-cole.org

Ⓓ The *McLaren Memorial Comedy Playwriting Competition* is a nationwide contest for original, unproduced comedy scripts of any length. Three to five finalists receive a staged reading of their work at the McLaren Comedy Festival; grand-prize winner is then chosen for a cash stipend of $400. MCT may produce the winning script at a future date. The playwright retains all rights to work submitted. A $5 entry fee per script is required.

Available to: No restrictions
Deadline: Submissions accepted October 1–January 31
Apply to: McLaren Memorial Comedy Playwriting Competition, above address

Mid-List Press
4324 12th Avenue South
Minneapolis, MN 55407-3218
E-mail: guide@midlist.org
Web site: http://www.midlist.org
Fax: 612-823-8387

Ⓜ The *First Series Awards for the Novel, Poetry, Short Fiction, and Creative Nonfiction* offer publication and an advance against royalties to a writer who has never published a book in the particular genre (a chapbook is not considered a book of poetry). Novelists and short fiction and creative nonfiction writers receive a $1,000 advance; poets receive $500. Novels, collections of short fiction, and creative nonfiction manuscripts must be at least 50,000 words in length; poetry manuscripts at least 60 pages. There is a $20 reading fee in each category. Send #10 SASE for guidelines and entry form.

Available to: Unpublished writers
Deadline: Novel and poetry submissions accepted October 1–February 1; short fiction and creative nonfiction, April 1–July 1
Apply to: Above address

Midwest Theatre Network
5031 Tongen Avenue, NW
Rochester, MN 55901

Ⓓ The *Midwest Theatre Network Original Play Competition/Rochester Playwright Festival* biennially offers four to eight awards of $300 to $1,000 each (contingent on funding) and full production at cooperating theaters for unpublished works (full-length plays, collections of one-acts, musicals, experimental works) that have not received professional production. The winning playwrights also receive paid travel, and room and board to attend the performance. Send SASE for guidelines and entry form.

Available to: No restrictions
Deadline: November 30, 2001
Apply to: Joan Sween, Executive Director/Dramaturg, above address

Milkweed Editions
430 First Avenue North, Suite 668
Minneapolis, MN 55401-1743
Web site: http://www.milkweed.org
Fax: 612-332-6248

Ⓕ The annual *Milkweed National Fiction Prize* offers a $2,000 cash advance on any royalties agreed on in a negotiated contract for the best work of fiction accepted for publication, by a writer not previously published by Milkweed. Manuscript may be a novel, a collection of short stories, one or more novellas, or a combination of short stories and one or more novellas. All manuscripts submitted to Milkweed are considered for the prize. Send SASE or visit the Web site for guidelines before submitting.

Available to: No restrictions

Deadline: Ongoing
Apply to: Above address

©   The *Milkweed Prize for Children's Literature* ofers a $2,000 cash advance on any royalties agreed on in a negotiated contract for the best manuscript for children ages eight to twelve accepted for publication, by a writer not previously published by Milkweed. Novels only are eligible; collections of stories are not, nor are the retellings of legends or folktales. Texts should be of high literary quality, and "embody humane values that contribute to cultural understanding." Send SASE or visit the Web site for guidelines.

Available to: No restrictions
Deadline: Ongoing
Apply to: Above address

Mill Mountain Theatre
One Market Square, SE
Roanoke, VA 24011-1437
Web site: http://www.millmountain.org
Fax: 540-342-5745

Ⓓ   The *Mill Mountain Theatre New Play Competition* annually awards $1,000, staged reading with possible production, and travel stipend and housing for an unproduced, unpublished play, preferably with a cast of no more than ten. One work per playwright must be submitted by an agent or accompanied by the professional recommendation of a director, literary manager, or dramaturg. Send SASE for guidelines.

Available to: U.S. residents
Deadline: October 1–January 1
Apply to: Jo Weinstein, Literary Manager, above address

Millay Colony for the Arts
PO Box 3
Austerlitz, NY 12017-0003
E-mail: application@millaycolony.org

Ⓡ   The Millay Colony for the Arts provides work space, meals, and sleeping accommodations for qualified writers, composers, and visual artists for a period of one month. The Colony can accommodate six artists monthly; its main building is fully accessible and includes two work/living spaces. Samples of work must accompany applications. Send SASE for application, or e-mail.

Available to: No restrictions
Deadlines: February 1 for June–September residences; May 1 for October–January; September 1 for February–May
Apply to: Gail Giles, Director of Admissions, above address

Milton Center
Newman University
3100 McCormick Avenue
Wichita, KS 67213
E-mail: miltonc@newman.edu

The Milton Center awards two postgraduate fellowships to "new writers of Christian commitment." Fellows are expected to complete their first book-length manuscript while in residence. Each fellow receives a stipend of $1,225 per month for a nine-month tenure. The Center also offers assistance in placing manuscripts with publishers and agents, and provides a supportive community in which to work. Write or e-mail for further information and application.

Available to: See above
Deadline: February 1
Apply to: Postgraduate Fellowships, above address

Minnesota Monthly
10 South Fifth Street, Suite 1000
Minneapolis, MN 55402

Ⓕ The *Tamarack Award* offers $800 and publication in *Minnesota Monthly*, the magazine of Minnesota Public Radio, for an unpublished work of fiction by a resident of the upper Midwest: Iowa, Michigan, Minnesota, North Dakota, South Dakota, or Wisconsin. Applicants may submit one unpublished story of up to 3,500 words. Send SASE for guidelines.

> Available to: Residents of Iowa, Michigan, Minnesota, North Dakota, South Dakota, and Wisconsin
> Deadline: May (inquire for exact date)
> Apply to: Tamarack Award, above address

Minnesota State Arts Board
400 Sibley Street, Suite 200
St. Paul, MN 55101-1928
E-mail: msab@state.mn.us
Web site: http://www.arts/state.mn.us
Fax: 651-215-1602

Artist Assistance Fellowship Grants of $8,000 are given annually for new works, advanced study, and works-in-progress. Short-term *Career Opportunity Grants*, which range from $500 to $1,500, are awarded three times a year.

> Available to: Minnesota residents
> Deadline: Early fall for fellowships; inquire for career grants (3 deadlines per year)
> Apply to: Above address

Mississippi Arts Commission
239 North Lamar Street, Suite 207
Jackson, MS 39201
E-mail: wilkins@arts.state.ms.us
Web site: http://www.arts.state.ms.us
Fax: 601-359-6008

Ⓜ *Fellowships in Literary Arts*, $5,000 each, are given to Mississippi writers each year. Write or e-mail for further information.

> Available to: Mississippi residents
> Deadline: March 1
> Apply to: Above address

Mississippi Review
University of Southern Mississippi
Box 5144 USM
Hattiesburg, MS 39406-5144
E-mail: rief@netdoor.com

Ⓕ Ⓟ The *Mississippi Review Prize in Fiction* and *Poetry* awards $500 for the winning story and $500 for the winning poem, plus publication in print and on-line editions of *Mississippi Review*. All runners-up are also published. The fee is $10 per entry , with one story or three poems constituting an entry. There is no limit on the number of entries. Send SASE or e-mail for guidelines.

> Available to: U.S. citizen or resident
> Deadline: May 31
> Apply to: Prize in Fiction or Prize in Poetry, above address

The Missouri Review
University of Missouri, Columbia
1507 Hillcrest Hall, UMC
Columbia, MO 65211
Web site: http://www.missourireview.org

Ⓜ The *Larry Levis Editors' Prize in Poetry* offers $1,500 and publication for an unpublished poem. *Editors' Prize Awards* of $1,000 and $1,500, plus publication in the *Review*, are offered for an essay and a short story, respectively. All entries must be typed double-spaced, poems no more than 10 pages in length, stories and essays no more than 25. The $15 entry fee covers a one-year subscription to the magazine.

Available to: No restrictions
Deadline: October 15
Apply to: Larry Levis Editor's Prize or Editors' Prize Awards, above address

Ⓕ Ⓟ The *William Peden Prize* offers $1,000 annually for the best fiction published in the *Review*. The *Tom McAfee Discovery Feature in Poetry* offers $125 to $250 once or twice a year for the best group of poems to be published in the journal by a poet who has not yet published a book. Write for submission guidelines.

Available to: Writers published in *The Missouri Review*

Mixed Blood Theatre Company
1501 South 4th Street
Minneapolis, MN 55454

Ⓓ The Mixed Blood Theatre Company sponsors the *"We Don't Need No Stinkin' Dramas" Playwriting Contest*, designed for full-length contemporary comedies, particularly those on race or sports or with a political edge. Scripts must be at least 65 pages long; no translations or adaptations are accepted. The winner of the contest receives a cash prize of $2,000 if Mixed Blood chooses to produce the winning script, or $1,000 if Mixed Blood declines. The contest is open to the first 300 submissions received. Send SASE for guidelines.

Available to: U.S. playwrights who have had at least one work produced or workshopped
Deadline: February 1
Apply to: "We Don't Need No Stinkin' Dramas" Playwriting Contest, above address

Modern Language Association of America
10 Astor Place
New York, NY 10003
E-mail: awards@mla.org
Web site: http://www.mla.org
Fax: 212-533-0680

Ⓝ The *Morton N. Cohen Award* offers $1,000 in odd-numbered years for an important collection of letters published in the two-year period preceding the award. The winning collection should give readers "a clear, accurate, and readable text; necessary background information; and succinct and eloquent introductory material and annotations. The edited collection should be in itself a work of literature." Editors may apply regardless of the fields they and the authors of the letters represent; MLA membership is not required. To enter, send four copies of each eligible volume.

Available to: No restrictions
Deadline: May 1, 2001
Apply to: Morton N. Cohen Award, above address

Ⓝ The *Katherine Singer Kovacs Prize* offers $1,000 annually for the best book published in English in the field of Latin American and Spanish literatures and cultures.

Available to: No restrictions
Deadline: May 1
Apply to: Katherine Singer Kovacs Prize, above address

Ⓝ The *James Russell Lowell Prize* of $1,000 is awarded annually to an MLA member who has published an outstanding literary or linguistic study, a critical edition of an important work, or a critical biography. Nominations may be made by publisher or author. To enter, send six copies of the work.

Available to: MLA members
Deadline: March 1
Apply to: James Russell Lowell Prize, above address

(N) The *Howard R. Marraro Prize* and the *Aldo and Jeanne Scaglione Prize in Italian Literary Studies* jointly award $1,000 every even-numbered year to the author of a distinguished book- or essay-length scholarly study on any phase of Italian literature or comparative literature involving Italian. Nominations may be made by publisher or author. To enter, send four copies of the work.

Available to: MLA members who have published works in this field
Deadline: May 1, 2000, and 2002
Apply to: Howard R. Marraro Prize, above address

(N) The *Kenneth W. Mildenberger Prize* is given annually to the author of a research publication in the field of teaching foreign languages and literatures. Books compete in even-numbered years, when the prize is $1,000; articles compete in odd-numbered years, for $500. To enter, send four copies of the work.

Available to: No restrictions
Deadline: May 1
Apply to: Kenneth W. Mildenberger Prize, above address

(N) The *MLA Prize for a Distinguished Bibiliography* awards $1,000 in even-numbered years for an enumerative and descriptive bibliography published in serial, monographic, book, or electronic format. A multivolume bibliography is eligible if at least one volume was published during the specified period. The prize will be given without regard to the language of the compiler or of the text presented in the bibliography, as long as it falls within the subject scope of the MLA (e.g., modern languages and literatures, composition theory, folklore, linguistics). For the next award, the prize committee considers editions published in 1998 and 1999. To enter, send four copies of the work.

Available to: No restrictions
Deadline: May 1, 2000
Apply to: MLA Prize for a Distinguished Bibliography, above address

(N) The *MLA Prize for a Distinguished Scholarly Edition* awards $1,000 and a certificate in odd-numbered years. For the current award, the prize committee considers editions published in 1999 or 2000. A multivolume edition is eligible if at least one volume has been published during that period. An edition should be based on an examination of all available relevant textual sources; the source texts and the edited text's deviations should be fully described; the edition should employ editorial principles appropriate to the materials edited, and clearly articulate those principles; the text should be accompanied by appropriate textual and other historical contextual information; the edition should exhibit the highest standards of accuracy in the presentation of text and apparatus; and text and apparatus should be presented as accessibly and elegantly as possible. To enter, send four copies of the work.

Available to: No restrictions
Deadline: May 1, 2001
Apply to: MLA Prize for a Distinguished Scholarly Edition, above address

(N) The *MLA Prize for a First Book* annually awards $1,000 for the first book-length scholarly publication by an MLA member. The book must be a literary or linguistic study, a critical edition of an important work, or a critical biography. To enter, send six copies of the book and a letter identifying the work and confirming the author's MLA membership.

Available to: MLA members
Deadline: April 1
Apply to: MLA Prize for a First Book, above address

(N) The *MLA Prize for Independent Scholars* for distinguished published research in modern languages and literatures, including English, is awarded annually to a person who at the time of publication was not enrolled in a program leading to an academic degree and did not hold a tenured, tenure-track, or tenure-accruing position in a postsecondary educational institution. (Tenure is understood as any comparable provision for job security in a postsecondary educational institution.) The award consists of a certificate, a check for $1,000, and a year's MLA membership. To enter, send six copies of the work and a completed application form.

Available to: See above
Deadline: May 1
Apply to: MLA Prize for Independent Scholars, above address

The *Aldo and Jeanne Scaglione Prize for Comparative Literary Studies* awards $1,000 annually for an outstanding scholarly work in comparative literary studies, involving at least two literatures, by a MLA member. Works of literary history, literary criticism, philology, and literary theory are eligible, as are works dealing with literature and other arts and disciplines, including cinema. To enter, send four copies of the book and a letter confirming the author's MLA membership.

Available to: MLA members
Deadline: May 1
Apply to: Aldo and Jeanne Scaglione Prize for Comparative Literary Studies, above address

The *Aldo and Jeanne Scaglione Prize for French and Francophone Studies* awards $1,000 annually for an outstanding scholarly work in French or Francophone linguistic or literary studies by an MLA member. Works of literary history, literary criticism, philology, and literary theory are eligible. To enter, send four copies of the book and a letter confirming the author's MLA membership.

Available to: MLA members
Deadline: May 1
Apply to: Aldo and Jeanne Scaglione Prize for French and Francophone Studies, above address

The *Aldo and Jeanne Scaglione Prize for Literary Translation* awards $1,000 in even-numbered years for an outstanding translation into English of a book-length literary work, and $1,000 in odd-numbered years, for an outstanding translation into English of a book-length work of literary history, literary criticism, philology, or literary theory. Translators need not be MLA members. Books published during the preceding two years are eligible to compete for each year's prize. To enter, send five copies of the book and a letter of nomination.

Available to: No restrictions
Deadline: April 1
Apply to: Aldo and Jeanne Scaglione Prize for Literary Translation, above address

The *Aldo and Jeanne Scaglione Prize for Studies in Germanic Languages and Literatures* offers $1,000 each even-numbered year for an outstanding scholarly work on the linguistics or literatures of the Germanic languages, including Danish, Dutch, German, Icelandic, Norwegian, Swedish, and Yiddish, by an MLA member. Works of literary history, literary criticism, philology, and literary theory are eligible. To enter, send four copies of the book and a letter confirming the author's MLA membership.

Available to: MLA members
Deadline: May 1, 2000
Apply to: Aldo and Jeanne Scaglione Prize for Studies in Germanic Languages and Literatures, above address

The *Aldo and Jeanne Scaglione Prize for Studies in Slavic Languages and Literatures* offers $1,000 each odd-numbered year for an outstanding scholarly work on the linguistics or literatures of the Slavic languages. Works of literary history, literary criticism, philology, and literary theory are eligible; books that are primarily translations will not be considered. To enter, send four copies of the book.

Available to: No restrictions
Deadline: May 1, 2001
Apply to: Aldo and Jeanne Scaglione Prize for Studies in Slavic Languages and Literatures, above address

ⓝ The *Mina P. Shaughnessy Prize* awards $1,000 annually to the author of a research publication in the field of teaching English language and literature. To enter, send four copies of the work.

> Available to: No restrictions
> Deadline: May 1
> Apply to: Mina P. Shaughnessy Prize, above address

Money for Women/Barbara Deming Memorial Fund
PO Box 630125
Bronx, NY 10463

ⓜ The Fund provides grants of up to $1,000 to U.S. or Canadian women poets, fiction writers, and nonfiction writers "whose work addresses women's concerns or speaks for peace and justice from a feminist perspective." The *Gerty, Gerty, Gerty in the Arts, Arts, Arts Award*, named for Gertrude Stein, honors "outstanding work by a lesbian [that] gives voice to a lesbian sensibility or confronts homophobia." The *Fannie Lou Hamer Award* is given to a woman "whose work combats racism and celebrates women of color." Send SASE for application.

> Available to: See above
> Deadline: December 31 and June 30
> Apply to: Above address

Montana Artists Refuge
PO Box 8
Basin, MT 59631
E-mail: mtrefuge@pop.mcn.net
Fax: 406-225-9225

ⓡ The Montana Artists Refuge, located in Basin, provides a place for artists of all types to find respite from the rigors of modern life. Visiting artists may stay for three months to one year; three to five artists are in residence at a time. Rents range from $300 to $600 per month, plus heat. Financial assistance is available to a limited number of artists. Write or e-mail for additional information and application procedures.

> Available to: No restrictions
> Deadline: November 1 for May–September residences; ongoing for October–April
> Apply to: Above address

Montana Arts Council
PO Box 202201
Helena, MT 59620
E-mail: mac@state.mt.us
Fax: 406-444-6548

ⓜ Up to ten *Individual Artists Fellowships*, of $2,000 each, are available in even-numbered years to Montana residents ages twenty-one and over in categories including fiction and nonfiction. Write for guidelines and application.

> Available to: Montana residents age twenty-one and older
> Deadline: Summer 2000 (inquire for exact date)
> Apply to: Above address

Montclair State University
Upper Montclair, NJ 07043
Web site: http://www.montclair.edu
Fax: 973-655-5335

ⓓ The *TheatreFest Regional Playwriting Contest* annually offers $500, full production, and housing to a Connecticut, New Jersey, or New York playwright for an unproduced, unpublished full-length play exploring contemporary issues. Plays should have a maximum cast of eight. Send SASE for guidelines.

Available to: Connecticut, New Jersey or New York playwrights
Deadline: January 1
Apply to: TheatreFest, Regional Playwriting Contest, above address

Monterey County Film Commission
PO Box 111
Monterey, CA 93942
E-mail: mryfilm@aol.com
Web site: http://www.filmmonterey.org
Fax: 831-655-9244

Ⓢ The *Monterey County Film Commission Screenwriting Competition* offers a first prize of $1,000, a second of $500, and a third of $250 for a full-length film or television movie script. (Scripts for one-hour television dramas or sitcoms are not accepted.) Only writers who have not earned money writing for television or film are eligible. Submitted work must not have been optioned for more than $1,000 or sold at the time of submission. There is a $50 entry fee. Send SASE or visit the Web site for guidelines and application form.

Available to: See above
Deadline: Inquire
Apply to: Screenwriting Competition, above address

Jenny McKean Moore Writers Program. *See* **George Washington University**

William Morris Society in the United States
PO Box 53263
Washington, DC 20009
E-mail: Biblio@aol.com
Web site: http://www.ccny.cuny.edu/wmorris/morris/html

The William Morris Society offers fellowships of up to $1,000 for research and other expenses incurred in individual projects related to the life and work of William Morris. Projects may deal with any subject—biographical, historical, social, literary, political, artistic, typographical—pertaining to Morris, and may be scholarly or creative.

Available to: U.S. citizens or permanent residents
Deadline: December 1
Apply to: Mark Samuels Lasner, President, above address

Mountain West Center for Regional Studies
Utah State University–UMC 0735
Logan, UT 84322-0735
E-mail: mwc@cc.usu.edu
Web site: http://www.usu.edu/~pioneers/evans.html
Fax: 435-797-3899

Ⓝ The *Evans Biography Award* of $10,000 and the *Evans Handcart Prize* of $1,000 are designed to encourage fine writing about people who have shaped the growth and character of an important part of the United States. The Biography Award recognizes outstanding scholarship and writing; the Handcart Prize recognizes a biography of merit that contributes to an understanding of any region characterized by Mormon settlement during the period of the biography in question. Judges will consider book-length biographies, published during the given calendar year, of any person who lived a significant portion of his or her life in Mormon country. Neither the biography subject nor the author need be Mormon. Authors or publishers should submit four copies of the book and the author's vita.

Available to: No restrictions
Deadline: December 1
Apply to: Evans Biography Award or Evans Handcart Prize, above address

Mountaineers Books
1001 SW Klickitat Way, Suite 201
Seattle, WA 98134
E-mail: mbooks@mountaineers.org
Fax: 206-223-6306

Ⓝ The *Barbara Savage "Miles from Nowhere" Memorial Award* is given in even-numbered years for an outstanding unpublished book-length manuscript of personal-adventure nonfiction. The prize consists of a $3,000 cash award, publication, and a $12,000 guaranteed advance against royalties. Send SASE for details.

Available to: No restrictions
Deadline: May 1, 2000
Apply to: Barbara Savage "Miles from Nowhere" Memorial Award, above address

Mountains and Plains Booksellers Association
19 Old Town Square, Suite 238
Fort Collins, CO 80524
E-mail: lknudsen@mountainsplains.org
Web site: http://www.mountainsplains.org
Fax: 970-407-1479

Ⓜ The *Regional Book Awards* honor outstanding books set in the Mountains and Plains region, which includes Arizona, Colorado, Idaho, Kansas, Montana, Nebraska, New Mexico, South Dakota, Texas, Utah, and Wyoming. The awards, of $500 each, are given in fiction, poetry, nonfiction, and children's literature, for books published between the November 1 and the October 31 preceding the submission deadline. Publishers and booksellers may nominate books throughout the year.

Available to: No restrictions
Deadline: November 1
Apply to: Regional Book Awards, above address

Municipal Art Society of New York
457 Madison Avenue
New York, NY 10022
Fax: 212-753-1816

[IN] The *Brendan Gill Prize*, consisting of a cash award and an engraved Steuben crystal vessel, is given annually to the creator of "a single work of art which best captures the energy, vigor and verve of New York City." The award is open to all artistic disciplines, including writing. Nominations should be submitted by April 15 for work completed in the prior calendar year.

Museum of Science
Science Park
Boston, MA 02114

The *Bradford Washburn Award*, consisting of $10,000 and a gold medal, is presented annually to an individual who has made "outstanding contributions toward public understanding of science, its importance, its fascination, and the vital role it plays in all of our lives." The award honors a writer or lecturer of national or international influence, and is not meant to reward specific research, technical accomplishment, or teaching, although it may be given to an outstanding teacher or researcher who also is a highly effective writer or lecturer. There is no application process, and the prize committee does not consider self-nominators. Presentation is made at an annual autumn dinner.

Available to: Writers, lecturers, or scientists of any nationality
Deadline: Inquire for nomination procedures
Apply to: Bradford Washburn Award, Community Relations Department, above address

Mystery Writers of America
17 East 47th Street, 6th floor
New York, NY 10017
Fax: 212-888-8107
E-mail: mwa_org@earthlink.net
Web site: http://www.mysterywriters.net

Ⓕ The *Robert L. Fish Memorial Award* offers $500 for the best first mystery or suspense short story published during the calendar year. A copy of each eligible short story should be sent to the judges of the short story committee by the editor of the magazine that first published it, and an entry form and copy to the MWA office. Under special circumstances, writers may submit their own work. Write for additional information and guidelines.

Available to: No restrictions
Deadline: December 1
Apply to: Robert L. Fish Memorial Award, above address

National Arts Journalism Program
Columbia University
2950 Broadway, Mail Code 7200
New York, NY 10027
E-mail: najp@columbia.edu
Web site: http://www.najp.org
Fax: 212-854-8129

Ⓙ Supported by a grant from the Pew Charitable Trusts, the National Arts Journalism Program offers fellowships to mid-career and senior journalists in arts and culture. Ten mid-career fellows, supported by stipends of $40,000, spend an academic year at Columbia engaged in a blend of study and work with arts and cultural organizations. Eligible fellows are working critics, reporters, or editors with at least five years' experience and demonstrated dedication to arts and cultural journalism. Several senior fellows spend shorter periods at Columbia, with a generous stipend and research assistance. Nominees for senior fellowships must have achieved singular and measurable distinction in arts and cultural journalism. Write or e-mail for additional information and application.

Available to: See above
Deadline: February (inquire for exact date)
Apply to: Above address

National Association of Black Journalists
8701-A Adelphi Road
Adelphi, MD 20783-1716
Web site: http://www.nabj.org
Fax: 301-445-7101

Ⓙ Fifteen *NABJ Summer Internships* are awarded annually to college sophomores, juniors, and seniors and graduate students committed to journalism careers. Candidates are offered a paid position in print, radio, or television at selected news organizations. Interns, who receive an all-expenses-paid trip to the NABJ convention, are required to participate in student convention projects. Write for additional information and application procedures.

Available to: See above
Deadline: Inquire
Apply to: Summer Internships, above address

Ⓙ At least ten *NABJ Scholarships* of $2,500 each are awarded annually to African-American college students planning to pursue a career in journalism. Any student currently attending an accredited four-year U.S. college or university is eligible. Recipients, who receive an all-expenses-paid trip to the NABJ convention, are required to participate in student convention projects. In addition, two four-year college scholarships are offered to African-American high school students. Write for additional information and application procedures.

Available to: See above
Deadline: Inquire
Apply to: Scholarship Program, above address

ⓙ Two *Ethel Payne Fellowships* are offered annually to African-American journalists interested in obtaining international reporting experience through assignments in Africa. The fellowships, designed for journalists who have a strong interest in Africa but limited opportunities to cover the continent for their news organizations, allow recipients to spend up to three weeks there and to produce news reports for NABJ. Write for additional information and application procedures.

> Available to: NABJ members with at least five years' experience as full-time or freelance journalists for a newspaper, magazine, or broadcast station
> Deadline: Inquire
> Apply to: Ethel Payne Fellowships, above address

National Association of Hispanic Journalists
1193 National Press Building
Washington, DC 20045
E-mail: nahj@nahj.org
Web site: http://www.nahj.org

ⓙ Up to thirty scholarships ranging from $1,000 to $5,000 are awarded each academic year to Hispanic students interested in pursuing careers in the media. Scholarships are open to high school seniors, college undergraduates, and graduate students. Applicants are judged according to financial need, scholastic achievement, journalistic ability, and commitment to the field. Write, e-mail, or visit the Web site for additional information and application.

> Available to: See above
> Deadline: Late February (inquire for exact date)
> Apply to: Educational Programs, above address

National Association of Science Writers
PO Box 294
Greenlawn, NY 11740
Web site: http://www.nasw.org

ⓙ The *Science in Society Journalism Awards* "recognize investigative and interpretive reporting about the sciences and their impact for good and bad." Three awards, of $1,000 each, are offered in the categories of newspapers, magazines, and television and radio. Work must be written, or spoken, in English, intended for the layperson, and published or broadcast in North America between June 1 of the previous year and May 31 of the current application year. Write or visit the Web site for guidelines and entry form.

> Available to: No restrictions
> Deadline: Applications must be postmarked by July 1
> Apply to: Above address

National Book Awards
c/o National Book Foundation
260 Fifth Avenue, Room 904
New York, NY 10001
Web site: http://www.publishersweekly.com/NBF/docs/nbf.html
Fax: 212-213-6570

Ⓜ The *National Book Awards* recognize American literary excellence in four categories: fiction, nonfiction, poetry, and young people's literature. Each winner receives a cash prize of $10,000; runners-up receive $1,000. Eligible books must be published in the United States between the December 1 preceding and November 30 of the award year, and nominated by their publishers only.

> Available to: U.S. authors
> Deadline: July 15
> Apply to: Above address

National Council for the Social Studies
3501 Newark Street, NW
Washington, DC 20016

Ⓜ The *James A. Michener Prize in Writing* of $5,000 is awarded every five years to "an individual who has enhanced the social studies profession through his or her writing." Nominees must have demonstrated ability in one of more of the following: a career devoted to writing of and about social studies; a body of work that has made social studies come alive through fiction, nonfiction, children's literature, young people's literature, or poetry; works in history or social studies that have contributed to the evolution of the social studies profession; works that affect the understanding, growth, and future of society. Write for nomination and application procedures.

Available to: No restrictions
Deadline: June 1, 2001
Apply to: Michener Prize in Writing Subcommittee, above address

National Education Association
1201 Sixteenth Street, NW
Washington, DC 20036
E-mail: clehane@nea.org
Web site: http://www.nea.org/he

The *Excellence in the Academy Awards,* consisting of the prizes listed below, are intended to advance the NEA's commitment in higher education. Winning entries will be published in *Thought and Action,* the NEA higher education journal. Prizewinners will be asked to be guest presenters at the NEA Higher Education Conference. The competition is open to the entire academic community. Write, e-mail, or visit the Web site for additional information and guidelines.

The NEA *Art of Teaching Prize* offers $2,500 for an essay that "illuminates one professor's approach to the complex and intangible dynamic that inspires students with a love of learning" or an article that "offers practical approaches to improving teaching and learning at the college level."

The NEA *Democracy in Higher Education Prize* offers $2,500 for an article that "contributes to the expansion of the welcoming and democratic culture of higher learning and the ideal of tolerance, justice, and the unfettered pursuit of truth traditional to the academy."

The NEA *New Unionism in the Academy Prize* offers $2,500 for an article that "describes a higher education local union's collective approach to uniting the academic community in pursuit of quality higher education for all."

The NEA *New Scholar Prize* offers $2,500 for an article by a scholar with less than seven years' full- or part-time employment in higher education. The submission can be made in any of the categories listed above.

Available to: No restrictions
Deadline: September 30
Apply to: Con Lehane, Editor, Higher Education Publications, above address

National Endowment for the Arts
Literature Program
Nancy Hanks Center
1100 Pennsylvania Avenue, NW
Washington, DC 20506
E-mail: webmgr@arts.endow.gov
Web site: http://www.arts.endow.gov

Ⓜ *Fellowships in Creative Writing* of $20,000 each are available, in alternating years, to published creative writers of exceptional talent in poetry and prose (fiction and creative nonfiction). Fellowships are awarded to enable recipients to set aside time for writing, research, travel, and/or general career advancement. In 2001, fellowships will be offered to poets.

Applicants must meet specific prior-publication requirements to be eligible. Write, e-mail, or visit the Web site for additional information and current guidelines.

Available to: U.S. citizens
Deadline: March 14, 2000, for poetry; inquire in 2001 for prose
Apply to: Information Management Division, Room 815, Fellowships in Creative Writing, above address

Ⓣ *Translation Project Grants* of $20,000 each are available to published translators of literature for projects that involve the specific translation of prose (fiction, creative nonfiction, drama) or poetry (including verse drama) from other languages into English. Translations of writers and of work insufficiently represented in English are encouraged. All projects must be creative translations of published literary material into English; the work to be translated should be of interest for its literary excellence and value. Priority will be given to projects that involve work that has not yet been translated into English. Grants will be awarded to translators of poetry in 2001. Applicants must meet specific prior-publication requirements to be eligible. Write, e-mail, or visit the Web site for additional information and guidelines.

Available to: U.S. citizens
Deadlines: March 14, 2000, for translators of poetry; inquire for 2001
Apply to: Translation Project Grants, Information Management Division, Room 815, above address

National Endowment for the Humanities
1100 Pennsylvania Avenue, NW
Washington, DC 20506
E-mail: fellowsuniv@neh.gov (for Fellowships for University Teachers);
  Fellowscollind@neh.gov (for Fellowships for College Teachers and Independent Scholars);
  Research@neh.gov (for Collaborative Research Grants)
Web site: http://www.neh.fed.us

Fellowships for University Teachers, *Fellowships for College Teachers and Independent Scholars*, and *Collaborative Research Grants* are offered through the NEH Division of Research for research, editing, and writing in the humanities. These grants are made for scholarly writing rather than for fiction or poetry. The term "humanities" includes, but is not limited to, the study of the following: language, both modern and classical; linguistics; literature; history; jurisprudence; philosophy; archaeology; comparative religion; ethics; history, criticism, and theory of the arts; aspects of the social sciences that have humanistic content and employ humanistic methods; and the study and application of the humanities to the human environment, with particular attention to the diverse heritage, traditions, and history of Americans, and to the relevance of the humanities to conditions of national life. Write, e-mail, or visit the Web site for further information on stipends, eligibility requirements, and application procedures.

Available to: U.S. citizens and permanent residents
Deadline: May 1 for both types of fellowships; September 1 for Collaborative Research Grants
Apply to: Division of Research, above address

National Foundation for Advancement in the Arts
800 Brickell Avenue, Suite 500
Miami, FL 33131
E-mail: nfaa@nfaa.org
Web site: http://www.nfaa.org
Fax: 305-377-1149

The *Arts Recognition and Talent Search Program* honors the achievements of high school seniors and other artists seventeen or eighteen years of age. Awards of $3,000, $1,500, $500, and $100 are offered to students demonstrating talent in writing, dance, jazz, theater, music, voice, photography, film and video, and the other visual arts. Award candidates will receive an invitation to Arts Week in Miami, which includes live adjudications, master and technique classes, workshops, studio exercises, and interviews. NFAA pays all travel expenses. A $25 entry fee is required for applications postmarked by June 1, a $35 fee for those postmarked June 2– October 1. Write for additional information and the required registration form.

Available to: Seventeen- and eighteen-year-olds
Deadline: June 1 (June 2–October 1, with late fee)
Apply to: ARTS Program, above address, or contact high school teachers or counselors

National Gallery of Art
Center for Advanced Study in the Visual Arts
Washington, DC 20565
E-mail: advstudy@nga.gov
Web site: http://www.nga.gov/resources/casva.htm
Fax: 202-842-6733

Senior Fellowships and *Visiting Senior Fellowships* are available to scholars who have held a Ph.D. for five years or more or who possess an equivalent record of professional accomplishment, for study in the history, theory, and criticism of the visual arts of any geographical area and any period. Senior Fellowships are normally awarded for an academic year, early fall to late spring; Visiting Senior Fellowships are available for up to sixty days. Fellowships are for full-time research, and scholars are expected to reside in Washington for the duration and participate in the activities of the Center. All grants are based on individual need. Senior Fellowships will normally be limited to half of an applicant's salary, up to a maximum of $30,000, on the expectation that applicants will bring sabbatical stipends or research grants from their home institution. Visiting senior fellows receive a stipend that covers round-trip travel and local expenses. Write for additional information and application materials, which may be found also at the Center's Web site.

Available to: See above
Deadline: October 1 for Senior Fellowships; March 21 and September 21 for Visiting Senior Fellowships
Apply to: Senior Fellowship Program, above address

National Humanities Center
PO Box 12256
Research Triangle Park, NC 27709-2256
E-mail: nhc@ga.unc.edu
Web site: http://www.nhc.rtp.nc.us:8080

The National Humanities Center offers thirty-five to forty residential fellowships for advanced study in all fields of the humanities. Applicants must hold a doctorate or equivalent credentials and have a record of publication. The Center provides an environment for individual research and fosters the exchange of ideas among scholars. Both senior and younger scholars are eligible for fellowships; the latter should be engaged in research well beyond the subject of their doctoral dissertations. Fellowships are for the academic year (September through May). Humanistically inclined individuals from the natural and social sciences, the arts, the professions, and public life may also apply. Fellowships are individually determined, the amount of a stipend depending on the needs of the fellow and on the Center's ability to meet them. The average stipend is $35,000, with a few available up to $50,000. Write, e-mail, or visit the Web site for further information and application.

Available to: No restrictions
Deadline: October 15
Apply to: Fellowship Program, above address

National Institute for Labor Relations Research
5211 Port Royal Road, Suite 510
Springfield, VA 22151
Web site: http://www.nilrr.org

Ⓙ The *William B. Ruggles Journalism Scholarship* of $2,000 is available yearly to graduate or undergraduate students majoring in journalism or related mass media or mass communications studies who have demonstrated a financial need for tuition assistance. A 500-word essay on the right-to-work principle is required of applicants.

Available to: See above
Deadline: Applications accepted January 1–March 31
Apply to: Public Relations Department, above address

National League of American Pen Women
1300 17th Street, NW
Washington, DC 20036

Ⓜ The *NLAPW Scholarship for Mature Women in Letters*, in memory of Dr. Adeline Hoffman, offers $1,000 in even-numbered years to an American woman over thirty-five years old to "further creative goals at an age when encouragement can lead to realization of long-term purposes." Applicants may submit a published or unpublished article, short story, editorial, drama, teleplay, three poems, or first chapter of a novel. NLAPW members are ineligible. There is an $8 handling fee. Send SASE for guidelines.

Available to: Women over age thirty-five
Deadline: January 1 of even-numbered years
Apply to: Scholarship for Mature Women in Letters, above address

National Museum of American Art
Research and Scholars Center
Smithsonian Institution
Washington, DC 20560
E-mail: plynagh@nmaa.si.edu
Web site: http://www.nmaa.si.edu
Fax: 202-786-2583

Ⓝ The *Charles C. Eldredge Prize* is awarded annually for outstanding scholarship in the field of American art. A cash award of $2,000 is given to the author of a recent book-length publication that provides new insight into works of American art, the artists who made them, or aspects of history and theory that enrich our understanding of the artistic heritage. Single-author book-length publications—including monographs, exhibition catalogues, catalogues raisonnées, and collected essays—in the field of American art history appearing within the three calendar years before the application deadline are eligible. Write for additional information and nomination procedures.

Available to: No restrictions
Deadline: December 1
Apply to: Charles C. Eldredge Prize, above address

National Poetry Series
PO Box G
Hopewell, NJ 08525

Ⓟ The National Poetry Series oversees an annual open competition. Five book-length manuscripts of poetry will be selected by five well-known poets and published by participating publishers. Each of the five winning poets receives a $1,000 cash award. Manuscripts must be accompanied by an entry fee of $25. Send SASE for guidelines.

Available to: U.S. citizens
Deadline: Submissions accepted January 1–February 15
Apply to: Above address

National Press Club
529 14th Street, NW, 13th floor
Washington, DC 20045
Web site: http://npc.press.org

Ⓙ The *National Press Club Scholarship for Minorities in Journalism* annually awards a $20,000 college scholarship to a minority high school student planning to pursue a career in journalism (newspaper, magazine, trade paper, radio, television). The scholarship is awarded over four years, at $5,000 per year. Write for additional information and application form.

Available to: Minority high school students with an ongoing interest in journalism
Deadline: March 1
Apply to: Scholarship Committee, above address

National Press Foundation
1211 Connecticut Avenue NW, Suite 310
Washington, DC 20036
E-mail: npf@natpress.org
Web site: http://www.natpress.org
Fax: 202-530-2855

Ⓙ The *Evert Clark Award* of $1,000 is given in recognition of outstanding reporting and writing in any field of science by young writers. The winner will also receive an all-expenses-paid trip to the annual meeting of the American Association for the Advancement of Science. The award is limited to nontechnical print journalism. Write, e-mail, or visit the Web site for additional information and application.

Available to: No restrictions
Deadline: Early December (inquire for exact date)
Apply to: Evert Clark Award, above address

Ⓙ The *Everett McKinley Dirksen Award for Distinguished Reporting of Congress* annually offers $5,000 each to a print and a broadcast journalist whose work on the activities of Congress was published or broadcast during the calendar year. Write, e-mail, or visit the Web site for application procedures.

Available to: No restrictions
Deadline: October 1
Apply to: Everett Dirksen Award, above address

Ⓙ The Foundation *Spanish Language Fellowships*, given to six working journalists, offer three consecutive months of intensive Spanish language study during the academic year at the Cemanahuac Educational Community School in Cuernavaca, Mexico. The fellowships are given annually in recognition of the importance of Spanish in covering the growing Hispanic communities in the United States as well as Latin American affairs. Write, e-mail, or visit the Web site for information and application.

Available to: No restrictions
Deadline: Mid-June (inquire for exact date)
Apply to: Spanish Language Fellowships, above address

Ⓙ The Foundation awards several fellowships for working print and broadcast journalists to attend specific professional seminars. Write, e-mail, or visit the Web site for information on current offerings and application procedures.

Available to: No restrictions
Deadline: Varies with program (inquire)
Apply to: Above address

National Repertory Theatre Foundation
PO Box 286
Hollywood, CA 90078
E-mail: nrtf@aol.com
Web site: http://www.nrtf.org
Fax: 323-417-4722

Ⓓ The *National Play Award* of $5,000 and production or a staged reading is given annually for original unpublished full-length plays that have not been produced with a paid Equity cast, and have not won a major award or been submitted previously. Four runners-up receive $500 each. There is a $25 submission fee. Send SASE for additional information.

Available to: No restrictions
Deadline: January 1–March 31
Apply to: National Play Award, above address

National Science Foundation
4201 Wilson Boulevard
Arlington, VA 22230
Web site: http://www.nsf.gov

To enable interpretation and presentation of the nation's Antarctic endeavors , the *Antarctic Artists & Writers Program* considers requests from particularly well qualified writers, historians, artists, or others in the liberal arts to work in Antarctica. This limited opportunity provides field support but no direct award of funds. Candidates must be well established and working full-time in the appropriate field and have a means of presenting their work to the public. Write to the Polar Information Program for USAP Information Series No. 31 for further details.

Available to: No restrictions
Deadline: Inquire
Apply to: Antarctic Artists & Writers Program, USAP Information Series No. 31, above address

National Screenwriting Competition
755 Highway 34
Matawan, NJ 07747
E-mail: director@skyweb.net
Web site: http://www.nationalscreenwriting.com

Ⓢ The *National Screenwriting Competition* offers a first prize of $2,500, a second of $500, and a third of $250 for full-length film scripts. All winning entries will be considered for possible production or development as feature films. There is a $45 entry fee. Send SASE, e-mail, or visit the Web site for rules and guidelines.

Available to: No restrictions
Deadline: May 31, 2000; inquire for 2001
Apply to: Above address

National Society of Arts and Letters
4227 46th Street, NW
Washington, DC 20016
Web site: http://www.arts-nsal.org

The *National Society of Arts and Letters Literature Awards* offer a first prize of $10,000, a second of $5,000, a third of $3,000, and a fourth of $1,000 for creative work in a variety of disciplines by artists age twenty-six and younger. The NSAL, comprising regional chapters, is a nonprofit volunteer organization founded in 1944 to create opportunities for young artists. The regional and national competitions rotate among various artistic disciplines, with literature awards offered every five years. The next round of literature awards will be in 2003. Write or consult the Web site for additional information in 2002.

Available to: Writers age twenty-six and younger
Deadline: Inquire for 2003
Apply to: Above address

National Space Club
2000 L Street NW, Suite 710
Washington, DC 20036

Ⓝ The *Robert H. Goddard Historical Essay Award Competition* offers $1,000 for an essay, no longer than 5,000 words, that explores any significant aspects of the historical development of rocketry and astronautics. Entries will be judged on their originality and scholarship. Write for guidelines.

Available to: U.S. citizens
Deadline: Early December (inquire for exact date)
Apply to: Robert H. Goddard Historical Essay Contest, above address

National Steinbeck Center
One Main Street
Salinas, CA 93901
E-mail: celeste@steinbeck.org
Web site: http://www.steinbeck.org

(F)   The *National Steinbeck Center Writing Competition* offers a first prize of $1,000 and a travel stipend to attend the Steinbeck Festival, for an unpublished short story of up to 5,000 words on a given theme. The winner is announced at the annual Festival, held in Salinas, California, in August. There is a $15 entrance fee. Send SASE, e-mail, or visit the Web site for competition theme and guidelines.

Available to: No restrictions
Deadline: June 15
Apply to: Writing Competition, above address

National Women's Studies Association
7100 Baltimore Avenue, Suite 500
College Park, MD 20740
E-mail: nwsa@umail.umd.edu

The *Graduate Scholarship Award* of $1,000 is given to a student who will be engaged in the research or writing stages of a master's thesis or Ph.D. dissertation in the interdisciplinary field of women's studies in the fall. The research project must be on women and must enhance the NWSA mission.

Available to: NWSA members
Deadline: Inquire
Apply to: Graduate Scholarship Award, above address

The *Graduate Scholarship in Lesbian Studies* awards $500 to a student who will be doing research or writing a master's thesis or Ph.D. dissertation in lesbian studies in the fall.

Available to: See above
Deadline: Inquire
Apply to: Graduate Scholarship in Lesbian Studies, above address

The *Jewish Caucus Prize* awards $500 to a graduate student enrolled for the fall semester whose area of research is Jewish women's studies.

Available to: See above
Deadline: Inquire
Apply to: Jewish Women's Studies Scholarship, above address

National Writers Association
3140 South Peoria, #295
Aurora, CO 80014
E-mail: contests@nationalwriters.com
Web site: http://www.nationalwriters.com

(F)   The *Novel Writing Contest* offers a first prize of $500, a second of $250, and a third of $150 for unpublished novels of any genre. Manuscripts may be up to 90,000 words. There is a $35 entry fee; a critique of the submitted manuscript is available for an additional $1.25 per 1,000 words. Judging sheets are sent to applicants if SASE is enclosed with the submission. Send SASE or visit the Web site for guidelines and application.

Available to: No restrictions
Deadline: April 1
Apply to: Novel Writing Contest, above address

National Writers' United Service Organization
113 University Place, 6th floor
New York, NY 10003
Fax: 212-254-0673

Ⓕ The *Bellwether Prize*, established and funded by Barbara Kingsolver, biennially offers $25,000 and publication by a major publisher (HarperCollins for the 2000 prizewinner) for a literary novel whose content addresses issues of social justice and the impact of culture and politics on human relationships. Writers should contact NWUSO for guidelines, eligibility requirements, and application form before submission. The next prize will be given in 2002.

Available to: U.S. citizens
Deadline: October 2001 (inquire for exact date)
Apply to: Bellwether Prize, above address

Native American Journalists Association
3359 36th Avenue, South
Minneapolis, MN 55406
E-mail: info@naja.com
Web site: http://www.naja.com
Fax: 612-729-9373

Ⓙ The Native American Journalists Association offers scholarships and internships. Scholarship recipients receive financial assistance for books and tuition costs. Interns have on-the-job learning opportunities with Native and mainstream organizations. Write for additional information.

Available to: Native American journalism students
Deadline: March 31
Apply to: Above address

Native Writers' Circle of the Americas
English Department
University of Oklahoma
Norman, OK 73019-0240

ⅠⓃ *Lifetime Achievement Awards for Literature* are given to Native American writers selected by fellow Native American writers. The awards carry a cash prize that varies yearly according to funding. There is no application process. *By Internal Nomination Only.*

Ⓜ The *North American Native Authors First Book Awards*, consisting of the *Diane Decorah Memorial Award for Poetry* and the *Louis Littlecoon Oliver Memorial Award for Short Fiction*, offer $500 in each genre and publication in book form by the University of Arizona Press. The awards are open to Native Americans of American Indian, Aleut, Inuit, or métis ancestry who have not yet published a book. Writers may be from North America, Mexico, or Central America; manuscripts must be in English or in bilingual format. Write for guidelines and further information.

Available to: Native Americans
Deadline: Inquire
Apply to: North American Native Authors First Book Awards, above address

Naval Historical Center
Washington Navy Yard
805 Kidder Breese SE
Washington, DC 20374-5060
Web site: http://www.history.navy.mil

Ⓝ The *Ernest M. Eller Prize in Naval History* annually offers $1,000 to the author of the best article on United States naval history published in a scholarly journal. Write or visit the Web site for further information.

Available to: No restrictions
Deadline: June 1
Apply to: Senior Historian, above address

Ⓝ The *Rear Admiral John D. Hayes Pre-Doctoral Fellowship* offers a stipend of $10,000 to support dissertation research and writing on any aspect of U.S. naval history. Write or visit the Web site for further information.

> Available to: U.S. citizens enrolled in a recognized graduate school who will complete all requirements for a Ph.D. except the dissertation by June 30 of the application year and who have an approved dissertation topic in U.S. naval history
> Deadline: February 28
> Apply to: Senior Historian, above address

Ⓝ The *Vice Admiral Edwin B. Hooper Research Grant* offers two awards, of up to $2,500 each, to scholars engaged in the research or writing of books or articles; awards are to be used for travel, living, and document duplication costs related to the research project. Write or visit the Web site for further information.

> Available to: U.S. citizens with a Ph.D. from an accredited university or equivalent attainment as published authors
> Deadline: February 28
> Apply to: Senior Historian, above address

Nebraska Arts Council
3838 Davenport
Omaha, NE 68131-2329
E-mail: stwnac@infobridge.com
Web site: http://www.nebraskaartscouncil.org
Fax: 402-595-2334

Ⓜ *Individual Artist Fellowships* in literature are given every three years to Nebraska writers with demonstrated records of professional achievement. Distinguished Achievement Awards of $5,000 and Merit Awards of $2,000 are available. Writers must be residents of Nebraska for at least two years before applying, and may not be students in an undergraduate or graduate degree program in the fellowship field.

> Available to: Nebraska residents
> Deadline: November 15, 2000
> Apply to: Above address

The Nebraska Review
University of Nebraska at Omaha
College of Fine Arts
Omaha, NE 68182-0324

Ⓕ Ⓟ The *Nebraska Review Fiction Prize* and *Poetry Prize* each offer $500 and publication for the best story of 5,000 words or less, and for the best poem or group of poems, not to exceed five poems or 6 pages. There is a $10 entry fee. All entrants receive a one-year subscription to *The Nebraska Review*.

> Available to: No restrictions
> Deadline: November 30
> Apply to: Fiction Prize or Poetry Prize, above address

Negative Capability Magazine
62 Ridgelawn Drive East
Mobile, AL 36608

Ⓕ Ⓟ The *Negative Capability Short Fiction Award* and the *Eve of St. Agnes Award in Poetry* each offer a cash prize of $500 and publication in *Negative Capability*. Fiction writers should submit unpublished short fiction of 1,500 to 4,500 words with a $10 reading fee; poets may submit as many poems as they like, with $3 per poem. Send SASE for guidelines.

> Available to: No restrictions
> Deadline: January 15
> Apply to: Short Fiction Award or Eve of St. Agnes Award in Poetry, above address

Nevada Arts Council
602 North Curry Street
Carson City, NV 89703
Fax: 775-687-6688

Ⓜ *Jackpot Grants* of various amounts up to $1,000 are available quarterly to Nevada resident professional artists in fiction, nonfiction, and poetry. Fellowships of $5,000 each are offered annually to two Nevada writers working in any genre. Write or fax for additional information and guidelines.

Available to: Nevada residents
Deadline: Inquire
Apply to: Artist Services Program, above address

New Dramatists
424 West 44th Street
New York, NY 10036
E-mail: NewDram@aol.com
Web site: http://www.fargo.itp.tsoa.nyu.edu/~diana/ndintro.html

Ⓓ New Dramatists, a service organization, offers seven-year memberships to emerging playwrights of talent and ability. During this period, they are encouraged to use the organization's resources to develop and refine their artistry and vision. Primary among the services offered to members are play development workshops; playwright exchange programs with Australia, Chile, England, Ireland, Israel, and Los Angeles; and ScriptShare, a national script distribution service. Additional services include screenplay development and musical theater workshops; writer work spaces; a free ticket program; script-copying facilities; and a summer playwriting residency in Lake Placid, New York. Write for additional information and guidelines.

Available to: Playwrights who live in the New York City area or who visit enough to take advantage of the programs
Deadline: Inquire
Apply to: Above address

New England Poetry Club
2 Farrar Street
Cambridge, MA 02138

Ⓟ The *Daniel Varoujan Prize* annually awards $500 for a poem "worthy of the Armenian poet Daniel Varoujan, who was killed by the Turks in 1915." Translations are not eligible. There is a $5 reading fee for entrants who are not members of the New England Poetry Club. Send SASE for guidelines.

Available to: No restrictions
Deadline: June 30
Apply to: Above address

The Club offers several other awards, with lesser cash prizes, for individual poems. Inquire for further information.

New England Theatre Conference
Northeastern University
360 Huntington Avenue
Boston, MA 02115
E-mail: netc@world.std.com
Web site: http://world.std.com/~netc
Fax: 617-424-1057

Ⓓ The *John Gassner Memorial Playwriting Competition* offers first- and second-place cash awards for commercially unpublished, unproduced full-length plays. Send SASE for guidelines before submitting.

Available to: New England residents and NETC members
Deadline: April 15
Apply to: John Gassner Memorial Playwriting Competition, above address

© ⑩ The *Aurand Harris Memorial Playwriting Competition* offers a first prize of $1,000 and a second prize of $500 for unpublished, unproduced plays for young audiences. Send SASE for guidelines before submitting.

Available to: New England residents and NETC members
Deadline: April 15
Apply to: Aurand Harris Memorial Playwriting Competition, above address

New Hampshire State Council on the Arts
40 North Main Street
Concord, NH 03301-4974
Web site: http://www.state.nh.us/nharts
Fax: 603-271-3584

Ⓜ *Individual Artist Fellowships* of up to $3,000 are available to New Hampshire writers in fiction, poetry, and playwriting. Write or visit the Web site for guidelines and application.

Available to: New Hampshire residents of at least one year, over eighteen years of age, not enrolled as full-time students, and not recipients in preceding two years
Deadline: Inquire
Apply to: Above address

New Hampshire Writers and Publishers Project
PO Box 2693
Concord, NH 03302-2693
E-mail: nhwp@nh.ultranet.com
Web site: http://www.orbit.unh.edu/nhwp

Ⓜ The New Hampshire Writers and Publishers Project biennially offers the *Jane Kenyon Award*, for an outstanding book of poetry published by a New Hampshire poet; the *Outstanding Emerging Writer Award*, given to a promising New Hampshire writer (published or unpublished) who has not yet been recognized widely; the *Outstanding Children's Book Award*; the *Outstanding Work of Fiction Award* and *Outstanding Work of Nonfiction Award* for published work by a New Hampshire writer; and the *Lifetime Achievement Award*. Each award carries a cash prize of $500 and are given in even-numbered years. Write for guidelines and nomination form. There is a $10 submission fee.

Available to: New Hampshire writers
Deadline: Inquire
Apply to: Above address

The New Harmony Project
613 North East Street
Indianapolis, IN 46202
Fax: 317-635-4201

Ⓓ Ⓡ The *New Harmony Project* seeks writers and scripts that "explore the human journey by offering hope and showing respect for the positive values of life" for an annual development conference in historic New Harmony, Indiana. Writers and their work are offered a series of rehearsals and readings with actors, dramaturgs, and other media professionals, and are given time and freedom to explore their work in a setting removed from the pressures of production. Send SASE for guidelines.

Available to: No restrictions
Deadline: Mid-November (inquire for exact date)
Apply to: Selection Committee, above address

New Issues Press
Department of English
Western Michigan University
1201 Oliver Street
Kalamazoo, MI 49008-5092
Web site: http://www.wmich.edu/english/fac/nipps

Ⓟ The *Green Rose Prize in Poetry* annually awards $1,000 and publication for a book of poems by a poet who has published one or more full-length collections. Poets may submit manuscripts of 50 to 120 pages. The Press will consider individual collections and volumes of new and selected poems. New Issues may publish as many as three other manuscripts from the competition. There is a $20 reading fee. Send SASE or visit the Web site for guidelines.

Available to: Established poets writing in English
Deadline: September 30
Apply to: Green Rose Prize, above address

Ⓟ The *New Issues First Book of Poetry Prize* annually awards $1,000 and publication for a first book of poems by a poet who has not published a full-length collection in an edition of 500 or more copies. Poets may submit manuscripts of 48 to 72 pages; there is a $12 reading fee. All entries will be considered for publication. Send SASE or visit the Web site for guidelines.

Available to: U.S. citizens or residents
Deadline: November 30
Apply to: New Issues First Book of Poetry Prize, above address

New Jersey Council for the Humanities
28 West State Street, 6th floor
Trenton, NJ 08608-1602
E-mail: njch@njch.org

Ⓝ The *New Jersey Council for the Humanities Book Award* of $1,000 is given annually for the best book in the humanities directed toward a general audience and written by an individual with a New Jersey connection (birth, current residence, place of work, subject matter, etc.). Write or e-mail for additional information.

Available to: See above
Deadline: May 1
Apply to: Above address

New Jersey State Council on the Arts
225 West State Street
PO Box 306
Trenton, NJ 08625-0306
Web site: http://www.njartscouncil.org
Fax: 609-989-1440

Ⓜ The *New Jersey State Council on the Arts Fellowship Program* awards fellowships in poetry, prose, and playwriting in odd-numbered years. Fellowships are highly competitive and are given on the basis of artistic excellence. Applications are reviewed anonymously by a peer panel. Write or visit the Web site for application.

Available to: New Jersey residents
Deadline: July 15, 2001
Apply to: NJSCA Fellowships, c/o MAAF, 22 Light Street, Baltimore, MD 21202

The *New Jersey Writers Project* places dozens of professional writers, playwrights, and poets in short-term residences in approximately two hundred New Jersey schools each year. Schools make the request for writer visits. Council funds pay for a portion of the writers' fees. Writers may apply to become certified to conduct residences.

Available to: Professional, practicing writers
Deadline: Inquire
Apply to: Above address

New Letters Magazine
University of Missouri–Kansas City
University House
5101 Rockhill Road
Kansas City, MO 64110
E-mail: mccraryg@umkc.edu
Web site: http://www.umkc.edu/newletters
Fax: 816-235-2611

In addition to receiving the monetary prize listed below, winners will have their work published in the annual awards issue of *New Letters*, an international magazine of arts and letters. Each entry for each prize must be accompanied by a $10 reading fee. All entries must be previously unpublished. Send SASE for guidelines.

Ⓝ The *New Letters Creative Nonfiction Prize* awards $1,000 plus publication for the best creative nonfiction of 5,000 words or less. Applicants are strongly discouraged from submitting annotated, footnoted, or academic work.

Ⓕ The *New Letters Fiction Prize* awards $1,000 plus publication for the best short story of 5,000 words or less.

Ⓟ The *New Letters Poetry Prize* awards $1,000 plus publication for the best group of three to six poems.

> Available to: No restrictions
> Deadline: May 15
> Apply to: New Letters Literary Awards (specify genre), above address

New Millennium
PO Box 2463
Knoxville, TN 37901

Ⓜ The *New Millennium Awards* biannually offer $1,000 each for fiction, poetry, and nonfiction. All winning submissions will be published in *New Millennium Writing*. There are no restrictions as to style or content; stories and essays should be no longer than 6,000 words, and poetry should be kept to three poems totaling no more than 5 pages. There is a $15 fee for each contest entry (one story; one essay; up to three poems). All contestants will receive a copy of the issue in which the winning submissions appear. Send SASE for rules.

> Available to: No restrictions
> Deadline: June 1 for fall issue; December 1 for spring
> Apply to: NMW Contest, above address

Ⓜ The *2001 Writing Prize* offers a one-time award of $1,000 for the work that best expresses the significance of the coming millennium either personally or to society at large. The winner will be published in the special spring 2001 issue of *NMW*. Each story, poem, or essay is counted as a separate entry and should total no more than 2,000 words. There is a $15 fee for each entry. All contestants will receive a copy of the special issue. Send SASE for rules.

> Available to: No restrictions
> Deadline: Submissions accepted throughout 2000
> Apply to: 2001 at NMW, above address

New Orleans Literary Festival. *See* Tennessee Williams/New Orleans Literary Festival

New Professional Theatre
424 West 42nd Street, 3rd floor
New York, NY 10036
E-mail: newprof@aol.com
Fax: 212-290-8202

Ⓓ The *New Professional Theatre Writers Festival* annually offers three awards of $2,000 each for a full-length play by an African-American playwright, with special consideration given to work by women. Each selected playwright receives dramaturgical support and mentoring, and is given the opportunity to attend business seminars. Excerpts of the winning plays are performed at the Theatre's October gala. There is a $15 administrative fee. Send SASE, fax, or e-mail for guidelines.

Available to: African-American playwrights
Deadline: June 1
Apply to: Writers Festival, above address

New Rivers Press
420 North 5th Street, Suite 938
Minneapolis, MN 55401
E-mail: newrivpr@mtn.org
Web site: http://www.mtn.org/~newrivpr
Fax: 612-339-9047

Ⓜ The *Headwaters Literary Competition* offers $500 and publication by New Rivers in the categories of poetry, short fiction, novella, and personal essay/memoir to writers residing in Illinois, Iowa, Michigan, North Dakota, South Dakota, or Wisconsin. Send SASE for further guidelines and application.

Available to: Illinois, Iowa, Michigan, North Dakota, South Dakota, or Wisconsin writers
Deadline: Early September (inquire for exact date)
Apply to: Headwaters Literary Competition, above address

Ⓜ The *Minnesota Voices Project* offers $500 and publication by New Rivers in the categories of poetry, short fiction, novella, and personal essay/memoir. Writers must be Minnesota residents and must not have been published by a commercial house. Send SASE for further guidelines and application.

Available to: Minnesota residents
Deadline: April 1
Apply to: Minnesota Voices Project, above address

New York Foundation for the Arts
155 Avenue of the Americas, 14th floor
New York, NY 10013
Web site: http://www.nyfa.org
Fax: 212-366-1778

Ⓜ *Artists' Fellowships* are granted to individual New York State creative artists, on the basis of the excellence of recent work, submitted as described below. The 2000–2001 cycle is for nonfiction and poetry; the 2001–2002 cycle is for fiction and playwriting/screenwriting. The $7,000 fellowship award may be used however the recipient sees fit. Recipients are required to provide a mutually agreed-upon public service during the grant period.

Applicants for *Fellowships in Fiction* must submit six copies of a portion of a completed manuscript; this may be an excerpt from a novel or collection of short stories, at most 20 double-spaced pages.

Applicants for *Fellowships in Nonfiction* should submit six copies of up to 20 double-spaced pages from a collection of essays, creative writing depicting actual events, biography, autobiography, or other nonfiction.

Applicants for *Fellowships in Playwriting/Screenwriting* should submit six copies of up to 20 pages of a play or film script, and one copy of the entire script.

Applicants for *Fellowships in Poetry* must submit six copies of at least two examples of work, at most 10 pages.

Available to: New York State residents of at least two years, nonstudents, over eighteen years old
Deadline: Mid-October 2000 for poetry and nonfiction; mid-October 2001 for fiction and

playwriting/screenwriting (inquire for exact dates)
Apply to: Artists' Fellowships, above address

New York Mills Arts Retreat
24 North Main Avenue
PO Box 246
New York Mills, MN 56567
E-mail: nymills@uslink.net
Fax: 218-385-3366

® Two- or four-week residences are offered at the New York Mills Arts Retreat in a small, rural Minnesota community. Through the Jerome Foundation, each resident artist is offered a stipend amounting to $750 for two weeks or $1,500 for four. In exchange, retreat residents are asked to work within the community for eight hours a week—teaching in local schools, conducting workshops, or pursuing another creative activity involving the community. Residents are given studio space and their own small retreat house in town. Send SASE for additional information and application.

Available to: U.S. citizen
Deadline: April 1 and October 1
Apply to: Above address

New York Public Library
Fifth Avenue & 42nd Street
New York, NY 10018-2788
Web site: http://www.nypl.org

Ⓙ Ⓝ The *New York Public Library Helen Bernstein Book Award for Excellence in Journalism* annually offers $15,000 to an outstanding journalist "whose book has made an impact on public consciousness, events, or policy." Four finalists receive $1,000 honorable mentions. To be eligible for the award, a book must be an outgrowth of the author's work as a journalist. Publishers, agents, or journalists may nominate books published within the calendar year by submitting five copies (or bound galleys), biographical information about the author, and available reviews. Authors may not nominate their own work. Write or visit the Web site for further details and required nomination form.

Available to: No restrictions
Deadline: October 1
Apply to: Publications Office, New York Public Library, 8 West 40th Street, 6th floor, New York, NY 10018-2788

New York Public Library
Center for Scholars and Writers
Fifth Avenue & 42nd Street
New York, NY 10018-2788
Web site: http://www.nypl.org
Fax: 212-768-7439

The *Scholars and Writers Fellowship Program* annually awards fifteen resident fellowships to scholars, nonacademic research professionals, scientists engaged in the humanities, and creative writers of demonstrated achievement whose proposed work would benefit from access to the rich and diverse collections of the Humanities and Social Science Libraries. Fellows are required to be in continuous residence for the academic year and to participate as much as possible in Center activities including daily lunches, readings, lectures, colloquia, symposia, and conferences, and are responsible for a public presentation of publishable quality. Each fellow receives access to the Library's collections, a private office with computer and Internet access, and a stipend of $50,000. Up to five of the awards are offered jointly by the NYPL and the American Council of Learned Societies; for these joint fellowships, applicants must be U.S. citizens or residents who have had a Ph.D. conferred prior to October 1, 1997. Write or visit the Web site for additional information.

Available to: See above

Deadline: October 1
Apply to: Scholars and Writers Fellowship Program, above address

New York State Archives Partnership Trust
Cultural Education Center, Room 9C49
Albany, NY 12230
E-mail: jrydberg@mail.nysed.gov
Web site: http://www.sara.nysed.gov
Fax: 518-473-7058

The *Larry J. Hackman Research Residency Program* awards funds to pursue research using the holdings of the New York State Archives. The program supports advanced work in New York State history, government, or public policy, with preference given to projects that relate to enduring public policy, particularly in New York State, and that demonstrate a high probability of publication or other public dissemination. Applicants working on doctoral dissertations and those at the postdoctoral level are especially encouraged to apply; any proposal for advanced research will be considered. Award amounts generally are $1,500 to $2,000 a month, but are greater for in-depth research over a substantial period of time. Awards are intended to defray travel, living, and research expenses. Write or visit the Web site for guidelines and application.

Available to: No restrictions
Deadline: Inquire
Apply to: Jill Rydberg, above address

New York State Historical Association
PO Box 800
Cooperstown, NY 13326
Web site: http://www.nysha.org
Fax: 607-547-1405

Ⓝ The *Dixon Ryan Fox Manuscript Prize of the New York State Historical Association*, consisting of $3,000 and assistance in publication, is awarded annually to the best unpublished book-length monograph on an aspect of New York State history, as judged by a special editorial committee.

Available to: No restrictions
Deadline: January 20
Apply to: Wendell Tripp, Director of Publications, above address

New York State Writers Institute
Humanities 355
State University at Albany
Albany, NY 12222
E-mail: writers@uamail.albany.edu
Web site: http://www.albany.edu/writers-inst/

ⒾⓃ The *New York State Edith Wharton Citation of Merit* (State Author) and the *New York State Walt Whitman Citation of Merit* (State Poet) are awarded biennially to a New York State fiction writer and a New York State poet for a lifetime of works of distinction. Winners receive an honorarium of $10,000 and must give two public readings a year. Fiction writers and poets living in New York State are nominated by an advisory panel. There is no application process. *By Internal Nomination Only.*

New York Stories
English Department, E-103
La Guardia Community College
31-10 Thomson Avenue
Long Island City, NY 11101

Ⓕ The *New York Stories Fiction Prize* offers $750 and publication for an unpublished short story not longer than 6,500 words. There is a $15 entry fee. Send SASE for guidelines.

Available to: No restrictions
Deadline: May 31, 2000; inquire for 2001
Apply to: New York Stories Fiction Prize, above address

New York University Press
838 Broadway, 3rd floor
New York, NY 10003-4812
Web site: http://www.nyupress.nyu.edu

(F) (P) The *New York University Press Prize for Fiction* and *Prize for Poetry* offer a $1,000 honorarium and publication by the press for book-length manuscripts of fiction and poetry by authors who have not previously published in book form and by published authors who "remain unrecognized relative to the quality and ambition of their writing." Write or visit the Web site for additional information and guidelines.

Available to: No restrictions
Deadline: Early May (inquire for exact date)
Apply to: NYU Press Prizes (specify genre), above address

The New Yorker
4 Times Square
New York, NY 10036
Web site: http://www.newyorker.com
Fax: 212-286-5028

(IN) *The New Yorker Literary Awards* offer $10,000 each for the best books of poetry, fiction, and nonfiction published in the preceding year. A committee made up of *New Yorker* editors and writers who have not published books in the year under consideration nominate five books each year. *New Yorker* readers select the winner by voting via a prepaid postcard ballot inserted in the magazine, a toll-free telephone number, or an on-line ballot. Awards for the best debut book (fiction or nonfiction) and for lifetime achievement in writing are also given to writers chosen by a panel of senior editors.

New Yorkers Need to Know
PO Box 1942
New York, NY 10021

(J) The *New Yorkers Need to Know Prizes for Journalism* offer two annual prizes of $10,000 each, one for investigative reporting on New York City government and one for investigative reporting on New York City nonprofit institutions. For the next set of prizes, which will be awarded in 2001, articles must have been published in 1999 or 2000. Contact the address above for further information and guidelines.

Available to: No restrictions
Deadline: December 31, 2000
Apply to: Prizes for Journalism, above address

Newberry Library
60 West Walton
Chicago, IL 60610
E-mail: research@newberry.org
Web site: http://www.newberry.org

Long-Term Fellowships are available to postdoctoral scholars, and in some cases, Ph.D. candidates, for periods of six to eleven months. They include the *National Endowment for the Humanities Fellowship;* the *Lloyd Lewis Fellowship in American History;* the *Monticello College Foundation Fellowship for Women,* designed for a woman early in her academic career whose work gives clear promise of scholarly productivity; the *Mellon Postdoctoral Research Fellowship;* and the *Spencer Foundation Fellowship in the History of Education.* Stipends and application procedures vary. Write, e-mail, or visit the Web site for further information and application.

Available to: See above
Deadline: Mid-January (inquire for exact date)
Apply to: Committee on Awards, above address

Short-Term Residential Fellowships in the Humanities are available to scholars, including those at the dissertation stage, who desire a short period of residency to use particular Newberry collections. These include the *Newberry Library/American Antiquarian Society Short-Term Fellowship*; the *American Society for Eighteenth-Century Studies Fellowships*, for scholars wishing to use the Newberry's collections to study the period 1660–1815; the *Frances C. Allen Fellowship* for women of Native American heritage; and the *Arthur Weinberg Fellowship for Independent Scholars* for people working outside the academy who have demonstrated excellence through publishing and are working in a field appropriate to the Newberry's collections. Stipends and application procedures vary. Write, e-mail, or visit the Web site for further information and application.

Available to: No restrictions
Deadline: March 1
Apply to: Committee on Awards, above address

The Center for Renaissance Studies at the Newberry Library offers three types of awards: *Consortium Funds*, for faculty members and graduate students of the Center's member institutions, to participate in a broad range of interdisciplinary and archival programs at the Library or the Folger Institute; the *Audrey Lumsden-Kouvel Fellowship*, carrying a stipend of up to $3,000 for postdoctoral scholars in late medieval or Renaissance studies who wish to carry on research in residence at the Library for three months; and the *Rockefeller Foundation Fellowship in Gender Studies in Early Modern Europe*, for postdoctoral scholars in literature, history, and other humanities fields who will spend ten months in full-time residence at the Library.

Available to: See above
Deadline: March 1
Apply to: Center for Renaissance Studies, above address

The *Newberry–British Academy Fellowship for Study in Great Britain* offers a three-month exchange fellowship for study in Great Britain to scholars in any field in which the Newberry holdings are strong. This postdoctoral award pays £40 per day in Great Britain. Preference is given to readers and staff of the Newberry and to scholars who have used the Library. Write for further information and application.

Available to: Ph.D. scholars
Deadline: Mid-January (inquire for exact date)
Apply to: Newberry–British Academy Fellowship, above address

Newcomen Society in the United States
412 Newcomen Road
Exton, PA 19341

Ⓝ The *Thomas Newcomen Book Award in Business History* is given in cooperation with *Business History Review* to the author of an outstanding book dealing with the history of business in the United States or Canada. One award of $4,000 is granted triennially. It will be awarded next in spring 2001 to the author of a book published in 1998, 1999, or 2000.

Available to: No restrictions
Deadline: Inquire
Apply to: Book Review Editor, Business History Review, Harvard Business School Publishing, 60 Harvard Way, Boston, MA 02163

Newspaper Guild
501 Third Street, NW, 2nd floor
Washington, DC 20001
Web site: http://www.newsguild.org

Ⓙ The *Heywood Broun Award* is given annually for work published or broadcast during the preceding calendar year that embodies "the spirit of Heywood Broun," the newspaper columnist who was the Guild's founder. Eligible are nonmanagerial employees of newspapers, news services, newsmagazines, and radio and television stations in the United States, Canada, and Puerto Rico, whether members of the Guild or not. One award of $5,000 is given annually. Write or visit the Web site for guidelines.

Available to: See above
Deadline: January (inquire for exact date)
Apply to: Broun Award Committee, above address

Nieman Foundation
Harvard University
Walter Lippmann House
One Francis Avenue
Cambridge, MA 02138
E-mail: sgoldstein@harvard.edu
Web site: http://www.nieman.harvard.edu
Fax: 617-495-8976

Ⓙ Ⓡ The *Lucius W. Nieman Fellowships for Journalists* offer working journalists a mid-career opportunity to study and broaden their intellectual horizons in residence at Harvard. Applicants must have at least three years' media experience and must obtain employer consent for a leave of absence for the academic year. Fellows agree to refrain from professional work during that period; to complete all work in at least two academic courses, one each semester; to remain in residence during term time; and to return at the end of the sabbatical year to the employer who granted the leave of absence. Each year fellowships are awarded to some twelve U.S. and ten to twelve international journalists. U.S. journalists receive tuition and a $40,000 stipend for living expenses. Funding arrangements vary for international journalists, who must obtain funding by competing successfully for restricted grants available to the Nieman Foundation, or securing their own financial backing.

Available to: Working journalists
Deadlines: January 31 for U.S. journalists; March 1 for international
Apply to: Program Officer, above address

Nimrod International Journal of Fiction & Poetry
University of Tulsa
600 South College
Tulsa, OK 74104
E-mail: nimrod@utulsa.edu
Web site: http://www.utulsa.edu/nimrod
Fax: 918-631-3033

Ⓕ Ⓟ *Nimrod* sponsors the *Pablo Neruda Prize for Poetry* and the *Katherine Anne Porter Prize for Fiction*, each offering a first prize of $2,000 and a second prize of $1,000. Winners are flown to Tulsa for readings and an awards dinner with the judges. The $20 entry fee covers a subscription to *Nimrod*. Send business-size SASE for guidelines.

Available to: Authors of previously unpublished works
Deadline: Submissions accepted January 1–April 20, 2000 (inquire for 2001)
Apply to: Nimrod Prize Competition, above address

96 Inc.
PO Box 15559
Boston, MA 02215

The *Bruce Rossley Literary Award* of $1,000, named for Boston's first commissioner of the arts and humanities, is presented biennially to a writer of merit by 96 Inc., an artists' collaborative and literary magazine. There are no specific publication requirements for eligibility; anyone may nominate a writer by sending a letter of recommendation and support materials. The writer's accomplishments in teaching and community service will be considered.

Available to: No restrictions
Deadline: Nominations accepted August 1–September 30 in even-numbered years
Apply to: Bruce Rossley Literary Award, above address

Norcroft
32 East 1st Street, Suite 330
Duluth, MN 55802

® Residences of one to four weeks from May through October at a remote lodge on the shores
of Lake Superior are available to feminist women writers whose work demonstrates an
understanding of and commitment to feminist change. Each resident has her own private
bedroom and individual "writing shed." Housing is free; groceries are provided for
residents to do their own cooking. Send SASE for application.

Available to: Feminist writers
Deadline: October 1
Apply to: Above address

North American Conference on British Studies
Department of History
University of Texas
Austin, TX 78712
E-mail: levack@mail.utexas.edu

Ⓝ The *John Ben Snow Foundation Prize* awards $1,000 for the best book published annually on
any topic in British studies before 1800. The *British Council Prize* awards $1,000 for the
best book published annually on any topic in British studies after 1800. Inquire for
submission procedures.

Available to: U.S. or Canadian citizens
Deadline: Submissions accepted January 1–April 1
Apply to: Brian Levack, above address

North Carolina Arts Council
Department of Cultural Resources
Raleigh, NC 27699-4632
E-mail: dmcgill@ncacmail.dcr.state.nc.us
Web site: http://www.ncarts.org
Fax: 919-733-4834

Ⓜ ® Fellowships of $8,000 are available to North Carolina artists in rotating disciplines. Fellowships
in the literary arts (fiction, literary nonfiction, poetry, playwriting, screenwriting, and
translation) will be offered in 2001. The Council also supports residence opportunities
for writers at Headlands Center for the Arts in California, the La Napoule Foundation in
France, and the Vermont Studio Center. Write, e-mail, or visit the Web site for additional
information and guidelines.

Available to: North Carolina residents
Deadline: November 1, 2000, for literature fellowships; inquire for residences
Apply to: Literature Director, above address

North Carolina Writers' Network
Box 954
Carrboro, NC 27510
E-mail: mail@ncwriters.org
Web site: http://www.ncwriters.org
Fax: 919-929-0535

Ⓓ The *Paul Green Playwrights Prize* of $500 is given annually for an unpublished, unproduced
play on any theme (no musicals). Playwrights should submit two copies and a synopsis.
There is a $12 entry fee.

Available to: No restrictions
Deadline: September 30
Apply to: Paul Green Playwrights Prize, North Carolina Writers' Network, 3501 Highway
54 West, Studio C, Chapel Hill, NC 27516

Ⓟ The *Randall Jarrell Poetry Prize* of $1,000 is given annually for an unpublished poem composed in any form or genre. The winner will be published in *Parnassus: Poetry in Review*. Two copies of up to three poems should be submitted, not exceeding a total of 10 single-spaced pages. There is a $10 entry fee.

Available to: No restrictions
Deadline: November 1
Apply to: Randall Jarrell Poetry Prize, North Carolina Writers' Network, 3501 Highway 54 West, Studio C, Chapel Hill, NC 27516

(F) The *Thomas Wolfe Fiction Prize*, of $1,000 with possible publication, is given annually for an unpublished work of fiction. Writers should submit two copies of up to 12 pages (novel excerpt or short story). There is a $7 entry fee.

Available to: No restrictions
Deadline: August 31
Apply to: Thomas Wolfe Fiction Prize, North Carolina Writers' Network, 3501 Highway 54 West, Studio C, Chapel Hill, NC 27516

Northeastern University
English Department
406 Holmes Hall
Boston, MA 02115
Web site: http://www.casdn.neu.edu/~english/morse.htm

(P) The *Samuel French Morse Poetry Prize*, awarded annually for the manuscript of a first or second book of poems by a U.S. poet, consists of publication of the work by Northeastern University Press and a cash award of $1,000. A $15 reading fee must accompany the manuscript. Send SASE or visit the Web site for guidelines.

Available to: U.S. citizens and residents
Deadline: September 15
Apply to: Professor Guy Rotella, Editor, Morse Poetry Prize, above address

Northern Kentucky University
Department of Theatre
Highland Heights, KY 41099-1007
E-mail: forman@nku.edu
Fax: 606-572-6057

(D) The *Year-End-Series New Play Festival* biennially awards four prizes of $400 each, plus production and travel expenses to attend late rehearsals and performance, for unproduced musicals, adaptations, and plays. Preference is given to plays with roles that can be handled by actors eighteen to twenty-five years old. Write for application.

Available to: No restrictions
Deadline: October 31, 2000
Apply to: YES Project Director, above address

Northern Michigan University
Forest Roberts Theatre
1401 Presque Isle
Marquette, MI 49855-5364
E-mail: theater@nmu.edu
Web site: http://www.nmu.edu/theatre

(D) The *Mildred and Albert Panowski Playwriting Award* of $2,000 is given to the author of the best original full-length play, unproduced and unpublished, submitted to the competition. A full production of the winning play will be included in the Forest Roberts Theatre season. The playwright will act as artist-in-residence at the university during the run of the show, with transportation and room and board provided. Send SASE or visit the Web site for guidelines.

Available to: No restrictions
Deadline: Friday before Thanksgiving
Apply to: Panowski Playwriting Contest, above address

Northwood University
Alden B. Dow Creativity Center
3225 Cook Road
Midland, MI 48640-2398
Fax: 517-837-4468
E-mail: creativity@northwood.edu

®   The *Summer Resident Fellowship Program* is open to individuals in all professions who wish to
pursue innovative ideas with potential impact in their fields. Awards for the ten-week
residency include travel to/from Midland, room and board, and a $750 stipend to be
used at the discretion of the recipient. Fellows should be able to work independently and
live cooperatively. No accommodations for spouses/families are available. There is a $10
application fee. Write for additional information and guidelines.

Available to: No restrictions
Deadline: December 31
Apply to: Above address

NORWAY
Nordmanns-Forbundet
Rådhusgaten 23b
N-0158 Oslo
Norway
E-mail: dinatolf@nik.no
Web site: http://www.accn.no/mbr11.htm
Fax: 47-2-242-51-63

Ⓣ   The Nordmanns-Forbundet, in its desire to make Norwegian culture known abroad, awards
an annual grant to one or more publishing houses introducing Norwegian fiction or poetry
(preferably contemporary) in translation.

Available to: U.S. publishing houses
Deadline: Inquire
Apply to: Nordmanns-Forbundet Translation Grant, above address

NORWAY
NORLA—Norwegian Literature Abroad
Bygdoy alle 21
N-0262 Oslo
Norway
E-mail: øirmapost@nbr.no
Web site: http://www.boknett.no/norla
Fax: 47-2-212-25-44

Ⓣ   NORLA offers grants for the translation of Norwegian fiction, poetry, and children's books
into any language. Translators must apply for grants through their publisher, and grants
will be assessed on the basis of the quality of the book and its translation, and the
publisher's ability to market the translation satisfactorily. Contact NORLA for additional
information and application.

Available to: No restrictions
Deadline: December 15
Apply to: Kristin Brudevoll, above address

Nuclear Age Peace Foundation
PMB 121
1187 Coast Village Road, Suite 1
Santa Barbara, CA 93108-2794
E-mail: wagingpeace@napf.org
Web site: http://www.wagingpeace.org
Fax: 805-568-0466

Ⓟ   The *Barbara Mandigo Kelly Peace Poetry Awards* offer $500, publication in *Waging Peace
Worldwide*, the Nuclear Age Peace Foundation journal, and posting on the Nuclear Age

Peace Foundation Web site for a poem that explores and illuminates an aspect of peace and the human spirit. Send two copies of up to three unpublished poems, maximum 40 lines each, along with a $5 entry fee for one poem or $10 for two or three poems. Awards of $250 are offered for a poem by young adults (ages thirteen to eighteen) and children (twelve and under); there is no entry fee for these categories. Send SASE for guidelines.

Available to: No restrictions
Deadline: July 1
Apply to: Peace Poetry Awards, above address

Oberlin College Press
Oberlin College
10 North Professor Street
Oberlin, OH 44074
E-mail: ocpress@oberlin.edu
Web site: http://www.oberlin.edu/~ocpress/

(P) The *Field Poetry Prize* awards a $1,000 honorarium and publication by Oberlin College Press as part of its Field Poetry Series for a manuscript of poems, 50 to 80 pages long. There is a reading fee of $22, which covers a year's subscription to *Field*, a biannual journal of contemporary poetry and poetics. Send SASE or visit the Web site for guidelines.

Available to: No restrictions
Deadline: Submissions accepted in May only
Apply to: Field Poetry Prize, above address

Scott O'Dell Award for Historical Fiction
c/o Zena Sutherland
1700 East 56th Street #3906
Chicago, IL 60637
Fax: 773-702-0775

© The *Scott O'Dell Award for Historical Fiction* offers $5,000 for a distinguished work of historical fiction for children or young adults published in the United States during the calendar year under consideration. The book must be set in the New World (North, Central, or South America).

Available to: U.S. citizens
Deadline: December 31
Apply to: Above address

Oglebay Institute
c/o Stifel Fine Arts Center
1330 National Road
Wheeling, WV 26003

(D) The *Towngate Theatre Playwriting Competition* annually offers a cash prize of $300, production, and partial payment of travel expenses. Authors may submit more than one unproduced nonmusical play; co-authored plays are accepted. Scripts of a serious and thoughtful nature that may not have wide appeal are encouraged.

Available to: No restrictions
Deadline: January 1
Apply to: Towngate Theatre Playwriting Competition, above address

Ohio Arts Council
727 East Main Street
Columbus, OH 43205-1796
E-mail: kemerick@oac.state.oh.us
Web site: http://www.oac.state.oh.us
Fax: 614-466-4494

(M) Fellowships of $5,000 and $10,000 are given annually to Ohio poets, fiction writers, nonfiction writers, playwrights, and critics. Write for guidelines and application.

Available to: Ohio residents at least eighteen years old who are not students
Deadline: September 1
Apply to: Ken Emerick, Coordinator, Individual Artists Fellowship Program, above
address

Ohio State University Press
1070 Carmack Road
Columbus, OH 43210
E-mail: ohiostatepress@osu.edu
Web site: http://www.ohiostatepress.org

(P) The *Ohio State University Press/The Journal Award in Poetry* selects one full-length manuscript each year for a $1,000 cash prize and publication by the Press. Entries must be at least 48 pages; a $20 reading fee is required. Everyone submitting a manuscript and the fee receives a one-year subscription to the *Journal,* the literary magazine of Ohio State University.

Available to: No restrictions
Deadline: Submissions accepted in September only
Apply to: David Citino, Poetry Editor, above address

(F) The *Sandstone Prize in Short Fiction* annually awards $1,500 and publication by the Press under a standard book contract for a collection of short fiction. The winner is invited to direct a workshop and to give a paid reading at OSU. Writers should submit a book-length collection (150 to 300 manuscript pages) of short stories, a novella (not exceeding 125 pages), or a combination. There is a $20 entry fee. Send SASE or visit the web site for guidelines.

Available to: No restrictions
Deadline: Submissions accepted in January only
Apply to: Bill Roorbach, Fiction Editor, above address

Ohio University Press
Scott Quadrangle
Athens, OH 45701
Web site: http://www.ohiou.edu/oupress/
Fax: 740-593-4536

(P) The *Hollis Summers Poetry Prize,* named after a poet who taught at Ohio University, annually awards $500 and publication by the Press for an unpublished poetry manuscript. The contest is open to all poets, regardless of previous publication. Submit poetry manuscripts of 60 to 95 pages and a $15 entry fee. Write for complete guidelines.

Available to: No restrictions
Deadline: October 31
Apply to: Hollis Summers Poetry Prize, above address

Ohioana Library Association
65 South Front Street, Suite 1105
Columbus, OH 43215-4163
E-mail: ohioana@winslo.ohio.gov
Web site: http://www.oplin.lib.oh.us/OHIOANA
Fax: 614-728-6974

The *Walter Rumsey Marvin Grant* of $1,000 is given annually to an unpublished writer under age thirty. Up to six pieces of prose may be submitted.

Available to: Ohio natives or residents for at least five years
Deadline: January 31
Apply to: Walter Rumsey Marvin Grant, above address

(C) The *Ohioana Award for Children's Literature/Alice Wood Memorial Award* of $1,000 is given to an author whose body of published work has made a significant contribution to literature for children or young adults.

Available to: Ohio natives or residents for at least five years

Deadline: December 31
Apply to: Alice Wood Memorial Award, above address

Ⓟ The *Ohioana Poetry Award/Helen and Laura Krout Memorial Award* of $1,000 is given to a poet whose body of published work has contributed significantly to poetry, and through whose writing, teaching, administrating, or community service other people's interest in poetry has developed.

Available to: Ohio natives or residents for at least five years
Deadline: December 31
Apply to: Ohioana Poetry Award, above address

Omicron World Entertainment
32 Alfred Street, Suite A
New Haven, CT 06512
E-mail: newcenturywriter@yahoo.com
Web site: http://www.newcenturywriter.org
Fax: 203-468-0333

Ⓜ The *New Century Writer Awards* offer a first prize of $3,000, a second of $1,000, and a third of $500 for short stories and novels, and a first prize of $5,000, a second of $2,000, and a third of $1,000 for screenplays and stage plays. The awards provide a new and valuable outlet to recognize and develop screenplays, stage plays, and fiction by undiscovered writers, and to connect these new writers with publishers, producers, and agents. The best work in each genre will be forwarded to such interested parties as AMH Entertainment and *Zoetrope: All Story,* and one of the top three screenplays or stage plays will be given a staged reading at Film Fest New Haven, where the awards are presented each April. The entry fee is $30 for each screenplay, stage play, novel excerpt, or group of up to three short stories. Write, e-mail, or visit the Web site for additional information and application.

Available to: No restrictions
Deadline: January 31
Apply to: New Century Writer Awards, above address

Omohundro Institute of Early American History and Culture
Box 8781
Williamsburg, VA 23185-8781
E-mail: mkburd@facstaff.wm.edu
Fax: 757-221-1047

Ⓝ The *Jamestown Prize* of $3,000 plus publication is offered annually for the best book-length scholarly manuscript on early American history or culture before 1815, or on the related history of the British Isles, Europe, West Africa, or the Caribbean during the same period. The competition is open only to authors who have not published a book.

Available to: See above
Deadline: None
Apply to: Editor of Publications, above address

Eugene O'Neill Theatre Center
234 West 44th Street, Suite 901
New York, NY 10036

Ⓓ The *National Playwrights Conference* offers staged readings at the Eugene O'Neill Theatre Center in Waterford, Connecticut, of nine to twelve original stage plays. The authors of the selected plays receive a stipend, transportation to and from the Conference, plus room and board. Attendance for the duration of the Conference, held in July, is required. Send SASE for guidelines in August.

Available to: U.S. citizens or permanent residents
Deadline: November 15
Apply to: National Playwrights Conference, Mary F. McCabe, Managing Director, above address

Oregon Arts Commission
775 Summer Street NE
Salem, OR 97310
E-mail: oregon.artscomm@state.or.us
Web site: http://art.econ.state.or.us
Fax: 503-986-0260

(M) *Individual Artists Fellowships* of $3,000 are available to Oregon residents in fiction, nonfiction, poetry, and playwriting. Write for application.

> Available to: Oregon residents
> Deadline: September 1
> Apply to: Individual Artists Fellowship Program, above address

Organization of American Historians
112 North Bryan Street
Bloomington, IN 47408-4199
Web site: http://www.indiana.edu/~oah

The organization sponsors or co-sponsors the following awards and prizes given in recognition of scholarly and professional achievements in American history:

(N) The *ABC-Clio America: History and Life Award* of $750, given biennially to recognize and encourage scholarship in American history in journal literature that advances new perspectives on accepted interpretations or previously unconsidered topics.

> Available to: No restrictions
> Deadline: November 15 of even-numbered years
> Apply to: ABC-Clio America: History and Life Award, above address

(N) The *Ray Allen Billington Prize* of $1,000, given biennially to the author of a book on American frontier history, defined broadly so as to include the pioneer periods of all geographical areas and comparisons between American frontiers and others.

> Available to: No restrictions
> Deadline: October 1 of even-numbered years
> Apply to: Ray Allen Billington Prize, above address

(N) The *Binkley-Stephenson Award* of $500, given for the best scholarly article published in *Journal of American History* during the preceding calendar year.

> Available to: Contributors to *Journal of American History*
> Deadline: December 31
> Apply to: Journal of American History, above address

(N) The *Avery O. Craven Award* of $500, given annually for the most original book on the coming of the Civil War, the Civil War years, or the era of Reconstruction, with the exception of works of purely military history. The exception recognizes and reflects the Quaker convictions of Craven.

> Available to: No restrictions
> Deadline: October 1
> Apply to: Avery O. Craven Award, above address

(N) The *Merle Curti Award* of $1,000, given to a book on American intellectual history in odd-numbered years and to one on American social history in even-numbered years; books must have been published during the preceding two years.

> Available to: No restrictions
> Deadline: October 1
> Apply to: Merle Curti Award, above address

(N) The *Ellis W. Hawley Prize* of $500, given annually for the best book-length historical study of the political economy, politics, or institutions of the United States, in its domestic or international affairs, from the Civil War to the present.

> Available to: No restrictions

Deadline: October 1
Apply to: Ellis W. Hawley Prize, above address

The *Huggins-Quarles Awards*, given annually to minority graduate students in American history at the dissertation research stage of their Ph.D. programs. Amounts vary but do not exceed $1,000.

Available to: Minority doctorate students
Deadline: Inquire (generally early January)
Apply to: Huggins-Quarles Awards, above address

Ⓝ The *Richard W. Leopold Prize* of $1,500, given biennially for the best book written by a historian connected with federal, state, or municipal government, in the areas of foreign policy, military affairs broadly construed, or the historical activities of the federal government, or in biography in one of the foregoing areas. The winner must have been employed in a government position for at least five years, and the publisher should include verification of this fact when a book is submitted.

Available to: See above
Deadline: September 1 of odd-numbered years
Apply to: Richard W. Leopold Prize, above address

The *Lerner-Scott Prize* of $1,000 and a certificate, given annually for the best doctoral dissertation in U.S. women's history completed during the previous academic year (July 1–June 30).

Available to: Doctoral candidates
Deadline: November 1
Apply to: Lerner-Scott Prize, above address

Ⓝ The *Horace Samuel & Marion Galbraith Merrill Travel Grants in Twentieth-Century American Political History*, which promote access of younger scholars to the Washington, D.C., region's rich primary- source collections in late-nineteenth- and twentieth-century American political history. The program offers stipends to underwrite travel and lodging expenses for members of the Organization of American Historians who are working toward completion of a dissertation or first book. Grants range from $500 to $3,000.

Available to: See above
Deadline: January (inquire for exact date)
Apply to: Horace Samuel & Marion Galbraith Merrill Travel Grants, above address

Ⓝ The *Louis Pelzer Memorial Award*, given annually for the best essay (up to 7,000 words) about any topic or period of U.S. history written by a graduate student in any field. The award includes publication of the essay in *Journal of American History*, a medal, and a prize of $500.

Available to: Graduate students
Deadline: November 30
Apply to: Louis Pelzer Memorial Award, Journal of American History, 1125 East Atwater, Indiana University, Bloomington, IN 47401

Ⓝ The *James A. Rawley Prize* of $750, given annually for a book dealing with the history of race relations in the United States.

Available to: No restrictions
Deadline: October 1
Apply to: James A. Rawley Prize, above address

Ⓝ The *Elliott Rudwick Prize* of $2,000 and a certificate, given biennially for a book on the experience of racial and ethnic minorities in the United States. Books on interactions between two or more minority groups, or comparing the experience of two or more groups are especially welcomed.

Available to: No restrictions
Deadline: September 1 of even-numbered years
Apply to: Elliott Rudwick Prize, above address

Ⓝ The *Frederick Jackson Turner Award* of $1,000, given annually for an author's first book on a significant phase of American history. Write for specific rules.

    Available to: No restrictions
    Deadline: September 1
    Apply to: Frederick Jackson Turner Award, above address

Orion Society
195 Main Street
Great Barrington, MA 01230
E-mail: orion@orionsociety.org
Web site: http://www.orionsociety.org

Ⓘ The *John Hay Award* annually offers $3,000 to a person who "has succeeded in two of the three following categories: writing that addresses the relationship between people and nature, environmental education, and conservation." There is no application process. *By Internal Nomination Only.*

Overseas Press Club of America
40 West 45th Street
New York, NY 10036
Web site: opcofamerica.org

The Overseas Press Club annually offers nineteen awards for newspaper, magazine, wire service, radio, television, cartoon, book, and photographic reporting from abroad. Work must be published or broadcast by a U.S.-based publication during the calendar year. Each award offers a $1,000 cash prize; each submission must be accompanied by a $100 entry fee. The following are awards for print journalists:

Ⓙ The *Whitman Bassow Award*, sponsored by AT&T, for the best reporting, in any medium, on international environmental issues.

Ⓙ The *Robert Spiers Benjamin Award*, sponsored by the Robert S. Benjamin Fund, for the best reporting in any medium on Latin America.

Ⓙ The *Hal Boyle Award*, sponsored by AT&T, for the best daily newspaper or wire service reporting from abroad.

Ⓙ The *Bob Considine Award*, sponsored by King Features Syndicate, for the best daily newspaper or wire service interpretation of foreign affairs.

Ⓙ The *Ed Cunningham Memorial Award*, sponsored by Lexis-Nexis, for the best magazine reporting from abroad.

Ⓙ The *Joe and Laurie Dine Award*, for the best reporting in a print medium dealing with human rights.

Ⓙ The *Malcolm Forbes Award*, sponsored by *Forbes* magazine, for the best business reporting from abroad in a newspaper or wire service.

Ⓙ The *Morton Frank Award*, for the best business reporting from abroad in magazines.

Ⓙ The *Madeline Dane Ross Award*, for international reporting, in any medium, showing a concern for the human condition.

Ⓙ The *Cornelius Ryan Award*, sponsored by the Carol Mann Agency, for the best nonfiction book on foreign affairs.

    Available to: No restrictions
    Deadline: January 31
    Apply to: Sonya Fry, Executive Director, above address

Paintbrush
Truman State University
MC335
Kirksville, MO 63501
Web site: http://www.paintbrush.org

(P) The *Ezra Pound Poetry Award* annually offers $2,000 and publication of a 32-page collection of poetry in *Paintbrush: A Journal of Poetry and Translation*. The award is given in honor of Pound's contribution to modern poetry and to modernism as a whole. Send SASE or visit the Web site for additional information and guidelines.

Available to: No restrictions
Deadline: October 30
Apply to: Ezra Pound Poetry Award, above address

The Paris Review
541 East 72nd Street
New York, NY 10021

(F) The *Aga Khan Prize for Fiction* is awarded annually by the editors of *The Paris Review* for the best previously unpublished short story (1,000 to 10,000 words). Translations are acceptable and should be accompanied by a copy of the original text. The winner receives $1,000 in addition to publication in the *Review*. One submission per envelope; SASE is required for a response or the return of a manuscript.

Available to: No restrictions
Deadline: Ongoing
Apply to: Aga Khan Prize for Fiction, above address

(P) The *Bernard F. Conners Prize for Poetry* is awarded annually for the best previously unpublished long poem (more than 200 lines). The winner receives $1,000 plus publication. One submission per envelope; SASE is required for a response or the return of a manuscript.

Available to: No restrictions
Deadline: Ongoing
Apply to: Bernard F. Conners Prize for Poetry, above address

Passager
School of Communications Design
University of Baltimore
1420 North Charles Street
Baltimore, MD 21201

(P) The *Passager Poetry Contest* awards a cash prize ($500 in 1999) and publication in *Passager: A Journal of Remembrance and Discovery* for an original poem or group of poems by a writer over age fifty. *Passager* is a quarterly journal of poetry, fiction, essays, and interviews that promotes the writing of older writers. Poets may submit up to five poems of not more than 30 lines each, along with a $10 reading fee; the fee is waived with a new $18 subscription to the journal. Write for guidelines.

Available to: Writers over age fifty
Deadline: June 15
Apply to: Poetry Contest, above address

Passages North
Department of English
Northern Michigan University
1401 Presque Isle Avenue
Marquette, MI 49855

(P) The *Elinor Benedict Poetry Prize* biennially awards $500 for an unpublished poem. Two poems may be submitted with an entry fee of $4 each; for additional poems, $3 each. All entries will be considered for publication. Send SASE for guidelines.

Available to: No restrictions
Deadline: Inquire
Apply to: Elinor Benedict Poetry Prize, above address

Passaic County Community College
Poetry Center
One College Boulevard
Paterson, NJ 07509-1179
E-mail: mgillan@pccc.cc.nj.us
Web site: http://www.pccc.cc.nj.us/poetry
Fax: 973-684-5843

Ⓟ The *Allen Ginsberg Poetry Award* offers a first prize of $1,000 for an original unpublished poem. Applicants may submit up to three poems, not exceeding 10 pages. Send SASE for guidelines.

Available to: No restrictions
Deadline: March 31
Apply to: Allen Ginsberg Poetry Award, above address

Ⓕ The *Paterson Fiction Prize* awards $500 for the novel or collection of short fiction that, in the opinion of the judges, is the strongest work published in the preceding year. The winning writer will participate in an awards ceremony and give a public reading as part of the Meet-the-Authors Series at the college. Publishers should submit three copies of each book, along with an application form. Send SASE for application.

Available to: No restrictions
Deadline: April 1
Apply to: Maria Mazziotti Gillan, Director, above address

Ⓟ The *Paterson Poetry Prize* offers $1,000 for a book of poetry published in the preceding year. The poet will be asked to participate in an awards ceremony and to give a reading at the Poetry Center. Books must be at least 48 pages in length, with a minimum press run of 500 copies. Publishers should submit three copies of each book, along with an application form. Send SASE for application.

Available to: No restrictions
Deadline: February 1
Apply to: Paterson Poetry Prize, above address

Ⓒ The *Paterson Prize for Books for Young People* offers a $500 award in each of three categories: pre-K through grade 3, grades 4 to 6, and grades 7 to 12. For each category, one book will be selected that, in the opinion of the judges, is the most outstanding book for young people published in the preceding year. Publishers should submit three copies of each book, along with an application form. Send SASE for application.

Available to: No restrictions
Deadline: March 15
Apply to: Maria Mazziotti Gillan, Director, above address

Alicia Patterson Foundation
1730 Pennsylvania Avenue, NW, Suite 850
Washington, DC 20006
E-mail: execdirector@aliciapatterson.org
Web site: http://www.aliciapatterson.org

Ⓙ Five to seven *APF Fellowships* are given yearly to working print journalists who wish to pursue independent projects of significant interest and write articles based on their investigation for *The APF Reporter*. Each fellowship is for one year and carries a stipend of $35,000. Applicants must be U.S. citizens who are full-time print journalists or, if not U.S. citizens, must work full-time for U.S. print publications, either in America or abroad. Write, e-mail, or visit the Web site for additional information and application.

Available to: See above
Deadline: October 1
Apply to: APF Fellowship Program, above address

Pavement Saw Press
PO Box 6291
Columbus, OH 43206
E-mail: baratier@megsinet.net

(P) The *Pavement Saw Press Transcontinental Poetry Award* offers $1,000 and publication by the Press for a full-length book of poetry. There is a $15 entry fee. Send SASE or e-mail for guidelines.

Available to: No restrictions
Deadline: Inquire
Apply to: Transcontinental Poetry Award, above address

Pearl Editions
3030 East Second Street
Long Beach, CA 90803

(P) The *Pearl Poetry Prize* annually awards $1,000 and book publication for an original poetry manuscript, 48 to 64 pages in length. A $20 entry fee covers a copy of the winning book. The winning author will receive 25 copies. Send SASE for guidelines.

Available to: No restrictions
Deadline: Submissions accepted May 1–July 1
Apply to: Pearl Poetry Prize, above address

PeaceWriting
2582 Jimmie
Fayetteville, AR 72703-3420
E-mail: jbennet@comp.uark.edu

(M) The *PeaceWriting International Writing Awards* are given for unpublished book-length manuscripts about the causes, consequences, and solutions to violence and war, and about the ideas and practices of nonviolent peacemaking and the lives of nonviolent peacemakers. A prize of $500 is given in each of three categories: nonfiction (history, biography, political science, international law, etc.), imaginative work (novel, short stories, poems, play), and work for young people (nonfiction or imaginative). Send SASE or e-mail for guidelines.

Available to: No restrictions
Deadline: December 1
Apply to: International Writing Awards, above address

PEN American Center
568 Broadway
New York, NY 10012-3225
E-mail: jm@pen.org
Web site: http://www.pen.org
Fax: 212-334-2181

(T) The *Gregory Kolovakos Award* of $2,000 is given triennially to an American literary translator, editor, or critic whose work honors the richness of Hispanic literature and expands its English-language audience. The award's primary purpose is to recognize work from Spanish, but contributions from other languages of the Hispanic world are accepted. Candidates are considered for individual works as well as for collections of criticism or distinguished careers as translators or editors. Candidates may not nominate themselves. A letter of nomination must be received from the candidate's editor or a colleague, with the candidate's vita. As the award honors a sustained contribution over time to Latin American literatures in English translation, nominating letters should not focus exclusively on a single work, but rather document the candidate's qualifications with particular attention to the depth and vision of the work.

Available to: No restrictions
Deadline: January 2, 2001
Apply to: Gregory Kolovakos Award, above address

Ⓝ The *PEN/Martha Albrand Award for the Art of the Memoir* of $1,000 is given to an American author for a first published memoir, distinguished by qualities of literary and stylistic excellence. Eligible books must have been published in the calendar year under consideration. Authors may have published books in another literary genre, but the work submitted for this prize must be their first published memoir. Books submitted for this award may not be submitted for the PEN/Martha Albrand Award for First Nonfiction. There is no application form; three copies of the book should be submitted.

Available to: U.S. citizens or permanent residents
Deadline: December 15
Apply to: PEN/Martha Albrand Award for the Art of the Memoir, above address

Ⓝ The *PEN/Martha Albrand Award for First Nonfiction* of $1,000 is given annually for a U.S. writer's first published book of general nonfiction, distinguished by literary and stylistic excellence. Eligible books must have been published in the calendar year under consideration. There is no restriction on content, but nonliterary texts (how-to guides, inspirational tracts, craft and exercise manuals) are not considered. Memoirs should be submitted for the PEN/Martha Albrand Award for the Art of the Memoir. There is no application form; three copies of each title should be submitted.

Available to: U.S. citizens or permanent residents
Deadline: December 15
Apply to: PEN/Martha Albrand Award for First Nonfiction, above address

Ⓝ The *PEN/Architectural Digest Award for Literary Writing on the Visual Arts* of $10,000 is given annually to an American writer of an outstanding book of criticism or commentary on one or more of the visual arts, including architecture, interior design, landscape studies, painting, photography, and sculpture. Eligible books must have been published in the United States in the calendar year under consideration. There is no application form; three copies of the book should be submitted.

Available to: U.S. citizens or permanent residents
Deadline: December 15
Apply to: PEN/Architectural Digest Award, above address

Ⓣ The *PEN Award for Poetry in Translation* of $3,000 is given for a book-length translation of poetry from any language into English published in the United States during the current calendar year. Translators may be of any nationality. Submission of a book for this award does not preclude simultaneous submission for the PEN/Book-of-the-Month Club Translation Prize. There is no application form; two copies of the eligible book should be submitted.

Available to: No restrictions
Deadline: December 15
Apply to: PEN Award for Poetry in Translation, above address

Ⓣ The *PEN/Book-of-the-Month Club Translation Prize*, sponsored by Book-of-the-Month Club, is awarded for the best book-length translation into English from any language published in the United States during the current calendar year. Technical, scientific, and reference works are not eligible. One prize of $3,000 is awarded annually. There is no application form; three copies of the eligible book should be submitted.

Available to: No restrictions
Deadline: December 15
Apply to: PEN/Book-of-the-Month-Club Translation Prize, above address

Ⓝ The *PEN/Jerard Fund Award* of $4,000 is awarded biennially for a book-length work-in-progress of general nonfiction, marked by high literary quality, by a woman writer early in her career. There are no restrictions on the content; emphasis is on the quality of the writing and the literary character of the subject. How-to manuals, cookery or craft books, vocational guides, and the like are not considered. Applicants should submit two copies of no more than 50 pages of the work-in-progress, accompanied by a list of publications.

Available to: Women U.S. residents who have published at least one article in a national magazine or major literary magazine, and who have published no more than one book of any kind

Deadline: January 2, 2001 (manuscripts not accepted before September 1, 2000)
Apply to: PEN/Jerard Fund Award, above address

©   The *PEN/Norma Klein Award* of $3,000 is given biennially to recognize an emerging voice of literary merit among American writers of children's fiction. Candidates are new authors whose books (for elementary school to young adult readers) demonstrate the adventuresome, innovative spirit that characterizes the best children's literature and Norma Klein's own work (books need not resemble hers stylistically). Candidates may not nominate themselves. Nominations are welcomed from authors and editors of children's books, and should include a list of the candidate's publications.

Available to: No restrictions
Deadline: December 15, 2000
Apply to: PEN/Norma Klein Award, above address

[IN]   The *PEN/Nabokov Award* of $20,000 recognizes a living author whose body of work, either written in or translated into English, represents achievement in a variety of literary genres and is of enduring originality and consummate craftsmanship. Honorees will be writers, principally novelists, whose works evoke Nabokov's brilliant versatility and commitment to literature as a search for the deepest truth and the highest pleasure—what he called the "indescribable tingle of the spine." Only authors who have published a book in the United States within the past two years will be considered. In light of the importance of translation in international letters, translators will also receive due recognition when the award is given to an author writing in a language other than English. The manner of acknowledging translators will be determined in consultation with the judges and will include a stipend and/or special mention in the award citation. There is no application process. *By Internal Nomination Only.*

Ⓕ ©   The *PEN/Naylor Working Writer Fellowship* of $5,000 is offered annually to a fiction writer in financial need who has published at least two, but no more than three, novels during the past ten years that were well reviewed and received by literary critics but were not widely recognized by the reading public. Candidates must be nominated by an editor or a fellow writer, who should submit a list of the candidate's published work (accompanied by copies of reviews, where possible), a description of the candidate's financial resources and needs, and three copies of up to fifty pages of the candidate's current work-in-progress. In odd-numbered years the fellowship will be given to a writer of adult fiction; in even-numbered years to a writers of children's or young adult fiction. Send SASE, e-mail, or visit the Web site for additional information.

Available to: See above
Deadline: January 2
Apply to: PEN/Naylor Working Writer Fellowship, above address

Ⓟ   The *PEN/Joyce Osterweil Award for Poetry* of $5,000 is given in odd-numbered years to a new and emerging American poet of any age whose published work to date is marked by a high literary character and the promise of further literary achievement. Candidates must be nominated by a PEN member, and must have published no more than one book of poetry. Letters of nomination should describe the literary character of the candidate's work, summarize the candidate's publications to date, and articulate the degree of promise indicated by the candidate's work.

Available to: See above
Deadline: January 2, 2001
Apply to: PEN/Joyce Osterweil Award for Poetry, above address

Ⓓ   The *PEN/Laura Pels Foundation Awards for Drama* are given to playwrights working indisputably at the highest level of achievement. Two U.S. playwrights will be selected annually: a medal will be presented to a master American dramatist, in recognition of his or her body of work; and a cash prize of $5,000 will be given to an American playwright in mid-career whose literary achievements are apparent in the rich and striking language of his or her work. Candidates for the mid-career award must write in English and must have had a professional production of two or more full-length works mounted in a theater of at least 299 seats and contracted specifically for either limited or open runs. Nominations are not accepted for the medal to a senior playwright. Nominations are accepted for the mid-career award, from producers, agents, critics, or other playwrights, who should write a letter of support, describing the literary character of the candidate's work, and submit a list of the candidate's produced plays. Do not send scripts.

Available to: U.S. playwrights
Deadline: Early January (inquire for exact date)
Apply to: PEN/Laura Pels Foundation Awards for Drama, above address

Ⓝ The *PEN/Spielvogel-Diamonstein Award for the Art of the Essay* of $5,000 is given for a distinguished book of previously uncollected essays on any subject by an American writer published in the calendar year under consideration. Individual essays included in books submitted may have appeared previously in magazines, journals, or anthologies, but must not have been published collectively in book form. There are no restrictions on subject matter; books are judged solely on the basis of literary character and distinction of writing, and equal consideration is given to the work of renowned essayists and more recently established writers. Essays may deal with a range of subjects or may explore one theme; the book should be a series of individual essays, not a single book-length work of nonfiction. There is no application form; four copies of each title should be submitted.

Available to: U.S. citizens or permanent residents
Deadline: December 15
Apply to: PEN/Spielvogel-Diamonstein Award, above address

Ⓟ The *PEN/Voelcker Award for Poetry* of $5,000 is given in even-numbered years to an American poet whose distinguished and growing body of work to date represents a notable and accomplished presence in American literature. Candidates may be nominated only by members of PEN. All letters of nomination should describe the scope and literary caliber of the candidate's work, summarize the candidate's publications, and articulate the degree of accomplishment the candidate has attained and the esteem in which his or her work is held within the American literary community.

Available to: U.S. poets
Deadline: January 2, 2002
Apply to: PEN/Voelcker Award for Poetry, above address

The *PEN Writers Fund* helps established writers in financial emergencies. Grants and loans—maximum $1,000—are given periodically. The *PEN Fund for Writers and Editors with AIDS* is administered under the Writers Fund and gives grants ranging from $500 to $1,000. Applications are reviewed every six to eight weeks.

Available to: U.S. residents
Deadline: None
Apply to: Writers Fund, above address

Ⓣ The *Renato Poggioli Translation Award* of $3,000 is given annually to encourage a promising beginning translator working on his or her first book-length translation from Italian into English. Letters of application should be accompanied by a vita describing the candidate's Italian studies, a statement of purpose, and a sample of the translation-in-progress (with the original Italian text) not exceeding 50 pages. It is preferable, though not necessary, that the candidate spend the award money in Italy.

Available to: No restrictions
Deadline: January 2
Apply to: Renato Poggioli Translation Award, above address

PEN Center USA West
672 South Lafayette Park Place, Suite 41
Los Angeles, CA 90057
Web site: http://www.pen-usa-west.org
Fax: 213-365-9616

Ⓜ *PEN Center USA West Literary Awards* recognize outstanding works published or produced by writers who live in the western United States. Cash prizes of $1,000 are given in the categories of fiction, creative nonfiction, research nonfiction, poetry, children's literature, translation, journalism, drama, screenplay, and teleplay. Winners are honored at an annual literary festival in Los Angeles. Submit four copies of each title, completed entry form, and $20 entry fee for book categories; non-book categories have no entry fee. Send SASE or visit the Web site for entry form.

Available to: Writers living west of the Mississippi River
Deadline: December 31, 2000 for book awards; January 31, 2001 for script awards
Apply to: Literary Awards, above address

PEN New England
PO Box 725
North Cambridge, MA 02140
Web site: www.pen-ne.org

Ⓕ The *Hemingway Foundation/PEN Award* of $7,500 is given annually to recognize distinguished first books of fiction by American writers. Only works published in the United States by an established house during the current calendar year will be considered. Genre fiction will not be included unless the commercial character of the work is deemed secondary to its overall literary purpose and quality. Eligible titles may be submitted by publishers, agents, or the authors themselves. Authors are not disqualified by the previous publication of nonfiction, poetry, drama, or books for children. One copy of the book should be mailed directly to each of the judges. Write for list of judges' names and addresses, and required form.

Available to: U.S. citizens or permanent residents
Deadline: December 15
Apply to: Above address

Ⓕ The *L. L. Winship/PEN New England Award*, sponsored by PEN New England and *The Boston Globe*, is given for the best book published in the calendar year preceding the deadline, with a New England topic or setting, and/or by an author whose principal residence is New England. Children's books and anthologies are not eligible. One award of $3,000 is available annually. Publishers should submit one copy of each eligible title to each of the five judges. Write for list of judges' names and addresses, and required form.

Available to: See above
Deadline: December 1
Apply to: Above address

PEN Northwest
23030 West Sheffler Road
Elmira, OR 97437

Ⓡ The *Margery Davis Boyden Writing Residency* offers a six-to-seven-month term in the wilderness of southern Oregon from April through October. The residency includes a house and a stipend of $1,200, with the resident providing an hour a day of routine caretaking. Interested writers may apply with their spouse or partner. There is a $10 entry fee. Send SASE for guidelines.

Available to: No restrictions
Deadline: February 28
Apply to: Margery Davis Boyden Writing Residency, above address

PEN/Faulkner Foundation
c/o Folger Shakespeare Library
201 East Capitol Street, SE
Washington, DC 20003
E-mail: delaney@folger.edu
Web site: http://www.penfaulkner.org

Ⓕ The *PEN/Faulkner Award for Fiction* of $15,000 is given annually to the most distinguished work of fiction by an American writer published in the United States in the calendar year preceding that of the award. Four nominees each receive $5,000. Publishers of book-length works of fiction (novels or short story collections; no juvenile titles), as well as authors and agents, are invited to submit four copies of each eligible title. No forms are needed.

Available to: U.S. citizens
Deadline: October 31
Apply to: PEN/Faulkner Award for Fiction, above address

[IN] The *PEN/Malamud Award for Excellence in Short Fiction* annually awards $2,000 to an author who has demonstrated long-term excellence in short fiction. Winners are chosen by a committee of PEN/Faulkner board members and Malamud's literary executors. There is no application process. *By Internal Nomination Only.*

Peninsula Community Foundation
1700 South El Camino Real, Suite 300
San Mateo, CA 94402-3042
E-mail: richard@pcf.org
Web site: http://www.pcf.org
Fax: 650-358-9817

Ⓜ The *Individual Artists Grant Program* offers support to artists living and working in San Mateo and northern Santa Clara counties in California. Grants of up to $1,000 are awarded twice annually, in January and July. Grantees are required to match the grant dollar for dollar. All media are eligible, including visual, performing, literary, and horticultural arts. Write, e-mail, or visit the Web site for additional information and application.

Available to: Residents of San Mateo and northern Santa Clara counties for the last two years, at least nineteen years of age
Deadline: Inquire
Apply to: Individual Artists Grant Program, above address

Pennsylvania Council on the Arts
Room 216, Finance Building
Harrisburg, PA 17120
E-mail: csavage@state.pa.us
Web site: http://www.artsnet.org/pca
Fax: 717-787-6883

Ⓜ The Pennsylvania Council on the Arts supports outstanding Pennsylvania artists by annually awarding fellowships of $5,000 to $10,000. Fellowships are awarded in prose (fiction and creative nonfiction) and poetry in alternate years. Applicants must have established careers as writers. Write, e-mail, or visit the Web site for guidelines and application.

Available to: Pennsylvania residents; no students
Deadline: August 1, 2000, for prose; August 1, 2001, for poetry
Apply to: Fellowship Partner, above address

Penumbra Theatre Company
270 North Kent Street
St. Paul, MN 55102-1794
Fax: 651-224-7074

Ⓓ The *Cornerstone Dramaturgy and Development Project* is intended to nurture the development of new and emerging playwrights who address the African-American and/or Pan-African experience. On the basis of artistic merit of submissions, one playwright a year is offered a main-stage production with a possible three-to-four-week residence, and one playwright is offered a four-week workshop-residence culminating in a staged reading. Financial assistance varies according to the need of playwright and project. Write for additional information.

Available to: No restrictions
Deadline: Ongoing
Apply to: Cornerstone Dramaturgy and Development Project, above address

Pew Center for Civic Journalism
1101 Connecticut Avenue, NW, Suite 420
Washington, DC 20036-4303
E-mail: news@pccj.org
Web site: http://www.pewcenter.org
Fax: 202-347-6440

Ⓙ The *James K. Batten Award for Excellence in Civic Journalism* of $25,000 is given for print or broadcast news reports, series, or accumulated bodies of work published or aired during the calendar year that support public involvement in the life of the community. Print submissions must be accompanied by a nominating letter from an editor or reporter describing the projects and the techniques used. Write, e-mail, or visit the Web site for guidelines and application form.

Available to: No restrictions
Deadline: Mid-February (inquire for exact date)
Apply to: Batten Award, above address

Pew Fellowships in the Arts
The University of the Arts
230 South Broad Street, Suite 1003
Philadelphia, PA 19102
Web site: http://www.pewarts.org
Fax: 215-875-2276

Ⓜ The *Pew Fellowships in the Arts* provide financial support to artists so that they may have the opportunity to dedicate themselves wholly to the development of their artwork for up to two years. Applicants must be residents of Bucks, Chester, Delaware, Montgomery, or Philadelphia counties in Pennsylvania, who are twenty-five years of age or older. Up to twelve fellowships of $50,000 each are awarded annually in three fields, which vary year by year. Write or visit the Web site for additional information and guidelines.

Available to: See above
Deadline: December (inquire for exact date)
Apply to: Above address

Phi Beta Kappa
17 Massachusetts Avenue, NW, 4th floor
Washington, DC 20036
E-mail: lsurles@pbk.org
Fax: 202-986-1601

Ⓝ The *Ralph Waldo Emerson Award* of $2,500 is given annually for an outstanding interpretation of the intellectual and cultural condition of man, published in the United States during the year preceding the submission deadline. Studies in history, religion, philosophy, sociology, anthropology, political science, and related fields are eligible. Submissions must be made by publishers.

Available to: U.S. citizens or residents
Deadline: April 30
Apply to: Ralph Waldo Emerson Award, above address

Ⓝ The *Christian Gauss Award* of $2,500 is given annually for an outstanding book of literary scholarship or criticism published in the United States during the year preceding the submission deadline. Submissions must be made by publishers.

Available to: U.S. citizens or residents
Deadline: April 30
Apply to: Christian Gauss Award, above address

Ⓝ The *Phi Beta Kappa Award in Science* of $2,500 is given annually for an outstanding book on science or interpretation of science written by a scientist and published in the United States during the year preceding the submission deadline. Submissions must be made by publishers.

Available to: U.S. citizens or residents
Deadline: April 30
Apply to: Science Award, above address

The *Mary Isabel Sibley Fellowship* is given annually for advanced study, research, or writing projects, in odd-numbered years for those dealing with Greek language, literature, history, or archaeology, and in even-numbered years for those dealing with any aspect of French language or literature. The fellowship carries a stipend of $20,000 for a period of one year.

Available to: Unmarried women between ages twenty-five and thirty-five who hold a doctorate or have fulfilled all the requirements except for the dissertation
Deadline: January 15
Apply to: Mary Isabel Sibley Fellowship Committee, above address

Phillips Exeter Academy
Exeter, NH 03833
Web site: http://www.exeter.edu

The *George Bennett Fellowship* is awarded annually to a person contemplating or embarking on a career as a writer who has under way a manuscript that he or she needs time and freedom from material considerations to complete. The fellow's official duties are to remain in residence while the Academy is in session and to write; the fellow is expected to be available to students interested in writing. The primary criterion for selection is the manuscript submitted (preferably a manuscript-in-progress). The election committee favors writers who have not issued a book-length work with a major publisher. The grant consists of a $6,000 stipend plus room and board for the writer and the writer's family during the academic year. Send SASE or visit the Web site for information and application.

Available to: See above
Deadline: December 1
Apply to: Above address

The Phillips Foundation
7811 Montrose Road, Suite 100
Potomac, MD 20854
Fax: 301-424-0245

ⓙ The *Phillips Foundation Journalism Fellowship Program* annually awards one $50,000 full-time fellowship and two $25,000 part-time fellowships to working journalists with less than five years' professional experience in print journalism. Awards are offered to assist fellows to undertake and complete a one-year project focusing on journalism supportive of American culture and a free society. Write for additional information and application.

Available to: U.S. citizens
Deadline: March 1
Apply to: John Farley, Journalism Fellowship Program, above address

Phoebe: A Journal of Literary Arts
MSN 2D6
George Mason University
4400 University Drive
Fairfax, VA 22030-4444
E-mail: phoebe@gmu.edu

Ⓕ Ⓟ The *Renee Sagiv Fiction Prize* and the *Greg Grummer Poetry Award* each offer $1,000 and publication in *Phoebe* for an unpublished short story and poem, respectively. Fiction writers may submit one story, not to exceed 25 pages; poets may submit up to four poems, not to exceed 10 pages. There is a $10 reading fee for each contest. Send SASE or e-mail for guidelines.

Available to: No restrictions
Deadline: December 15
Apply to: Fiction Contest or Poetry Contest, above address

Pig Iron Press
PO Box 237
Youngstown, OH 44501
Fax: 330-747-0599

Ⓕ Ⓟ The *Kenneth Patchen Competition* offers a $500 cash prize and publication for a full-length
manuscript of, in alternate years, poetry and fiction (novel or short story collection). The
2000 competition will be for poetry; fiction will be considered in 2001. The winning author
will receive 50 of the 1,000 paperback copies of the work printed. There is a $10 reading
fee. Send SASE for guidelines.

Available to: No restrictions
Deadline: December 31
Apply to: Kenneth Patchen Competition, above address

Pilgrim Project
Religion and Public Life
156 Fifth Avenue, Suite 400
New York, NY 10010
E-mail: davida@firstthings.com

Ⓓ The Pilgrim Project offers grants to playwrights ranging from $1,000 to $7,000, with an average
award of $3,350. Grants are intended to defray the cost of readings, workshop productions,
or full productions of plays dealing with "questions of moral significance." Applications
are reviewed year-round, on an ongoing basis. Write for further information.

Available to: No restrictions
Deadline: Ongoing
Apply to: Above address

Pioneer Drama Service
Box 4267
Englewood, CO 80155-4267
E-mail: piodrama@aol.com
Web site: http://www.pioneerdrama.com
Fax: 303-779-4315

Ⓓ The *Shubert Fendrich Memorial Playwriting Contest* offers publication with a $1,000 advance on
royalties (10 percent book royalty, 50 percent performance royalty) for produced,
unpublished work not longer than 90 minutes. Full-length plays, one-acts, translations,
adaptations, musicals, and plays for young audiences are eligible; subject matter and
language should be appropriate for schools and community theaters. Work with a
preponderance of female roles and minimal set requirements is preferred, but all entries
will be considered for publication. Send SASE for guidelines.

Available to: Anyone not already published by Pioneer Drama
Deadline: March 1
Apply to: Shubert Fendrich Memorial Playwriting Contest, above address

Pirate's Alley Faulkner Society
632 Pirate's Alley
New Orleans, LA 70116
Web site: http://www.wordsandmusic.org
Fax: 504-522-9725

Ⓜ The *William Faulkner Creative Writing Competition* offers $7,500 for a novel ($2,500 of which is
designated as an advance against royalties to encourage a publisher to print the winning
book); $2,500 for a novella ($1,000 as an advance against royalties); $1,500 for an individual
short story ($250 as an advance against royalties or writer's fees as an incentive for
publication); $1,000 for a personal essay; and $750 for a single poem of up to 750 words.
Novels should be of up to 100,000 words; novellas of up to 50,000; short stories of up to
15,000. Entry fees are $35 for novel, $30 for novella, and $25 for short story, essay, or
poem. The Society also sponsors a $1,000 award for a short story by a high school student
($750 for the winning student and $250 for the sponsoring teacher). The entry fee for this

competition is $10. Winners of the competitions should expect to make a presentation at the Society's annual meeting in September. Send SASE for further information, guidelines, and application, or visit the Web site.

Available to: U.S. citizens and residents
Deadline: April 15
Apply to: William Faulkner Creative Writing Competition, above address

Playboy Foundation
680 North Lake Shore Drive
Chicago, IL 60611

The *Hugh M. Hefner First Amendment Awards* of $5,000 each recognize the efforts of individuals working to protect and enhance First Amendment freedoms. Awards are given in the following categories: publishing, education, individual conscience, law, lifetime achievement, and arts and entertainment.

Available to: No restrictions
Deadline: Inquire
Apply to: Hugh M. Hefner First Amendment Awards, above address

Playboy Magazine
680 North Lake Shore Drive
Chicago, IL 60611
Web site: http://www.playboy.com/announcements/fiction-contest.html

Ⓕ The *Playboy College Fiction Contest* awards a first prize of $3,000 and publication in *Playboy* to a work of fiction, 25 pages or less, by a college or MFA graduate student. Second prize is $500 and a one-year subscription to *Playboy*. Enclose a 3-by-5-inch card listing name, age, college/university affiliation, permanent home address, and telephone number with manuscript submission. Send SASE for further information.

Available to: See above
Deadline: Submissions accepted September 1–January 1
Apply to: Playboy College Fiction Contest, above address

Playhouse on the Square
51 South Cooper Street
Memphis, TN 38104

Ⓓ The *Playhouse on the Square New Play Competition* annually awards $500 and production to an unproduced work with a small cast. Full-length plays and musicals are eligible.

Available to: No restrictions; southern playwrights preferred
Deadline: April 1
Apply to: New Play Competition, above address

Plays on Tape
Box 5789
Bend, OR 97708-5789
E-mail: theatre@playsontape.com
Web site: http://www.playsontape.com
Fax: 541-923-9679

Ⓓ The *Auricle Award* annually offers up to $600 and 10 copies of an audio recording for full-length plays and long one-acts suitable for audio production. Any play that has not been audio-produced, with a running time of approximately 74 minutes, is eligible. Scripts with two to five characters are preferred; minority playwrights are encouraged to apply. There is a $3 entry fee. Send SASE, e-mail, or visit the Web site for guidelines.

Available to: No restrictions
Deadline: December 31
Apply to: Auricle Award, above address

The Playwrights' Center
2301 Franklin Avenue, East
Minneapolis, MN 55406
E-mail: pwcenter@mtn.org
Web site: http://www.pwcenter.org
Fax: 612-332-6037

Ⓓ Ⓡ The *Jerome Playwright-in-Residence Fellowships* offer five playwright-in-residence positions with an accompanying stipend of $7,200 annually to promising playwrights who have not had more than two separate plays produced professionally. Playwrights have access to public readings and workshops. Recipients are required to participate in Center activities during the yearlong residence. Send SASE after July for application.

Available to: U.S. citizens or permanent residents
Deadline: September 15
Apply to: Jerome Fellowships, above address

Ⓓ Ⓡ The *McKnight Fellowship* offers $10,000 stipends and one-month residences to two playwrights with a minimum of two separate plays produced professionally. Additional funds of up to $2,000 per fellow are available for workshops and staged readings of scripts. Send SASE after November 15 for application.

Available to: U.S. citizens
Deadline: January 15
Apply to: McKnight Fellowship, above address

Ⓓ *PlayLabs*, held in July/August, is a two-week developmental workshop for new unproduced, unpublished plays, which allows playwrights to work with their choice of national professional directors, dramaturgs, and a professional company of local actors. Each selected play receives a public reading. Selected playwrights receive an honorarium, paid travel, and room and board. Send SASE after October 16 for application.

Available to: U.S. citizens
Deadline: December 15
Apply to: PlayLabs, above address

Playwrights' Center of San Francisco
Box 460466
San Francisco, CA 94146-0466
E-mail: playctrsf@aol.com
Web site: http://www.playwrights.org

Ⓓ *DramaRama*, an annual playwriting competition, offers a staged reading of up to eight scripts (four long plays and four short) at the Center's fall festival. A $500 prize will be awarded to the best long and the best short play on the basis of the readings. There is a $25 submission fee. Send SASE, e-mail, or visit the Web site for guidelines.

Available to: No restrictions
Deadline: March 15
Apply to: DramaRama, above address

Playwrights First
c/o The National Arts Club
15 Gramercy Park South
New York, NY 10003

Ⓓ The *Playwrights First Award* of $1,000 is given annually for the best unproduced play written within the last two years. Adaptations and translations are not accepted. Playwrights should submit script and résumé. Write for further information.

Available to: No restrictions
Deadline: October 15
Apply to: Above address

The Playwrights' Theater
Box 803305
Dallas, TX 75380

Ⓓ *Plays for the 21st Century* awards $1,500 and a public reading with possible production for a full-length play written in or translated into English. There is a $15 application fee. Send SASE for guidelines and application.

Available to: No restrictions
Deadline: January 31
Apply to: Plays for the 21st Century, above address

Pleasant Company Publications
8400 Fairway Place
Middleton, WI 53562
Fax: 800-257-3865

Ⓒ The *Pleasant T. Rowland Prize for Fiction* annually awards $10,000 for the unpublished best novel for girls ages ten and up. In addition, Pleasant Company (publisher of the American Girls Collection, AG Fiction, American Girl Library, and *American Girl* magazine) will award a royalty contract under its AG Fiction imprint. The competition hopes to encourage high-quality fiction for girls and to reward authors of novels that capture the spirit of contemporary American girls and reflect important concerns in America today. Send SASE for guidelines.

Available to: No restrictions
Deadline: September 1
Apply to: Submissions Editor, above address

Pleiades Press
Department of English and Philosophy
Central Missouri State University
Warrensburg, MO 64093
E-mail: kdp8106@cmsu2.cmsu.edu
Fax: 660-543-8544

Ⓟ The *Lena-Miles Wever Todd Poetry Series,* formerly the *Winthrop Poetry Series,* offers a $1,000 honorarium and publication by Pleiades Press and distribution by Louisiana State University Press for a poetry manuscript of more than 48 pages. There is a $15 reading fee, which covers a copy of the winning book. Send SASE for guidelines.

Available to: U.S. or Canadian residents
Deadline: March 31
Apply to: Lena-Miles Wever Todd Poetry Series, above address

Ploughshares
Emerson College
100 Beacon Street
Boston, MA 02116
Web site: http://www.emerson.edu/ploughshares
Fax: 617-824-8991

[IN] The *Cohen Award in Poetry and Fiction* offers $600 each to the best short story and poem published in *Ploughshares* each year. There is no application process. *By Internal Nomination Only.*

[IN] The *John C. Zacharis First Book Award* offers $1,500 for the best debut book of poetry or short fiction published by a *Ploughshares* writer. Writers are nominated by the advisory editors of *Ploughshares.* There is no application process or deadline. *By Internal Nomination Only*

Pockets Magazine
The Upper Room
1908 Grand Avenue
PO Box 340004
Nashville, TN 37203-0004
E-mail: pockets@upperroom.org (for queries only)
Web site: http://www.upperroom.org/pockets

© The *Pockets Fiction Writing Contest* awards $1,000 and publication in *Pockets*, a devotional magazine for children, for an unpublished short story of 1,000 to 1,600 words written for children grades 1 through 6. Send SASE for additional information and guidelines.

Available to: No restrictions
Deadline: Submissions must be postmarked March 1–August 15
Apply to: Fiction Writing Contest, above address

The Poetry Center & American Poetry Archives
San Francisco State University
1600 Holloway Avenue
San Francisco, CA 94132
E-mail: newlit@sfsu.edu
Web site: http://www.sfsu.edu/~newlit
Fax: 415-338-0966

℗ The Poetry Center's *Book Award* offers a $500 cash prize and an invitation to read in the Poetry Center reading series, to the author of an outstanding book of poems published in the current year. The award is for a volume by an individual poet; anthologies and translations are not acceptable. A $10 reading fee must accompany the submitted book.

Available to: No restrictions
Deadline: December 31
Apply to: Book Award, above address

Poetry Magazine
60 West Walton Street
Chicago, IL 60610
Web site: http://www.poetrymagazine.org

℗ Two *Ruth Lilly Poetry Fellowships* of $15,000 each are given annually to undergraduate or graduate students enrolled in English or creative writing programs who will not have received an MA or MFA degree as of December 31 of the year of the award. Program directors and department chairs in the United States should submit nominations on an official application form from *Poetry*. Send SASE after February 1 for application form and guidelines.

Available to: See above
Deadline: April 15
Apply to: Ruth Lilly Poetry Fellowships, above address

[IN] The *Ruth Lilly Poetry Prize* of $75,000 is given annually to a U.S. citizen in recognition of outstanding poetic achievement. Applications and nominations are not accepted. *By Internal Nomination Only.*

℗ Eight *Poetry Magazine Awards*, ranging from $200 to $3,000, are given annually for poetry published in the magazine. Applications are not accepted. All verse published in the magazine during the preceding year is automatically considered.

Available to: Poets whose work has appeared in *Poetry* during the previous year

Poetry Society of America
15 Gramercy Park
New York, NY 10003
Web site: www.poetrysociety.org

In addition to those listed below, other awards, some of which are open only to PSA members, are given annually. For guidelines, entry forms, and details of all awards, send SASE to the above address.

(P) The *George Bogin Memorial Award* of $500 is given for a selection of four or five poems that reflect "the encounter of the ordinary and extraordinary," use language in an original way, and take a stand "against oppression in any of its forms." There is a $5 entry fee for nonmembers.

Available to: U.S. citizens
Deadline: December 21
Apply to: George Bogin Memorial Award, above address

(P) The *Alice Fay Di Castagnola Award* of $1,000 is given for a manuscript-in-progress of poetry, prose, or verse drama by a PSA member.

Available to: PSA members
Deadline: December 21
Apply to: Alice Fay Di Castagnola Award, above address

(P) The *Norma Farber First Book Award* of $500 is given annually for a first book (not a chapbook) of original poetry by an American published during the calendar year. Submissions must be made by publishers. There is a $10 entry fee per book.

Available to: U.S. citizens
Deadline: December 21
Apply to: Norma Farber First Book Award, above address

(IN) The *Frost Medal*, with an accompanying prize of $2,500, is given annually to a living American poet for lifetime service to American poetry. *By Internal Nomination Only.*

(P) The *Lyric Poetry Award* of $500 is given for a lyric poem of no more than 50 lines by a PSA member.

Available to: PSA members
Deadline: December 21
Apply to: Lyric Poetry Award, above address

(P) The *Lucille Medwick Memorial Award* of $500 is given for an original poem in any form on freedom or a humanitarian theme by a PSA member.

Available to: PSA members
Deadline: December 21
Apply to: Lucille Medwick Memorial Award, above address

(IN) The *Shelley Memorial Award,* of between $2,000 and $6,000, is given annually to a living American poet selected with reference to genius and need. *By Internal Nomination Only.*

(P) The *William Carlos Williams Award* is a purchase prize between $500 and $1,000 for a book of poetry published by a small, nonprofit, or university press. Submissions must made by publishers and must be original works by one author who is a permanent resident of the United States. Translations are not eligible. There is a $10 entry fee per book.

Available to: U.S. permanent residents
Deadline: December 21
Apply to: William Carlos Williams Award, above address

(P) The *Robert H. Winner Memorial Award* of $2,500 is given to a poet more than forty years of age who has published no book or only one. Poets may submit a brief but cohesive manuscript of up to ten poems or 20 pages. There is a $5 entry fee for nonmembers.

Available to: Poets over age forty
Deadline: December 21
Apply to: Robert H. Winner Award, above address

Poets Out Loud
Fordham University at Lincoln Center
113 West 60th Street, Room 924
New York, NY 10023
E-mail: pol@mary.fordham.edu
Web site: http://www.fordham.edu/english/pol

(P)   The *Poets Out Loud Prize* offers $1,000 and publication by Fordham University Press for a previously unpublished poetry manuscript, 50 to 100 pages long. There is a $25 entry fee. Send SASE or visit the Web site for guidelines and application form.

    Available to: No restrictions
    Deadline: Submissions accepted September 1–October 15
    Apply to: Poets Out Loud Prize, above address

Poets & Writers
72 Spring Street
New York, NY 10012
Web site: http://www.pw.org
Fax: 212-226-3963

(M)   The *Poets & Writers Readings/Workshops Program* in California and New York State and in Chicago and Detroit provides matching fee money to pay poets, fiction writers, and literary performance poets for giving readings and writing workshops in various public settings. Eligible to apply for writers' matching funds are libraries, Y's, community centers, small presses, colleges and universities, correctional facilities, bookstores, religious organizations, and community groups interested in presenting literary events. Applications must be submitted by organizations; writers may contact them to initiate the application. Write or visit the Web site for additional information and application procedures.

    Available to: Organizations in New York State, California, Chicago, and Detroit
    Deadline: Ongoing; applications must be submitted 8 weeks before the event, or for a series of workshops, the date of the first
    Apply to: Readings/Workshops Program, above address; or Poets & Writers, 580 Washington Street, Suite 308, San Francisco, CA 94111

(F) (P)   The *Writers Exchange Program* is designed to encourage a sharing of works and resources among emerging writers nationwide. A poet and a fiction writer from a designated state will be chosen annually. Each will receive a $500 honorarium and will give readings and meet with the literary community in New York City. Winning writers must be available for a one-week tour on a schedule determined by Poets & Writers. All related travel and lodging expenses and a daily stipend are covered. Inquire for designated state for 2000, guidelines, and application form.

    Available to: Emerging writers from states designated by Poets & Writers
    Deadline: December 1
    Apply to: Writers Exchange Program, above address

(R)   The *Writers on Site* program, sponsored by Poets & Writers in California, offers multidisciplinary residences for California writers in visual arts sites. In addition to creating new work, writers selected develop community activities with the partnership site. The Program is currently in Eureka at the Ink People Center for the Arts and Redwood Coast Writers' Center; previous sites have been in Los Angeles and Oakland. Writers are in residence for sixteen weeks, during which they devote approximately ten hours per week to the development of community activities. Writers receive a $5,000 honorarium for the term of the residence.

    Available to: Published California writers
    Deadline: July 1
    Apply to: Poets & Writers, 580 Washington Street, Suite 308, San Francisco, CA 94111

Pope Foundation
211 West 56th Street
New York, NY 10019

ⓙ The Pope Foundation *Journalism Awards* offer honorariums of $15,000 to mid-career investigative journalists and social commentators to be used as working fellowships. Applicants should have a minimum of ten years' journalistic background. Send SASE for application and guidelines.

Available to: Mid-career journalists
Deadline: November 15
Apply to: Catherine Pope, Journalism Awards Program Director, above address

Potato Eyes Foundation
PO Box 76
Troy, ME 04987
E-mail: potatoeyes@uninet.net
Web site: http://www.maineguide.com/giftshop/potatoeyes

ⓟ The *William and Kingman Page Poetry Book Award* offers $1,000, publication by Nightshade Press, and 25 copies to the author for a poetry book. Poets may submit manuscripts of no more than 41 typewritten pages, no more than 43 lines of poetry per page, and should include a cover sheet with collection title only, a separate acknowledgments page with name and address, SASE, and $12 reading fee.

Available to: No restrictions
Deadline: November 15
Apply to: William and Kingman Page Poetry Book Award, above address

Prairie Schooner
201 Andrews Hall
University of Nebraska
Lincoln, NE 68588-0334
Web site: http://www.unl.edu/schooner/psmain.htm

Ⓜ Writers whose work has been published in *Prairie Schooner* during the preceding calendar year are eligible for the following annual awards:

The *Virginia Faulkner Award for Excellence in Writing* of $1,000 for the best writing of any kind.

The *Lawrence Foundation Award* of $1,000 for the best short story.

The *Larry Levis Poetry Prize* of $1,000.

The *Hugh J. Luke Award* of $250 for writing in any genre.

The *Bernice Slote Award* of $500 for the best work by a beginning writer.

The *Edward Stanley Award for Poetry* of $1,000.

The *Strousse Award* of $500 for the best poem or group of poems.

Available to: *Prairie Schooner* contributors

Prince William Sound Community College
PO Box 97
Valdez, AK 99686
E-mail: vndjc@uaa.alaska.edu
Web site: http://www.uaa.alaska.edu/pwscc
Fax: 907-834-1611

Ⓓ The Last Frontier Theatre Conference sponsors a Play Lab for the staged readings of new works. Of approximately fifty new works selected for the Lab, five will receive the *Yukon Pacific New Play Award* of $1,000 each. Top plays may also be selected for readings in New

York, and the highest-rated play will receive full production at the University of Alaska in Anchorage, and at the following year's conference in Valdez. Send SASE, e-mail, or visit the Web site for guidelines.

Available to: No restrictions
Deadline: March 1
Apply to: Above address

Princess Grace Foundation—USA
150 East 58th Street
New York, NY 10155
E-mail: pgfusa@pgfusa.com
Web site: http://www.pgfusa.com
Fax: 212-317-1473

Ⓓ The *Princess Grace Awards Playwright Fellowship*, given annually to a young American playwright, consists of a $7,500 grant and a ten-week residence, including paid travel, at New Dramatists, a playwright service organization, in New York City. The award is based primarily on the artistic quality of a submitted play and the potential of the fellowship to assist in the writer's growth. Write for guidelines.

Available to: U.S. citizens or permanent residents
Deadline: March 31
Apply to: Playwright Fellowship, above address

Princeton University
The Council of the Humanities
122 East Pyne
Princeton, NJ 08544-5264
Web site: http://www.princeton.edu/~humcounc
Fax: 609-258-2783

The *Alfred Hodder Fellowship* of $45,600 is given annually to each of two writers and/or scholars with "much more than ordinary intellectual and literary gifts," for the pursuit of independent work in the humanities. The selected fellows are usually from outside academia, and in the early stages of his or her career. Fellows spend an academic year in residence at Princeton working independently. Ph.D. candidates are not eligible. Write for further information and guidelines.

Available to: No restrictions
Deadline: November 1
Apply to: Alfred Hodder Fellowship, above address

Providence Athenaeum
251 Benefit Street
Providence, RI 02903

Ⓟ The *Philbrick Poetry Award* offers $500 and publication for a chapbook by a New England poet who has not yet had a poetry book published. Applicants must reside in Connecticut, Maine, Massachusetts, New Hampshire, Rhode Island, or Vermont. The winner will be invited to read at the Athenaeum. Send SASE for guidelines.

Available to: See above
Deadline: Submissions accepted July 15–October 15
Apply to: Philbrick Poetry Award, above address

PublishingOnline.com
1200 South 192nd Street, Suite 300
Seattle, WA 98148
E-mail: info@publishingonline.com
Web site: http://www.publishingonline.com

Ⓕ The *North American Authors and Fiction Writers Contest* offers a first prize of $10,000, four second prizes of $5,000 each, ten third prizes of $1,000 each, and twenty-five fourth prizes of $500 each for works of fiction more than 100 pages long. Work must be submitted in electronic format. The contest is limited to the first 500 qualified manuscripts received by the deadline. Romance, mystery, adventure, science fiction, fantasy, and horror writers are encouraged to enter. There is a $25 reading fee. Write, e-mail, or visit the Web site for guidelines.

Available to: North American authors
Deadline: September 1
Apply to: North American Authors and Fiction Writers Contest, above address

Publishing Triangle
17 East 47th Street, 3rd floor
New York, NY 10017
E-mail: info@publishingtriangle.org
Web site: http://www.publishingtriangle.org

Ⓓ The *Robert Chesley Award for Lesbian and Gay Playwriting* recognizes a body of work or an emerging talent. The award alternates yearly between a man and a woman, who receive an honorarium of $1,000. Write to the address below for more information.

Available to: Lesbian or gay playwrights
Deadline: Inquire
Apply to: Victor Bumbalo, 828 North Laurel Avenue, Los Angeles, CA 90046

Ⓕ The *Ferro-Grumley Awards* of $1,000 each are given annually to two writers for literary excellence in lesbian and gay fiction. Publishers should submit six copies of nominated books (or bound galleys if books are not available). Members of the Publishing Triangle may nominate books for free. There is a $25 nominating fee for nonmembers. Write, e-mail, or visit the Web site for additional information and nomination form.

Available to: No restrictions
Deadline: November 1
Apply to: Ferro-Grumley Awards, above address

Ⓝ The *Judy Grahn Award* for literary excellence in lesbian nonfiction and the *Randy Shilts Award* for literary excellence in gay nonfiction each annually offer an honorarium of $1,000. Publishers should submit four copies of nominated books (or bound galleys if books are not available). Members of the Publishing Triangle may nominate books for free. There is a $25 nominating fee for nonmembers. Write, e-mail, or visit the Web site for additional information and nomination form.

Available to: No restrictions
Deadline: October 1
Apply to: Judy Grahn Award or Randy Shilts Award, above address

[IN] The *Bill Whitehead Award for Lifetime Achievement* recognizes a body of work with significant gay content. In even-numbered years the award is given to a woman; in odd-numbered years, to a man. The award carries an honorarium of $3,000. There is no application process. *By Internal Nomination Only.*

Puffin Foundation
20 East Oakdene Avenue
Teaneck, NJ 07666

The Puffin Foundation offers grants to artists and performers, including writers, committed to "continuing the dialogue between art and the lives of ordinary people." The Foundation seeks to foster and encourage younger artists and projects that might find funding difficult because of genre and/or social philosophy. Average grants range from $500 to $2,000. Write for further information and application.

Available to: No restrictions
Deadline: Applications accepted October 1–December 31
Apply to: Above address

The Pulitzer Prizes
Columbia University
Graduate School of Journalism
2950 Broadway
New York, NY 10027
Web site: http://www.jrn.columbia.edu or http://www.pulitzer.org

Ⓜ *Pulitzer Prizes* are given to American authors for the most distinguished volume of original verse, book of fiction, produced play, biography or autobiography, and book of nonfiction, and to authors of all nationalities for the most distinguished book in American history. Prizes are also given for journalism published in U.S. daily or weekly newspapers. Several prizes of $5,000 each are awarded annually.

Available to: See above
Deadlines: July 1 and November 1 for books; February 1 for journalism; March 1 for plays
Apply to: Above address

Pulliam Journalism Fellowships
Indianapolis Newspapers
PO Box 145
Indianapolis, IN 46206-0145
E-mail: pulliam@starnews.com
Web site: http://www.starnews.com/pjf
Fax: 317-630-9549

Ⓙ The *Pulliam Journalism Fellowships* are awarded to twenty journalism or liberal arts graduates. Fellows participate in a ten-week summer internship and receive a stipend of $5,000. Write, e-mail, or visit the Web site for further information and application packet.

Available to: See above
Deadline: November 15 for early admission; March 1 for others
Apply to: Russell B. Pulliam, Fellowships Director, above address

Purdue University Press
1207 South Campus Courts—E
West Lafayette, IN 47907-1207

Ⓟ The *Verna Emery Poetry Competition* offers publication of an unpublished collection of original poems, 60 to 90 pages. Multiple submissions are acceptable as long as the Press is informed. There is a $15 reading fee. Write for guidelines and further information.

Available to: No restrictions
Deadline: April 15
Apply to: Verna Emery Poetry Competition, above address

Pushcart Press
Box 380
Wainscott, NY 11975

Ⓕ Ⓝ The *Editors' Book Award* offers $1,000 and hardcover publication for any book-length manuscript, fiction or nonfiction, submitted to but not yet accepted by a commercial publisher. Manuscripts must be nominated by an editor at a U.S. or Canadian publishing company.

Available to: No restrictions
Deadline: October 15
Apply to: Above address

Ⓜ The *Pushcart Prize* offers publication in *The Pushcart Prize: Best of the Small Presses* for the best literary works published by small presses in the current calendar year. Works of poetry, short fiction, essays, or self-contained portions of books or chapbooks are eligible. Submissions, in the form of tear sheets or photocopies, are accepted from editors only, who may nominate up to six works. Work to be published between the deadline and

December 31 may be submitted in manuscript form. Write for complete guidelines.

Available to: No restrictions
Deadline: December 1
Apply to: Pushcart Prize, above address

Quality Paperback Book Club
1271 Avenue of the Americas
New York, NY 10017
Web site: http://www.qpb.com

[IN] The *New Voices Award* and the *New Visions Award* offer $5,000 each annually to the most distinctive and promising works of fiction and nonfiction, respectively, by new authors. QPBC editors choose the winner from work selected as Book Club offerings. All publishers' submissions to QPBC will be considered. There is no application process.

© The *QPBC/Estés International Storyteller Prize* of $5,000 is awarded annually to an author "whose work demonstrates remarkable achievement in crossing national, cultural, ethnic, geographical, class, gender and/or age boundaries." All submissions must be published in English during the previous calendar year and submitted by publishers. QPBC will offer the winner's book in paperback to its nearly one million members. Contact for additional information.

Available to: No restrictions
Deadline: May 31
Apply to: QPBC/Estés Storyteller Prize, above address

Quarterly Review of Literature
Princeton University
26 Haslet Avenue
Princeton, NJ 08540

℗ The *Quarterly Review of Literature Poetry Book Awards* are presented annually to four or five winners for an unpublished manuscript of poetry. The award consists of $1,000, publication in the *QRL* poetry series, and 100 copies of the published book. Applicants should submit a collection of miscellaneous poems, a poetic play, a long poem, or poetry translation of 60 to 100 pages. Manuscripts in English from outside the United States are also invited. Send SASE for complete information. A $20 subscription to *QRL* is requested with submission.

Available to: No restrictions
Deadlines: Submissions accepted in May and November
Apply to: QRL Awards, above address

Quarterly West
University of Utah
200 South Central Campus Drive, Room 317
Salt Lake City, UT 84112-9109

Ⓕ The *Quarterly West Novella Competition* biennially awards two prizes of $500 and publication in *Quarterly West* for novellas of between 50 and 125 pages. There is a $20 reading fee. Send SASE for guidelines before submitting.

Available to: No restrictions
Deadline: Inquire
Apply to: Novella Competition, above address

Ragdale Foundation
1260 North Green Bay Road
Lake Forest, IL 60045
E-mail: ragdale1@aol.com

Ⓡ Ragdale offers writers, artists, and composers an opportunity to work undisturbed on their own projects. Comfortable living and working space is provided in beautiful buildings adjoining a large nature preserve. Studios are available for visual artists and composers. Maximum stay is two months. Those accepted for residence are asked to pay $15 per day; some waivers are available on the basis of financial need.

Available to: No restrictions
Deadline: Inquire
Apply to: Above address

® The *Frances Shaw Fellowship for Older Women Writers* offers a two-month residence to a woman whose serious writing career began after age fifty-five. Send SASE for information.

Available to: See above
Deadline: February 1
Apply to: Above address

Sonia Raiziss-Giop Charitable Foundation
PO Box 15
Andover, NJ 07821-0051

℗ Ⓣ The *Bordighera Bilingual Poetry Prize* is given annually for a manuscript of poetry written in English by an Italian-American poet and translated into Italian. The winning poet and translator each receive $1,000 and publication by Bordighera, Inc., in a bilingual edition. Poets must be U.S. citizens; translators may be of any nationality. Qualified poets may translate their own work. Poets and translators should submit 10 sample pages of poems in English, with each page of poetry followed by a page of its Italian translation. The complete book should not exceed 96 manuscript pages, including the translations. Send SASE for guidelines.

Available to: See above
Deadline: May 31
Apply to: Daniela Gioseffi and Alfredo de Palchi, Contest Coordinators, above address

Ayn Rand Institute
4640 Admiralty Way #406
Marina del Rey, CA 90292
E-mail: essay@aynrand.org
Web site: http://www.aynrand.org

Ⓝ The *Anthem Essay Contest* annually offers a first prize of $1,000, ten second prizes of $200 each, and 20 third prizes of $100 each for an essay by a ninth- or tenth-grader about one of three topics related to Ayn Rand's novelette *Anthem*. Essays should be between 600 and 1,200 words. Send SASE, e-mail, or visit the Web site for guidelines.

Available to: Ninth- or tenth-grade students
Deadline: April 1
Apply to: Anthem Essay Contest, Dept. W, Ayn Rand Institute, PO Box 6099, Inglewood, CA 90312

Ⓝ The *Atlas Shrugged Essay Contest* annually offers a first prize of $5,000, a second of $3,000, and a third of $1,000 for an essay by an undergraduate or graduate business student about one of two topics related to Ayn Rand's novel *Atlas Shrugged*. Essays should be between 1,000 and 1,200 words. Send SASE, e-mail, or visit the Web site for guidelines.

Available to: Undergraduate or graduate business students
Deadline: February 15
Apply to: Atlas Shrugged Essay Contest, above address

Ⓝ The *Fountainhead Essay Contest* annually offers a first prize of $10,000, five second prizes of $2,000 each, and ten third prizes of $1,000 each for an essay by an eleventh- or twelfth-grader about one of three topics related to Ayn Rand's novel *The Fountainhead*. Essays should be between 800 and 1,600 words. Send SASE, e-mail, or visit the Web site for guidelines.

Available to: Eleventh- or twelfth-grade students

Deadline: April 15
Apply to: The Fountainhead Essay Contest, Dept. W, Ayn Rand Institute, PO Box 6004, Inglewood, CA 90312

Red Hen Press
PO Box 902582
Palmdale, CA 93590-2582
E-mail: redhen@vpg.net
Web site: http://www.vpg.net/redhen
Fax: 818-831-0649

(P) The *Benjamin Saltman Poetry Award* offers $1,000 and publication by Red Hen Press for an original, full-length poetry manuscript. Poets may submit 64 to 96 pages of poetry with SASE, a $12 reading fee, and a cover sheet listing the title and the poet's name, address, and phone number. Send SASE, e-mail, or visit the Web site for guidelines.

Available to: No restrictions
Deadline: October 31
Apply to: Poetry Editor, above address

Red Rock Review
English Department, J2A
Community College of Southern Nevada
3200 East Cheyenne Avenue
North Las Vegas, NV 89030
E-mail: rich_logsdan@ccsn.nevada.edu

(P) The *Red Rock Poetry Award* offers $500 and publication in *Red Rock Review* for a poem of no more than 20 lines. Poets may submit up to three poems, with a $6 reading fee. Send SASE for guidelines.

Available to: No restrictions
Deadline: Inquire
Apply to: Red Rock Poetry Award, above address

(F) The *Mark Twain Award for Short Fiction* offers $1,000 and publication in *Red Rock Review*, a biannual journal of fiction, poetry, and creative nonfiction, for a short story of no more than 3,500 words. There is a $10 reading fee. Send SASE for guidelines.

Available to: No restrictions
Deadline: Inquire
Apply to: Mark Twain Award for Short Fiction

The Refined Savage
PO Box 754
Terre Haute, IN 47808
E-mail: Resavage3@aol.com

(P) *The Refined Savage Poetry Competition* offers $500 and publication in *The Refined Savage*, a bilingual poetry review, for a poem in English or Spanish. The top ten finalists will also be published and translated. There is a $7 reading fee for three poems; $2 each for additional poems. Send SASE or e-mail for guidelines.

Available to: No restrictions
Deadline: November 15
Apply to: Poetry Competition, above address

Rhode Island State Council on the Arts
95 Cedar Street, Suite 103
Providence, RI 02903-1034
E-mail: ride0600@ride.ri.net
Web site: http://www.risca.state.ri.us
Fax: 401-521-1351

Ⓜ Literature fellowships are given biennially in the categories of fiction, playwriting/ screenwriting, and poetry to encourage the creative development of professional Rhode Island artists by enabling them to set aside time to pursue their work and achieve specific career goals. One fellowship of $5,000 and one runner-up prize of $1,000 are awarded in each category.

Available to: Rhode Island residents at least eighteen years old who are not full-time undergraduate or graduate students
Deadline: Inquire
Apply to: Fellowships, above address

Richard Free Library
58 North Main Street
Newport, NH 03773
E-mail: rfl@sugar-river.net
Fax: 603-863-3022

Ⓘ Ⓝ The *Sarah Josepha Hale Award* of $500 is given annually in recognition of a distinguished body of literary work by a writer who was born or resides in New England or whose work is primarily associated with New England. There is no application process. *By Internal Nomination Only.*

Mary Roberts Rinehart Fund
George Mason University
English Department
MSN 3E4
4400 University Drive
Fairfax, VA 22030-4444
E-mail: writing@gmu.edu

Ⓜ The *Mary Roberts Rinehart Fund* awards three grants, from $2,000 to $2,500 each, to writers who have not yet published a book, to complete previously unpublished works of fiction, poetry, biography, autobiography, or history with a strong narrative quality. Candidates must be nominated by a sponsoring writer, agent, or editor. Inquire for details.

Available to: See above
Deadline: November 30
Apply to: Above address

River City
Department of English
University of Memphis
Memphis, TN 38152

Ⓕ Three *River City Writing Awards in Fiction* are given annually for unpublished short stories of up to 7,500 words. First prize is $2,000, second is $500, and third is $300. All winning stories are published in *River City*. There is a $10 entry fee, which, upon request, will be applied toward a new or continuing subscription to *River City*. Manuscripts will not be returned.

Available to: No restrictions
Deadline: Inquire
Apply to: Thomas Russell, Editor, River City Writing Awards, above address

River Oak Review
PO Box 3127
Oak Park, IL 60303

Ⓕ The *River Oak–Hemingway Foundation Short Story Contest* annually awards $500 and publication in *River Oak Review* to an unpublished short story of no more than 5,000 words. A $12 reading fee covers a one-year subscription to the *Review*. Send SASE for complete guidelines.

Available to: No restrictions
Deadline: June 1
Apply to: Short Story Contest, above address

Ⓟ The *River Oak Poetry Contest* annually awards $500 and publication in *River Oak Review* for an unpublished poem or group of poems. Poets may submit up to four poems of no more than 500 lines total. A $12 reading fee covers a one-year subscription to the *Review*. Send SASE for guidelines.

Available to: No restrictions
Deadline: December 1
Apply to: Poetry Contest, above address

River Styx
634 North Grand Boulevard, 12th floor
St. Louis, MO 63103

Ⓟ *River Styx*, a triquarterly journal of poetry, fiction, and art, sponsors an *International Poetry Contest* for a short body of work—no more than three poems or 14 pages. First prize is $1,000 and publication. Second- and third-place winners will also be published. There is a $20 entry fee that covers the cost of a one-year subscription to *River Styx*. Send SASE for guidelines.

Available to: No restrictions
Deadline: May 31
Apply to: International Poetry Contest, above address

Robinson Jeffers Tor House Foundation
PO Box 223240
Carmel, CA 93922
E-mail: thf@torhouse.org
Web site: http://www.torhouse.org
Fax: 831-624-3699

Ⓟ The *Robinson Jeffers Tor House Prize for Poetry* awards $1,000 for a single, unpublished poem. Poets may submit up to three poems, no more than 3 pages each, with a $10 reading fee, or up to six poems with a $15 reading fee; fee for each additional poem is $2.50. Send SASE, e-mail, or visit the Web site for guidelines.

Available to: No restrictions
Deadline: March 1
Apply to: Poetry Prize, above address

Rockefeller Foundation
Bellagio Study and Conference Center
420 Fifth Avenue
New York, NY 10018-2702
E-mail: bellagio@rockfound.org
Web site: http://www.rockfound.org

Ⓡ Four-week residences in the Italian Alps from approximately February 1 to December 15 are offered to artists and scholars. Writers must have at least one major book publication to their credit to be eligible. Room is available for spouses. Residents must pay for their own travel. Write, e-mail, or visit the Web site for additional information and guidelines. E-mail applications are accepted only from outside the United States.

Available to: No restrictions

Deadline: January, May, and September (inquire for exact date); apply nine months in
    advance of desired residence dates
Apply to: Above address

Rocky Mountain National Park
Estes Park, CO 80517

® The *Artist-in-Residence Program* offers professional writers and other artists the opportunity
    to pursue their particular art form surrounded by the inspiring landscape of Rocky
    Mountain National Park. The park offers each chosen participant use of the historic William
    Allen White cabin for two weeks from early June to late September. No additional stipend
    is available. In return, participants must donate to the park's collection a piece of work
    representative of their style and their stay (with the National Park Service holding the
    copyright of donated work), and participate in two public presentations during their
    residence. Write for additional information and guidelines.

Available to: No restrictions
Deadline: Inquire
Apply to: Artist-in-Residence Program, above address

Rocky Mountain Student Theater Project
Box 1626
Telluride, CO 81435
E-mail: playfest@aol.com
Web site: http://members.aol.com/PlayFest/RMSTP.html

Ⓓ The *Roy Barker Playwriting Prize* annually awards a first prize of $500, production, and paid
    travel and housing to attend the Rocky Mountain Playwriting Festival for a full-length
    play, one-act, translation, adaptation, play for young audience, or solo piece by a high
    school student. One-act plays, 30 to 45 minutes long, are preferred. There is a $5 entry fee.
    Write, e-mail, or visit the Web site for contest rules.

Available to: High school students
Deadline: May 1
Apply to: Above address

Rome Arts and Community Center
308 West Bloomfield Street
Rome, NY 13440

Ⓟ The *Milton Dorfman Poetry Prize* of $500 is awarded annually for original, previously
    unpublished poems. A second prize of $200 and a third of $100 are also given. There is no
    limit to the numbers of submissions; a reading fee of $5 per poem is required. The winning
    poem will be published and read by the contest judge at the Center's open house. Write
    for further information.

Available to: No restrictions
Deadline: November 1
Apply to: Milton Dorfman Poetry Prize, above address

St. Martin's Press
175 Fifth Avenue
New York, NY 10010

Ⓕ The *Best First Private Eye Novel Contest*, co-sponsored by Private Eye Writers of America, and
    the *Malice Domestic Best First Novel Contest*, for traditional mystery novels, each annually
    award $10,000 (as an advance against royalties) and publication. Send SASE for contest
    rules before submitting manuscript. Authors must be unpublished in the mystery genre
    and must have no novels under contract for publication in the genre.

Available to: No restrictions
Deadline: August 1 for Private Eye; October 15 for Malice Domestic
Apply to: Private Eye Contest or Malice Domestic Contest, Thomas Dunne Books, above
    address

Salmon Run Press
PO Box 672130
Chugiak, AK 99567-2130
E-mail: salmonrp@aol.com

(P) The *Salmon Run National Poetry Book Award* offers $1,000 and publication for a poetry manuscript of 48 to 96 pages. The winning book will be published in an edition of 500 or 1,000 copies, and will be advertised nationally. There is a $10 reading fee. Send SASE for guidelines.

Available to: No restrictions
Deadline: December 30
Apply to: Poetry Book Award, above address

Salt Hill Journal
Syracuse University
Department of English
Syracuse, NY 13244-1170
E-mail: salthill@cas.syr.edu
Web site: http://www-hl.syr.edu/cwp

(P) The *Salt Hill Journal Poetry Prize* offers a $500 first prize and publication in *Salt Hill Journal,* Syracuse University's literary magazine, for an unpublished poem. A $250 second prize and a $100 third prize, both with publication, will also be given. For a $10 entry fee, poets may submit up to three poems; $3 is the fee for every additional title. Send SASE for rules.

Available to: No restrictions
Deadline: May 1
Apply to: Poetry Contest, above address

(F) The *Salt Hill Journal Short Short Fiction Prize* offers a $500 first prize and publication for an unpublished piece of short short fiction up to 1,500 words. A $250 second prize and a $100 third prize, both with publication, will also be given. The reading fee is $10 per story. Send SASE for rules.

Available to: No restrictions
Deadline: September 15
Apply to: Fiction Contest, above address

Constance Saltonstall Foundation for the Arts
120 Brindley Street
Ithaca, NY 14850
E-mail: artsfound@clarityconnect.com
Web site: http://www.saltonstall.org

(R) The Constance Saltonstall Foundation for the Arts awards one-month summer residences at the Saltonstall Arts Colony to visual artists, poets, fiction and creative prose writers who live in New York State. The Foundation also awards grants of up to $5,000 to individual artists living in central and western New York counties. Send SASE for guidelines and application.

Available to: See above
Deadline: January 15
Apply to: Above address

San Francisco Chronicle
901 Mission Street
San Francisco, CA 94103-2988
Web site: http://www.sfgate.com/chronicle

(J) The *San Francisco Chronicle* offers summer and two-year newsroom internships. The summer internship is a twelve-week newsroom training program, beginning in mid-June, for college students and recent graduates. The two-year program offers newsroom training to new college graduates. Summer interns are paid approximately $510 a week; two-year interns receive approximately $33,000 the first year and $38,000 the second, and are eligible for comprehensive health benefits after three months. Write or visit the Web site for additional information and application procedures.

Available to: See above
Deadline: Applications must be postmarked October 1–November 15
Apply to: Leslie Guevarra, Director of Editorial Hiring and Development, above address (specify Summer or Two-Year Internship Program)

San Jose Center for Poetry and Literature
110 South Market Street
San Jose, CA 95113

(P) The San Jose Center for Poetry and Literature *Poetry Prize* annually awards $500 and publication in *Cæsura*, the Center's journal, for an unpublished poem of any length. Poems must not have been awarded a prize in any other competition. Poets may submit up to three poems with a $10 reading fee; the fee for additional poems is $3 each. Write for guidelines.

Available to: No restrictions
Deadline: October 15
Apply to: Poetry Prize, above address

Sarabande Books
2234 Dundee Road, Suite 200
Louisville, KY 40205
Web site: http://www.sarabandebooks.org

(F) The *Mary McCarthy Prize in Short Fiction* awards $2,000 and publication by Sarabande for a collection of short stories or novellas. Winners receive a standard royalty contract. Send SASE or visit the Web site for guidelines and entry form.

Available to: U.S. resident citizens
Deadline: Submissions accepted January 1–February 15
Apply to: Mary McCarthy Prize in Short Fiction, above address

(P) The *Kathryn A. Morton Prize in Poetry* awards $2,000 and publication by Sarabande for a full-length volume of poetry. Winners receive a standard royalty contract. Send SASE or visit the Web site for guidelines and entry form.

Available to: U.S. resident citizens
Deadline: Submissions accepted January 1–February 15
Apply to: Kathryn A. Morton Prize in Poetry, above address

Sasquatch Books
615 Second Avenue
Seattle, WA 98104
E-mail: books@sasquatchbooks.com
Web site: http://www.SasquatchBooks.com

(F) (N) The *Chinook Prize*, consisting of $10,000 and publication by Sasquatch Books, is given for an unpublished book-length literary work of fiction or nonfiction with Pacific Northwest themes, origins, characters, or sources. The winner is announced at Northwest Bookfest, an annual literary arts festival in Seattle. Send SASE or e-mail for additional information and guidelines.

Available to: No restrictions
Deadline: Inquire
Apply to: Chinook Prize, above address

Scholastic
555 Broadway
New York, NY 10012-3999
Web site: http://www.scholastic.com/artandwriting

The *Scholastic Writing Awards* offer junior and senior high school students (grades 7 through 12) cash prizes from $100 to $5,000 in ten categories. Several scholarship grants and publishing opportunities are also available. Write or visit the Web site for further information and application procedures.

Available to: Students grades 7 through 12
Deadline: Varies by geographic region (inquire)
Apply to: Scholastic Writing Awards, above address

Schomburg Center for Research in Black Culture
515 Malcolm X Boulevard
New York, NY 10037-1801
Web site: http://www.nypl.org/research/sc/scm/scholars.html

The *Scholars-in-Residence Program* at the Schomburg Center is designed to encourage research and writing in black history and culture. Fellows spend six months or a year in residence, with access to resources at the Schomburg Center and the New York Public Library; they receive a maximum stipend of $15,000 for six months and up to $30,000 for twelve. The program is open to scholars studying black history and culture from a humanist perspective and to professionals in fields related to the Center's collections. Studies in social sciences, the arts, science and technology, psychology, education, and religion are eligible if they use a humanistic approach and contribute to humanistic knowledge. Write or visit the Web site for additional information and application materials.

Available to: U.S. citizens or foreign nationals resident in the United States at least three years immediately before application
Deadline: January 15
Apply to: Scholars-in-Residence Program, above address

Schoolcraft College
18600 Haggerty Road
Livonia, MI 48152
E-mail: alindenb@schoolcraft.cc.mi.us

Ⓟ The *MacGuffin National Poet Hunt* awards a $500 first prize, a $250 second prize, and a $100 third prize for an unpublished poem. All winning entries will appear in *The MacGuffin*, a magazine published three times a year by Schoolcraft College. Poets may submit up to five poems, with a $15 entry fee. Send SASE for guidelines.

Available to: No restrictions
Deadline: Submissions accepted April 1–May 31
Apply to: MacGuffin National Poet Hunt, above address

Scripps Howard Foundation
312 Walnut Street, 28th floor
Cincinnati, OH 45202-5380
E-mail: cottingham@scripps.com
Web site: http://www.scripps.com/foundation
Fax: 513-977-3800

Ⓙ The *Business/Economic Reporting/William Brewster Styles Award* of $2,500 is given for outstanding business and/or economics reporting published during the preceding calendar year. There is a $25 entry fee. Write, e-mail, or visit the Web site for guidelines and entry form.

Available to: Daily newspaper journalists in the United States and its territories
Deadline: January 31
Apply to: Business/Economic Reporting Award, above address

Ⓙ The *Commentary Award* of $2,500 honors outstanding commentary by a columnist whose signed work appeared regularly in a daily newspaper in the United States or its territories during the preceding calendar year. There is a $25 entry fee. Write, e-mail, or visit the Web site for guidelines and entry form.

Available to: Daily newspaper journalists in the United States and its territories
Deadline: January 31
Apply to: Commentary Award, above address

☺ The *Editorial Writing/Walker Stone Award* of $2,500 annually honors outstanding achievement in editorial writing. Submitted material must have been published in a newspaper in the preceding calendar year; work published in magazines is not eligible. There is a $25 entry fee. Write, e-mail, or visit the Web site for guidelines and entry form.

Available to: Daily newspaper journalists in the United States and its territories
Deadline: January 31
Apply to: Editorial Writing Award, above address

☺ The *Environmental Reporting/Edward J. Meeman Awards* recognize outstanding environmental reporting published in daily newspapers during the preceding calendar year. A $2,500 prize is given in each of two categories: newspapers with a circulation over 100,000 and newspapers with a circulation under 100,000. The awards encourage journalists to help educate the public and public officials toward better understanding of the environment and environmental protection. There is a $25 entry fee. Write, e-mail, or visit the Web site for guidelines and entry form.

Available to: Daily newspaper journalists in the United States and its territories
Deadline: January 31
Apply to: Environmental Reporting Awards, above address

☺ The *Human Interest/Ernie Pyle Writing Award* of $2,500 is given annually to an individual whose newspaper writing "most exemplifies the style and craftsmanship of the late Ernie Pyle [who wrote] movingly about everyday people with everyday dreams." Warmth, human interest, and storytelling ability rank high in the judging. Submitted material must have been published in a newspaper in the preceding calendar year. There is a $25 entry fee. Write, e-mail, or visit the Web site for guidelines and entry form.

Available to: Daily newspaper journalists in the United States and its territories
Deadline: January 31
Apply to: Human Interest Award, above address

☺ The *Roy W. Howard National Reporting Competition* encourages college students who aspire to the profession to which Howard dedicated his life. The competition is open to college freshmen, sophomores, and juniors. Entrants may submit one story or a series, published in a campus or professional newspaper, involving events, trends, or personalities. The winners receive a cash prize and an all-expenses-paid trip to Indiana University. Write to the address listed below or visit the Web site for additional information and application.

Available to: See above
Deadline: Inquire
Apply to: Trevor Brown, Dean, School of Journalism, Indiana University, Bloomington, IN 47405. (812) 855-9249

☺ The *Public Service Reporting/Roy W. Howard Awards* recognize outstanding public service and/or investigative reporting published in daily newspapers during the preceding calendar year. A $2,500 prize is given in each of two categories: newspapers with a circulation over 100,000 and newspapers with a circulation under 100,000. There is a $25 entry fee. Write, e-mail, or visit the Web site for guidelines and entry form.

Available to: Daily newspaper journalists in the United States and its territories
Deadline: January 31
Apply to: Public Service Reporting Awards, above address

☺ The Scripps Howard Foundation awards internships to journalism students. Selected students at participating schools (in 1999, Ohio University's E.W. Scripps School of Journalism, the University of Tennessee College of Communications, Indiana University School of Journalism, and the University of Kentucky School of Journalism and Telecommunications) receive grants allowing them to work in a professional site agreeable to them and approved by the school. Professional organizations provide meaningful work and instructive supervision, and the schools monitor, evaluate, and counsel the students. Write for additional information.

Available to: Journalism students at participating schools
Deadline: Inquire
Apply to: Internship Program, above address

Seattle Arts Commission
312 First Avenue North
Seattle, WA 98109
Web site: http://www.pan.ci.seattle.wa.us/sac

Ⓜ   The *Seattle Artist Program* offers awards of $2,000 and $7,500 to Seattle artists in a variety of disciplines, including poetry, prose/fiction, scriptwriting, screenwriting, and critical writing/creative nonfiction. Write for further information. Art forms to be awarded vary by year; literature grants will be awarded in 2000. Write or visit the Web site for further information.

Available to: Seattle artists
Deadline: Summer (inquire for exact date)
Apply to: Above address

Seattle Post-Intelligencer
101 Elliot Avenue, West
Seattle, WA 98119
E-mail: janetgrimley@Seattle-PI.com

Ⓙ   The *Bobbi McCallum Memorial Scholarship* of $1,000 is given to women college students attending a Washington State college or university who are interested in pursuing a newspaper career. Selection is based on need, academic achievement, and motivation. Application must include five samples of work, published or unpublished, a financial statement, and two letters of recommendation.

Available to: Women journalism majors entering their junior or senior year in college in
        Washington State
Deadline: March 1
Apply to: Janet Grimley, Assistant Managing Editor, above address

The Seattle Times
1120 John Street
Seattle, WA 98109

Ⓙ   *Summer Newsroom Internships* at the Pulitzer Prize–winning *Seattle Times* are offered annually to ten to twelve outstanding students pursuing a career in journalism. Most of the positions are for general assignment reporters working at the metro desk and in suburban bureaus. Applicants must be sophomores, juniors, or seniors attending a four-year college or university, or graduate students, and must be majoring in journalism or have demonstrated a commitment to journalism. Previous experience is required. Selected interns are placed in full-time, paid twelve-week positions. Write for additional information and application procedures.

Available to: See above
Deadline: November 1
Apply to: Newsroom Intern Coordinator, above address

Ⓙ   The *Blethen Family Newspaper Internship Program for Minorities* is a one-year program for college graduates committed to print journalism who are African-American, Asian-American, Latino, Native American, or Pacific Islanders. Interns spend four months in training at the *Walla Walla Union-Bulletin*, four months at the *Yakima Herald-Republic*, and a final four months at *The Seattle Times*. They receive housing, medical coverage, and salary ($260–$320 per week). Write for additional information and application procedures.

Available to: African-American, Asian-American, Latino, Native American, or Pacific
        Islander college graduates
Deadline: October 15, February 15, and June 15
Apply to: Patricia Foote, Assistant Managing Editor for Hiring, above address

Serpentine
1761 Edgewood Road
Redwood City, CA 94062
E-mail: contest@serpentinia.com
Web site: http://www.serpentinia.com

Ⓕ The *Serpentine Annual Short Story Contest* offers a first prize of $1,000, a second prize of $200, and six third prizes of $50 for short stories no longer than 10,000 words. Winners must supply story text in common electronic format to qualify for prize money and be published in a special on-line edition. The reading fee is $18 per manuscript. E-mail or visit the Web site for guidelines.

Available to: No restrictions
Deadline: December 31
Apply to: Above address

Seventeen Magazine
850 Third Avenue
New York, NY 10022

Ⓕ The *Seventeen Magazine Fiction Contest* is open to anyone between thirteen and twenty-one years of age. Each entry should be an unpublished short story not exceeding 4,000 words and should include the writer's birthdate, address, and signature. The winning writer will receive $1,000, a gift from the contest sponsor, Sally Hansen, and publication in *Seventeen*; the second-place winner receives $500, third-place $250, and five honorable mentions receive $50 each. Send SASE for rules.

Available to: See above
Deadline: April 30, 2000; inquire for 2001, or see the November 2000 issue of *Seventeen*
Apply to: Fiction Contest, above address

The Sewanee Review
University of the South
735 University Avenue
Sewanee, TN 37383-1000

ⓘ The *Aiken Taylor Award for Modern American Poetry* of $10,000 is given annually to a writer who has had a substantial and distinguished career. *By Internal Nomination Only.*

Sewanee Writers' Conference
310 St. Luke's Hall
735 University Avenue
Sewanee, TN 37383-1000

Ⓡ Numerous fellowships and scholarships are available for the annual twelve-day summer Sewanee Writers' Conference. Fellows receive full tuition plus room and board; most scholarships cover two-thirds of Conference expenses. Fellowship applicants in poetry and fiction must have a book published or in press at a major university or commercial publisher; candidates in playwriting should send details of work that has seen amateur or professional production. Scholarship applicants should have a number of publications in major academic or popular magazines. Applications are reviewed as they are received; early applications are encouraged. Send SASE for additional information and application.

Available to: See above
Deadline: Applications accepted from February 1, until spaces are filled
Apply to: Cheri Peters, Conference Coordinator, above address

Shenandoah
Washington and Lee University
Troubadour Theater, 2nd floor
Lexington, VA 24450
Fax: 540-463-8461

Ⓜ The following annual awards are given to work published in *Shenandoah* during the calendar year: the *James Boatwright III Prize for Poetry* of $1,000, to the author of the best poetry; the *Thomas H. Carter Prize for the Essay* of $500, to the author of the best essay; the *Jeanne Charpiot Goodheart Prize for Fiction* of $1,000, to the author of the best story. Send SASE for general guidelines.

Available to: *Shenandoah* contributors

Shenandoah International Playwrights Retreat
ShenanArts, Inc.
Route 5, Box 167-F
Staunton, VA 24401
E-mail: shenarts@mail.cfw.com
Fax: 540-248-7728

Ⓓ Ⓡ Ten to twelve playwrights and screenwriters are offered a four-week retreat in the Shenandoah Valley of Virginia. This August/September retreat features writers from specific regions of the world, as well as American writers. All collaborate with a multicultural company of professional theater artists in the translation, development, and adaptation of new plays and screenplays. Writers receive fellowships that provide round-trip transportation, room and board, and the services of the professional company. Write for additional information.

Available to: No restrictions
Deadline: February 1
Apply to: Above address

Joan Shorenstein Center on the Press, Politics, and Public Policy
John F. Kennedy School of Government
Harvard University
Cambridge, MA 02128
E-mail: Alison_Kommer@harvard.edu (for Goldsmith Awards only)
Web site: http://ksgwww.harvard.edu/~presspol/home.htm
Fax: 617-495-8696

Ⓝ The *Goldsmith Book Prize* offers $5,000 to the author(s) of the best English-language book that aims at improving the quality of government or politics through an examination of the press and government or the intersection of press and politics in the formation of public policy. Publication must have occurred within twelve months preceding the submission deadline. Edited volumes are not accepted. Write, e-mail, or visit the Web site for guidelines and application.

Available to: No restrictions
Deadline: November 1
Apply to: Goldsmith Book Prize, above address

Ⓙ The *Goldsmith Prize for Investigative Reporting* annually awards $25,000 to the journalist or journalists whose investigative reporting in a story or series best promotes more effective and ethical conduct of government, the making of public policy, or the practice of politics. The subject may relate to foreign policy, but only insofar as it has an impact on U.S. public policy. Publication must have occurred within twelve months preceding the submission deadline. Print and broadcast submissions are accepted. Write, e-mail, or visit the Web site for guidelines and application.

Available to: Journalists with U.S. news organizations
Deadline: November 1
Apply to: Goldsmith Prize for Investigative Reporting, above address

The *Goldsmith Research Awards* offer grants of varying amounts, rarely exceeding $5,000, to stimulate and assist research by scholars, graduate students, and journalists in the field of press/politics. Applications are accepted throughout the year; award recipients will be notified quarterly. Write, e-mail, or visit the Web site for guidelines and application.

Available to: No restrictions
Deadline: Ongoing
Apply to: Goldsmith Research Awards, above address

A limited number of resident fellowships are also available at the Center for established scholars, journalists, and policymakers interested in the relationship between the press and politics. Fellowships are for one academic semester (September through December, or February through May). During the term of the fellowship, participants are expected to conduct research and write a 40-page paper on a press/politics topic. Fellows participate in informal weekly seminars with visiting journalists, scholars, and policymakers, and in other activities sponsored by the Center. The program offers a stipend of $15,000 for the semester; travel and living expenses are not covered. Office space and a computer and printer are provided. Write or visit the Web site for additional information.

Available to: See above
Deadline: February 1
Apply to: Fellowship Program, above address

Siena College
Department of Creative Arts, Theatre Program
515 Loudon Road
Loudonville, NY 12211-1462
Web site: http://www.siena.edu/theatre/playwrights.htm

Ⓓ The *Siena College International Playwrights' Competition* biennially awards a $2,000 honorarium, full production, and up to $1,000 for travel, housing, and board during a four-to-six-week production residence for full-length, unpublished, unproduced, nonmusical plays. Scripts with roles for college-age performers, small casts, and simple sets are encouraged. Send SASE or visit the Web site for guidelines before submitting.

Available to: No restrictions
Deadline: February 1–June 30 in even-numbered years
Apply to: Siena College International Playwrights' Competition, above address

Sierra Repertory Theatre
Box 3030
Sonora, CA 95370
E-mail: srt@mlode.com
Web site: http://www.sierrarep.com
Fax: 209-532-7270

Ⓓ The *Marvin Taylor Playwriting Award* offers $500 and production to a full-length play that has received no more than two productions or staged readings, and that has no more than fifteen cast members and two sets.

Available to: No restrictions
Deadline: August 31
Apply to: Marvin Taylor Playwriting Award, above address

Silverfish Review Press
PO Box 3541
Eugene, OR 97403
E-mail: SFRpress@aol.com
Web site: http://www.qspeed.com/silverfish

Ⓟ The *Gerald Cable Book Award* annually offers $1,000 and publication by Silverfish Review Press for a book-length manuscript of original poetry by an author who has not published a full-length collection. Translations are not eligible. There is a $20 reading fee. Send SASE or e-mail for guidelines.

Available to: See above
Deadline: November 1
Apply to: Gerald Cable Book Award, above address

Sitka Center for Art and Ecology
Neskowin Coast Foundation
PO Box 65
Otis, OR 97368
E-mail: sitka@oregonvos.net
Web site: http://www.oregonvos.net/~sitka

® Residences of up to four months are offered to writers, naturalists, and artists at Cascade
Head Ranch, located within the Cascade Head National Scenic Research Area, in three
categories: emerging artist/naturalist, mid-career artist/naturalist, and artist/naturalist
on sabbatical. Each resident is provided with living and studio space and is asked to
provide community service on behalf of Sitka. Residents must provide their own food.
Write, e-mail, or visit the Web site for additional information and application.

Available to: No restrictions
Deadline: April 15
Apply to: Above address

Slipstream
Box 2071
New Market Station
Niagara Falls, NY 14301
Web site: http://www.slipstreampress.org

℗ The *Slipstream Annual Poetry Chapbook Contest* awards $1,000, publication of a chapbook for
the winning manuscript, and 50 copies of the book. All other entrants receive a copy, as
well as one issue of *Slipstream*. Send up to 40 pages of poetry, a $10 reading fee, and SASE
with sufficient postage for return of manuscript, if desired.

Available to: No restrictions
Deadline: December 1
Apply to: Above address

Gibbs Smith, Publisher
PO Box 667
Layton, UT 84041
E-mail: info@gibbs-smith.com
Web site: http://www.gibbs-smith.com
Fax: 801-544-5582

℗ The *Peregrine Smith Poetry Competition* awards a $500 prize plus publication by Gibbs Smith
for a book-length manuscript of poems, 48 to 64 typewritten pages. Submissions must be
accompanied by a $15 reading fee and SASE. Send SASE, e-mail, or visit the Web site for
guidelines.

Available to: No restrictions
Deadline: Submissions accepted in April only
Apply to: Peregrine Smith Poetry Competition, above address

The Smithsonian Institution
Office of Fellowships
955 L'Enfant Plaza, Suite 7000
Washington, DC 20560-0902
E-mail: siofg@ofg.si.edu
Web site: http://www.si.edu/research+study

Fellowships are offered by the Smithsonian Institution to graduate students, predoctoral
students, and postdoctoral and senior investigators, for opportunities to conduct

research in association with members of the Smithsonian professional research staff and to use Smithsonian resources. Graduate student fellows are appointed for ten weeks with a stipend of $8,500. Predoctoral, postdoctoral, and senior fellows are appointed for three to twelve months with a stipend of $15,000 per year for predoctoral and $27,000 per year for postdoctoral and senior fellows. A travel allowance and an allowance for research-related expenses, up to $2,000, are possible. Write for additional information and application.

Available to: No restrictions
Deadline: January 15
Apply to: Above address

Snake Nation Press
110 No. 2 West Force Street
Valdosta, GA 31601

(P)   The *Violet Reed Haas Poetry Prize* offers $500 and publication by Snake Nation Press for a 50-to-75-page manuscript of poems. There is a $10 entry fee, which covers a copy of the winning book. Write for further information.

Available to: No restrictions
Deadline: February 15
Apply to: Violet Reed Haas Poetry Prize, above address

Soapstone, A Writing Retreat for Women
622 SE 29 Avenue
Portland, OR 97214
Fax: 503-233-0774
E-mail: soapston@teleport.com

(R)   Residences of one to four weeks are given to between twenty-four and thirty-six women writers, who will be selected to come in pairs. Soapstone is located in the Coast Range in Oregon, approximately nine miles from the ocean, on twenty-two acres of land along the banks of the Soapstone Creek. When writers apply in pairs, each must be accepted individually on the merit of her work; single writers will be paired. Applicants are judged on the strength of their writing, with attention given to promoting diversity and to assisting women of limited economic means who may never have had such an opportunity. Residents are provided with blankets, pillows, and limited kitchen equipment. There is a $20 application fee. Send SASE for application.

Available to: Women writers
Deadline: August 15
Apply to: Above address

Social Science Research Council
810 Seventh Avenue
New York, NY 10019
E-mail: lastname@ssrc.org
Web site: http://www.ssrc.org
Fax: 212-377-2727

The Social Science Research Council is an autonomous, nongovernmental, not-for-profit international association devoted to the advancement of interdisciplinary research in the social sciences. It pursues this goal through a wide variety of fellowship and grant programs for training and research. Stipends vary according to geographic region and type of grant. Write for complete information.

Available to: Restrictions vary by program; inquire
Deadline: Varies by program; inquire
Apply to: Above address

Society of American Historians
c/o Professor Mark C. Carnes
Department of History
Barnard College
New York, NY 10027
E-mail: es28@columbia.edu
Fax: 212-222-4902

Ⓕ   The *James Fenimore Cooper Prize for Historical Fiction* of $2,500 is awarded every two years for
a work of literary fiction that significantly advances the historical imagination. The
winning entry is chosen for its literary quality and historical scholarship. For the next
prize, books must be copyrighted in 1999 or 2000. Publishers should submit one copy of
each eligible book to each selection committee member. Write for guidelines and names
and addresses of committee members.

Available to: No restrictions
Deadline: January 17, 2001 (earlier submission preferred)
Apply to: Above address

Ⓝ   The *Allan Nevins Prize,* for the best Ph.D. dissertation on a significant theme in American
history, is open to graduates of any Ph.D.-granting department in the United States. One
award of $1,000 is made each year. The winning manuscript is normally published by
one of the distinguished houses that currently support the prize. Manuscripts must be
submitted by the chairman of the department awarding the degree or by the sponsor of
the dissertation.

Available to: No restrictions
Deadline: January (inquire for exact date)
Apply to: Above address

Ⓝ   The *Francis Parkman Prize* is awarded for the best nonfiction book, including biography, on
any aspect of the history of what is now the United States published during the calendar
year. One award of $2,500, a certificate, and an engraved bronze medal is given annually.
The Parkman winner automatically becomes a selection of the History Book Club.
Publishers should submit one copy of each nominated title to each of the selection
committee members. Write for additional information and names and addresses of
committee members.

Available to: No restrictions
Deadline: January 15 (earlier submission preferred)
Apply to: Above address

Society of American Travel Writers Foundation
c/o Society of American Travel Writers
4101 Lake Boone Trail, Suite 201
Raleigh, NC 27607-6518
Web site: http://www.satw.org/public/lowell4.htm

Ⓙ   The *Lowell Thomas Travel Journalist Awards* offer a gold award of $1,000 and a silver award of
$500 for the best collection of three to nine entries published during the calendar year in
three of the following categories: newspaper travel section, travel magazine, newspaper
article on U.S./Canada travel, magazine article on U.S./Canada travel, newspaper article
on foreign travel, and magazine article on foreign travel. The individual travel articles
listed above are also eligible for separate $500 awards, as is work in the following
categories: special package/project, self-illustrated article, article on land travel, article
on marine travel, article on adventure travel, travel news/investigative reporting, service-
oriented consumer article, environmental tourism article, cultural tourism article, personal
comment, travel book (more personal than a guidebook), guidebook, Internet travel article.
Write or visit the Web site for further information.

Available to: No restrictions
Deadline: January 31
Apply to: Lowell Thomas Awards, c/o Dr. William McKeen, College of Journalism and
Communications, University of Florida, PO Box 118400, 2069 Weimer Hall,
Gainesville, FL 32611-8400

Society of Children's Book Writers
8271 Beverly Boulevard
Los Angeles, CA 90038
E-mail: membership@scbwi.org
Web site: http://www.scbwi.org
Fax: 323-782-1892

© Four *Work-in-Progress Grants*, one for a contemporary novel for young people, one for a work whose author has never had a book published, one for a general work-in-progress, and one for a nonfiction research project, will be awarded annually. Each grant is $1,000, and each category offers a runner-up award of $500. Write, e-mail, or visit the Web site for additional information.

Available to: Full and associate members of the Society of Children's Book Writers
Deadline: Applications accepted February 1–March 1
Apply to: Above address

© The *Barbara Karlin Grant* recognizes and encourages the work of aspiring picture-book writers who have never had a picture book published. One grant of $1,000 is awarded annually. Write, e-mail, or visit the Web site for additional information.

Available to: Full and associate members of the Society of Children's Book Writers
Deadline: Applications accepted April 1–May 15
Apply to: Barbara Karlin Grant, above address

Society for Historians of American Foreign Relations
Wright State University
Department of History
Dayton, OH 45435

Ⓝ The *Myrna Bernath Book Award* of $2,500 is given biennially for a book on diplomatic affairs written by a woman. Books must have been published during the two years preceding the award year. Write to the contact below for the name and address of the current committee chair.

Available to: Women
Deadline: Inquire
Apply to: Katherine Sibley, St. Joseph's University, Department of History, 5600 City Avenue, Philadelphia, PA 19131

Ⓝ The *Stuart L. Bernath Book Prize* of $2,500 is given to a young author for a first book dealing with any aspect of the history of American foreign relations. One award is available annually for books published during the preceding year. Write to the contact below for the name and address of the current committee chair.

Available to: No restrictions
Deadline: February 1
Apply to: Doron Ben-Atar, Fordham University, Department of History, 113 West 60th Street, New York, NY 10023

Society for the History of Technology
John Hopkins University
Department of History
Baltimore, MD 21218
Web site: http://shot.press.jhu.edu/associations/shot

Ⓝ The *Dexter Prize* of $2,000 is offered annually to the author of an outstanding book on the history of technology published during the three years preceding the award. Publishers or authors may call attention to their books by writing to the secretary of the Society; three copies of the book must accompany letters of nomination.

Available to: No restrictions
Deadline: April 15
Apply to: Professor Stuart Leslie, Secretary, above address

(N) The *Society for the History of Technology Popular Book Prize* of $2,000 is given for the best popular book on the history of technology directed to a broad audience, including students and the interested public. The nominated book must have been written in the three years preceding the award. The book should assume that the reader has no prior knowledge of the subject or its method of treatment, and should provide an elucidating explanation of technological change in history with a minimum of technical or academic prose. Send SASE or visit the Web site for nomination and submission procedures.

Available to: No restrictions
Deadline: April 1
Apply to: Above address for submission procedures

Society for the Study of the Short Story
1817 Marengo Street
New Orleans, LA 70115

(F) The Society's *Short Story Contest* annually offers a first prize of $500 and a second of $100 for a short story. The winners are published in the journal *Short Story* and invited to read at the International Conference on the Short Story in English, which takes place in October. There is a $15 entry fee. Send SASE for guidelines.

Available to: No restrictions
Deadline: July 31
Apply to: Short Story Contest, above address

Society for the Study of Social Problems
University of Tennessee
906 McClung Tower
Knoxville, TN 37996-0490
E-mail: mkoontz3@utk.edu
Web site: http://www.it.ukt.edu/sssp
Fax: 423-974-7013

(N) The *C. Wright Mills Award* is an annual prize of $500 for the book that best exemplifies social science scholarship, published during the calendar year preceding that in which the award is made.

Available to: No restrictions
Deadline: January (inquire for exact date)
Apply to: Tom Hood, Executive Officer, above address

Sons of the Republic of Texas
1717 8th Street
Bay City, TX 77414
E-mail: srttexas@srttexas.org
Web site: http://www.srttexas.org
Fax: 409-245-6644

The *Presidio La Bahia Award* is given for writing that promotes research into and preservation of the Spanish colonial influence on Texas culture. A total of $2,000 is available annually as an award or awards (depending on number and quality of entries), with a minimum first prize of $1,200. Send SASE for additional information and guidelines.

Available to: No restrictions
Deadline: September 30
Apply to: Above address

(M) The *Summerfield G. Roberts Award* of $2,500 is given annually for the best book or manuscript of biography, essay, nonfiction, fiction (novel, or short story), or poetry that describes or represents the Republic of Texas, 1836–1846. The manuscript must be written or published during the calendar year for which the award is given. Send SASE for additional information and guidelines.

Available to: U.S. citizens

Deadline: January 15
Apply to: Above address

(N) The *Texas History Essay Contest* offers a first prize of $3,000, a second of $2,000, and a third of $1,000 for an essay on a particular topic related to Texas history by a graduating high school senior. Essays must be between 1,500 and 2,000 words. Send SASE, e-mail, or visit the Web site for guidelines.

Available to: Graduating high school seniors
Deadline: February 3, 2001
Apply to: Texas History Essay Contest, above address

Source Theatre Company
1835 14th Street, NW
Washington, DC 20009
Web site: http://www.dcmdva-arts.org/sourceth

(D) The *Source Theatre Company Literary Prize* annually offers $250 and workshop production at the Washington Theatre Festival for a professionally unproduced play. Send SASE for additional information and guidelines.

Available to: No restrictions
Deadline: January 15
Apply to: Keith Parker, Literary Manager, above address

South Carolina Academy of Authors
c/o College of Charleston
MSC 2700
Charleston, SC 29424

(M) Nine fellowship awards—three each in the categories of poetry, fiction, and drama—are offered annually to South Carolina writers who have not published more than one book. The awards in each category consist of a first prize of $500, a second of $300, and a third of $200. There is a $5 fee per entry. Send SASE for guidelines.

Available to: South Carolina residents
Deadline: December 15
Apply to: Above address

South Carolina Arts Commission
1800 Gervais Street
Columbia, SC 29201
Web site: http://www.state.sc.us/arts
Fax: 803-734-8526

(M) The *Individual Artist Fellowships in Literature*, $7,500 each, are given to poets, playwrights, and fiction or creative nonfiction writers of exceptional promise or proven professional ability, to set aside time, purchase materials, or otherwise advance their careers. Prose and poetry fellowships are awarded in alternating years. Full-time undergraduate students are not eligible.

Available to: South Carolina residents
Deadline: February 15, 2001, for prose; February 15, 2002 for poetry
Apply to: Fellowships Program, above address

(M) *Individual Artist Project Grants* of up to $5,000 in matching funds are offered to writers with specific projects.

Available to: South Carolina residents
Deadline: April 1 and September 1, 2000
Apply to: Project Grants, above address

(F) The *South Carolina Fiction Project*, co-sponsored by the South Carolina Arts Commission and the Charleston *Post and Courier*, offers a short story competition. Stories are selected by a panel of professional writers; the winners receive $500 each and publication in the *Post and Courier*. Up to twelve stories are selected annually with monthly publication in the paper.

Available to: South Carolina residents
Deadline: January 15
Apply to: South Carolina Fiction Project, above address

South Coast Repertory
Box 2197
Costa Mesa, CA 92628
Fax: 714-545-0391

Ⓓ The *Hispanic Playwrights Project* selects full-length plays by Hispanic-American playwrights for workshops at South Coast Repertory, at which the playwrights work with directors and casts of professional actors. New, unproduced plays are preferred; previously produced plays that would benefit from further development may also be considered. Musicals are not accepted, nor are plays written fully in Spanish. Manuscripts should be submitted with a synopsis and a biography of the playwright.

Available to: Hispanic-American playwrights
Deadline: January
Apply to: Juliette Carrillo, Director, Hispanic Playwrights Project, above address

South Dakota Arts Council
800 Governors Drive
Pierre, SD 57501-2294
E-mail: sdac@stlib.state.sd.us
Web site: http://www.sdarts.org
Fax: 605-773-6962

Ⓜ *Artist Grants* of $3,000 each are available annually to South Dakota residents of at least two years, in general writing, fiction, and nonfiction. Write for guidelines and application.

Available to: South Dakota residents
Deadline: March 1
Apply to: Dennis Holub, Executive Director, above address

Ⓜ Forty to fifty *Artists-in-Schools* grants of approximately $800 per week are available annually in general writing, fiction, and nonfiction. Write for guidelines and application.

Available to: Practicing professional artists living in neighboring states who wish to work
    in residence in South Dakota, at all grade levels
Deadline: October 1
Apply to: Michael Pangburn, Arts Coordinator, above address

Ⓜ Some thirty-six *Touring Arts Programs* (about one-half fee paid to presenter) are available annually in general writing, fiction, and nonfiction. Write for guidelines and application.

Available to: Practicing artists who wish to tour South Dakota cities
Deadline: October 1
Apply to: Michael Pangburn, Assistant Director, above address

Southeastern Theatre Conference
Box 9868
Greensboro, NC 27429-0868
E-mail: setc@mindspring.org
Web site: http://www.setc.org

Ⓓ The *Charles M. Getchell New Play Award* offers $1,000, a staged reading at the SETC Annual Convention, paid travel, and room and board to attend the convention, and submission of the winning work to the O'Neill Center for favored consideration at the National Playwrights Conference, for an unproduced, full-length play or bill of two related one-acts by a resident of the states in the SETC region. Send SASE for guidelines before submitting.

Available to: Residents of Alabama, Florida, Georgia, Kentucky, Mississippi, North Carolina, South Carolina, Tennessee, Virginia, or West Virginia
Deadline: Submissions accepted March 1–June 1
Apply to: New Play Award, above address

Southern Appalachian Repertory Theatre
Box 1720
Mars Hill, NC 28754-1720

Ⓓ The *Southern Appalachian Playwrights' Conference* selects up to five playwrights to participate in a three-day conference in April at which one work by each writer is given an informal reading and critiqued by a panel of theater professionals. One work may be selected each year for production in the theater's summer season. Playwrights receive room and board, and the writer of the work selected for production receives a $500 honorarium. Send SASE for guidelines.

Available to: No restrictions
Deadline: October 30
Apply to: Southern Appalachian Playwrights' Conference, above address

Southern Environmental Law Center
201 West Main Street, Suite 14
Charlottesville, VA 22902-5065
E-mail: selcva@selcva.org
Web site: http://www.southernenvironment.org
Fax: 804-977-1483

Ⓝ The *Phillip D. Reed Memorial Award for Outstanding Writing on the Southern Environment* is given for work that relates to the natural environment in any or all of the states of Alabama, Georgia, North Carolina, South Carolina, Tennessee, and Virginia. A prize of $1,000 is offered in journalistic nonfiction, such as a newspaper series or magazine article, and in literary nonfiction, such as a book or essay. Submissions must be at least 3,000 words and must have been published during the calendar year preceding the award deadline. Write, e-mail, or visit the Web site for guidelines.

Available to: No restrictions
Deadline: March 1
Apply to: Cathryn McCue, above address

Southern Historical Association
Department of History
University of Georgia
Athens, GA 30602
E-mail: gsdavis@arches.uga.edu
Web site: http://www.uga.edu/~sha
Fax: 706-542-2455

Ⓝ The *Frank Lawrence and Harriet Chappell Owsley Award*, given in odd-numbered years for a book published in even-numbered years, honors a distinguished work in southern history. The *H. L. Mitchell Award*, given in even-numbered years for a book published in the two preceding years, honors a distinguished work about the history of the southern working class, including but not limited to industrial laborers and/or small farmers and agricultural laborers. The *Francis Butler Simpkins Award*, given in odd-numbered years for a book published in the preceding two years, honors the best first book by an author in southern history. The *Charles S. Sydnor Prize*, given in even-numbered years for a book published in odd-numbered years, honors a distinguished work in southern history. All awards carry a cash prize.

Available to: U.S. citizens
Deadline: Inquire
Apply to: Above address

Southern Oregon University
Extended Campus Programs
1250 Siskiyou Boulevard
Ashland, OR 97250
E-mail: friendly@sou.edu

® The *Walden Residency Program* offers residences of six weeks for writers of drama, fiction, poetry, and creative nonfiction. Send #10 SASE for application form.

Available to: Oregon residents
Deadline: Last working day in November
Apply to: Brooke Friendly, above address

The Southern Poetry Review
Advancement Studies Department
Central Piedmont Community College
Charlotte, NC 28235

℗ The *Guy Owen Poetry Prize* of $500 is given annually for the best poem selected by an outside judge. A maximum of five poems may be submitted with an $8 entry fee, which covers a one-year subscription to *The Southern Poetry Review*.

Available to: No restrictions
Deadline: Submissions accepted April 1–May 1
Apply to: Guy Owen Poetry Prize, above address

The Southern Review
Louisiana State University
43 Allen Hall
Baton Rouge, LA 70803
E-mail: bmacon@unix1.sncc.LSU.edu
Web site: http://www.LSU.edu/guests/wwwtsm
Fax: 504-388-5098

Ⓕ The *Southern Review/Louisiana State University Short Fiction Award* offers $500 to the best first collection of short stories by a U.S. writer published in the United States in the preceding year. Publishers or authors should send two copies of qualifying books for consideration.

Available to: U.S. citizens
Deadline: January 31
Apply to: Above address

The Southerner
University of Tennessee
Box 8820
Knoxville, TN 37996
Web site: http://www.southerner.net/warrenprize.html

Ⓕ The *Robert Penn Warren Prize for Fiction* offers a first prize of $1,000, a second of $500, and a third of $250 for published writers and a first prize of $500, a second of $250, and a third of $100 for unpublished writers of short stories with southern themes, characters, or settings. Submissions should not exceed 5,000 words. For the purposes of this contest, only published novelists and short story authors are considered published writers; published poets and nonfiction writers, including journalists, should apply as unpublished writers. There is a $10 entry fee. Send SASE or visit the Web site for contest rules.

Available to: See above
Deadline: October 15
Apply to: Robert Penn Warren Prize, above address

The Southwest Review
307 Fondren Library West
Box 374
Southern Methodist University
Dallas, TX 75275
E-mail: SWR@mail.smu.edu
Fax: 214-768-1408

Ⓕ Ⓝ The *John H. McGinnis Memorial Awards* of $1,000 are given annually for the best essay and best story appearing in *The Southwest Review* during the preceding year.

Available to: *Southwest Review* contributors
Apply to: Above address

Ⓟ The *Elizabeth Matchett Stover Memorial Award* of $200 is awarded annually for the best poem or group of poems published in the magazine during the preceding year.

Available to: *Southwest Review* contributors
Apply to: Above address

Sow's Ear Poetry Review
19535 Pleasant View Drive
Abingdon, VA 24211-6827
E-mail: richman@prefered.com

Ⓟ The *Sow's Ear Chapbook Competition* offers a first prize of $500, publication, and 25 copies of the chapbook (and distribution to subscribers); a second prize of $200; and a third of $100 for the best collection of poems, 22 to 26 pages total. Simultaneous submissions are accepted. There is a $10 entry fee, which covers a copy of the winning chapbook, if specified. Send SASE or e-mail for guidelines.

Available to: No restrictions
Deadline: Submissions accepted March–April
Apply to: Chapbook Competition, above address

Ⓟ The *Sow's Ear Poetry Competition* offers a first prize of $1,000, a second of $250, and a third of $100 for the best unpublished poems. Winners as well as some fifteen to twenty finalists are published in the review. Simultaneous submissions are accepted. There is a reading fee of $2 per poem; submission of five poems or more entitles entrant to a subscription to *Sow's Ear*. Send SASE or e-mail for guidelines.

Available to: No restrictions
Deadline: Submissions accepted September–October
Apply to: Poetry Competition, above address

SPAIN
Cultural Office
Embassy of Spain
2375 Pennsylvania Avenue, NW
Washington, DC 20037

Ⓜ Several organizations and foundations in Spain offer sizable literary prizes to authors of all nationalities for unpublished work (fiction, poetry, nonfiction) written in Castilian. Information may be obtained from the Consulate General of Spain.

Available to: Authors writing in Castilian
Deadline: Inquire
Apply to: Above address

Spoon River Poetry Review
4241 Department of English
Publication Unit
Illinois State University
Normal, IL 61790-4241

(P)   The *Editor's Prize* awards $1,000 and publication in *Spoon River Poetry Review* for an unpublished poem. Two second-place prizes of $100 each are also awarded. All submissions are considered for publication. Poets may submit up to three poems, of no more than 10 pages total, in duplicate, with the poet's name on one copy only. A reading fee of $15 covers a one-year subscription to the review. Send SASE for guidelines.

Available to: No restrictions
Deadline: April 15
Apply to: Editor's Prize, above address

Spuyten Duyvil
PO Box 1852
Cathedral Station
New York, NY 10025
Web site: http://www.spuytenduyvil.net

(P)   The *Spuyten Duyvil Book Award* offers $500 and publication for a full-length poetry manuscript. Poets should submit manuscripts of 40 to 60 pages, with title page and table of contents. There is a $25 reading fee.

Available to: No restrictions
Deadline: Submissions accepted May 1–December 31
Apply to: Book Award, above address

SQUARE magazine
99 Park Avenue, Suite 387
New York, NY 10016
Web site: http://www.squaremagazine.com

(S)   The *SQUARE magazine Screenwriting Award* offers $2,000 for an original film or TV screenplay in any genre, up to 120 pages. There is a $40 entry fee. Send SASE or visit the Web site for guidelines and entry form.

Available to: No restrictions
Deadline: Inquire
Apply to: Screenwriting Award, above address

(S)   The *SQUARE magazine Television Award* offers a first prize of $500 for a spec script or pilot for a half-hour sitcom or a one-hour drama. The second-place winner is entitled to a $100 shopping spree at Amazon.com. There is a $30 entry fee. Send SASE or visit the Web site for guidelines and entry form.

Available to: No restrictions
Deadline: Inquire
Apply to: Television Award, above address

STAGE (Society for Theatrical Artists' Guidance and Enhancement)
PO Box 214820
Dallas, TX 75221
E-mail: stage_tx@swbell.net
Web site: http://www.stage-online.org
Fax: 214-630-4468

(D)   The *STAGE Festival of New Plays* offers productions of previously unproduced one-act plays no more than 30 minutes' long. Winning playwrights receive an honorarium and full production. Write for guidelines.

Available to: No restrictions

Deadline: Inquire
Apply to: Operations Manager, above address

Stanford University
Building 120, Room 424
Stanford, CA 94305-2050
E-mail: knightfellow@forsythe.stanford.edu
Web site: http://www.stanford.edu/dept/communication/general/knightfellow
Fax: 650-725-6154

Ⓙ   The *John S. Knight Fellowships* are offered each year to twelve U.S. mid-career journalists who have demonstrated uncommon excellence in their work and who have the potential of reaching the top ranks in their specialties. The fellowships are awarded for an academic year, from mid-September to mid-June. Fellows receive a stipend of $45,000, plus a book allowance. The program pays university tuition for all fellows. Applicants must have at least seven years' full-time professional experience. Write, e-mail, or fax for additional information and application.

Available to: Professional journalists
Deadline: February 1
Apply to: John S. Knight Fellowships, above address

Stanford University
Creative Writing Center
Department of English
Stanford, CA 94305-2087
E-mail: Gay.pierce@forsythe.stanford.edu
Web site: http://www.stanford.edu/dept/english/cw
Fax: 415-723-3679

Ⓕ Ⓟ   Ten *Wallace E. Stegner Fellowships* are offered to five promising fiction writers and five poets who can benefit from residence at the university and from the instruction and criticism of the staff of the writing program. The two-year fellowships provide a stipend of $15,000 each year, plus the required tuition (about $6,000). Previous publication is not essential.

Available to: No restrictions
Deadline: December 1
Apply to: Program Coordinator, Wallace E. Stegner Fellowships, above address

State Historical Society of Wisconsin
816 State Street
Madison, WI 53706-1488
Web site: http://www.shsw.wisc.edu
Fax: 608-264-6404

The *John C. Geilfuss Fellowship* of $2,000 is awarded for research at the graduate level and beyond in Wisconsin and U.S. business and economic history. Preference is given to topics on Wisconsin and the American Midwest and/or for research using the collections of the State Historical Society. Write for further information and guidelines.

Available to: No restrictions
Deadline: February 1
Apply to: Dr. Michael E. Stevens, State Historian, above address

The *Amy Louise Hunter Fellowship* of $2,500 is awarded in even-numbered years for research on topics related to the history of women and public policy, broadly construed. Preference is given to Wisconsin topics and/or for research using the collections of the State Historical Society. Write for further information and guidelines.

Available to: No restrictions
Deadline: May 1, 2000, and 2002
Apply to: Dr. Michael E. Stevens, State Historian, above address

The *Alice E. Smith Fellowship* of $2,000 is awarded to women doing research in American history. Preference is given to applicants doing graduate research in the history of Wisconsin or the Middle West. Write for further information and guidelines.

Available to: Women historians
Deadline: July 15
Apply to: Dr. Michael E. Stevens, State Historian, above address

Story Line Press
Three Oaks Farm
PO Box 1240
Ashland, OR 97520-0055
E-mail: mail@storylinepress.com
Web site: http://www.storylinepress.com
Fax: 541-512-8793

Ⓝ The *Beryl Markham Prize for Creative Nonfiction* awards $1,500 and publication by Story Line for a book-length work of creative nonfiction. Memoirs and book-length collections of essays are eligible; literary criticism and theory is not. There is a $25 reading fee. Send SASE or visit the Web site for guidelines.

Available to: No restrictions
Deadline: July 31
Apply to: Beryl Markham Prize for Creative Nonfiction, above address

Ⓟ The *Nicholas Roerich Poetry Prize* awards $1,000, publication by Story Line, and a reading at the Nicholas Roerich Museum in New York City to the author of a first book-length poetry manuscript. Submissions should be accompanied by SASE, $20 reading fee, and a brief biography. The runner-up receives a full scholarship as the Nicholas Roerich/Story Line Press Fellow to the Wesleyan Writers' Conference. Send SASE or visit the Web site for guidelines.

Available to: Poets who have not published a book-length volume of poetry
Deadline: October 31
Apply to: Nicholas Roerich Poetry Prize, above address

Ⓕ The *Three Oaks Prize for Fiction* awards $1,500 and publication by Story Line for a novel, novella, or book-length collection of short stories. There is a $25 entry fee. Send SASE or visit the Web site for guidelines.

Available to: No restrictions
Deadline: April 30
Apply to: Three Oaks Prize, above address

STUDIO for Creative Inquiry
Carnegie Mellon University
College of Fine Arts
Pittsburgh, PA 15213-3890
E-mail: info-studio@andrew.cmu.edu
Web site: http://www.cmu.edu/studio
Fax: 412-268-2829

Ⓡ Two to five residences per year are offered concurrently to artists in all disciplines who are interested in cross-disciplinary and exploratory work in the arts. The broad mission of STUDIO is to facilitate work in two major areas: artistic creation and development of educational tools. Projects include work with interactive electronic media, computer-based telecommunications, the environment, light, virtual reality, and artificial intelligence. Residents receive a stipend and have access to the resources of the University. Assistance is offered in finding housing in the community. Send SASE, e-mail, or visit the Web site for additional information.

Available to: No restrictions
Deadline: Inquire
Apply to: Above address

Sundance Institute
225 Santa Monica Boulevard, 8th floor
Santa Monica, CA 90401
E-mail: sundance@deltanet.com
Web site: http://www.sundance.org
Fax: 310-394-8353

Ⓓ Ⓢ The *Sundance Institute Feature Film Program* for playwrights, screenwriters, and filmmaking
teams includes a five-day screenwriters' lab in January and June offering participants
one-on-one problem-solving sessions with professional screenwriters; a three-week
filmmakers' lab in June, in which projects are explored with directors, writers, actors,
cinematographers, producers, editors, and others; and a network/advisory service
providing practical and creative assistance to selected projects. The program awards travel,
and room and board for at least one writer/filmmaker per project, with possible room
and board for additional team members. Special interest is given to supporting new talent
and artists in transition (e.g., theater artists who want to work in film, writers who want
to direct). There is a $25 entry fee. Send SASE for guidelines and application form, or visit
the Web site.

Available to: No restrictions
Deadline: Early May (inquire for exact date)
Apply to: Feature Film Program, above address

Ⓓ The *Sundance Theatre Laboratory* is a three-week workshop offering playwrights and other
theater artists the opportunity to develop new plays or explore new approaches to existing
scripts. Up to eight projects are selected for the Laboratory, which is held at Sundance in
Utah in July. The Laboratory provides professional actors, dramaturgs, rehearsal space,
stage management, round-trip air transportation, accommodations, and food for the team
working on each project. Applications may be submitted by individual playwrights,
though playwright/directors teams are preferred. There is a $25 entry fee. Write or visit
the Web site for guidelines and application.

Available to: No restrictions
Deadline: December 15
Apply to: Sundance Theatre Laboratory, above address

Sunset Center
Box 1950
Carmel, CA 93921

Ⓓ The *Festival of Firsts Playwriting Competition* offers up to $1,000 and possible production for
previously unproduced full-length plays. Musicals and operas are not eligible. Send SASE
for guidelines and entry form.

Available to: No restrictions
Deadline: Submissions accepted June 15–August 31
Apply to: Brian Donoghue, Director, above address

SWEDEN
Swedish Information Service
Bicentennial Fund
One Dag Hammarskjöld Plaza, 45th floor
New York, NY 10017-2201
Web site: http://www.swedeninfo.com
Fax: 212-752-4789

The Swedish Bicentennial Fund, which fosters the exchange of qualified persons between
the United States and Sweden, provides opportunity for study and contact, for two-to-
four-week periods, for individuals in a position to influence public opinion and contribute
to the development of their society in areas of current concern. Approximately ten grants,
usually equal to 25,000 Swedish crowns each, are awarded annually. Grants are intended
to be used for transportation and living expenses. Study projects must be carefully defined,
and should include a detailed plan for achieving specific goals. Applicants who have

visited Sweden many times will be considered only in exceptional cases. Two letters of recommendation are required. Send SASE or visit the Web site for guidelines and application.

Available to: U.S. citizens or permanent residents
Deadline: First Friday in February
Apply to: Above address

SWITZERLAND
Château de Lavigny International Writers' Colony
Fondation Ledig-Rowohlt
Montbenon 2
CH-1003 Lausanne
Switzerland

⑱ Residences are offered in June, July, and August, for two-week or one-month stays, to published writers. A private room and all meals are provided (breakfast and lunch are self-service; dinner is prepared and served). The château features shared common areas and gardens. Writers arrange their own transportation to and from Switzerland; they will be met at the Geneva airport or the Lausanne or Morges train stations. Write for additional information and guidelines.

Available to: No restrictions; fluency in French or English required
Deadline: March 1
Apply to: Anna Bourgeois, Program Director, above address

Syracuse University
Department of English
401 Hall of Languages
Syracuse, NY 13244-1170
E-mail: tazollo@syr.edu
Web site: http://sumweb.syr.edu/english

Ⓕ Ⓟ The Syracuse Department of English offers five one-year fellowships to applicants for the MFA degree in creative writing: the *Cornelia Carhart Ward Fellowship* (fiction), the *Elise G. Mead Fellowship* (poetry), and three *Creative Writing Fellowships*. In 1998–1999 the Ward Fellowship carried a stipend of $10,577, the Mead Fellowship a stipend of $12,000, and each of the Creative Writing Fellowships a stipend of $7,523. All fellowships include remitted tuition for a full-time load of twenty-four credit hours for the academic year.

Available to: Syracuse Creative Writing applicants
Deadline: January 1
Apply to: Director, Creative Writing Program, above address

Syracuse University Press
621 Skytop Road, Suite 110
Syracuse, NY 13244-5290

Ⓝ The *John Ben Snow Prize* of $1,500 is given annually for a nonfiction manuscript on some aspect of New York State that makes the most distinguished contribution to the study of the upstate area. The prize includes publication by the Press, and the money is given as an advance against royalties. No substantial portion of the manuscript submitted may have been previously published. Unrevised theses and dissertations are not eligible; dissertations available in photocopied and microfilm forms are considered published and therefore ineligible. Authors are urged to send a query letter before submitting manuscripts.

Available to: No restrictions
Deadline: December 31
Apply to: Director, Syracuse University Press, above address

Tanne Foundation
c/o Grants Management Associates
77 Summer Street
Boston, MA 02110-1006
E-mail: philanthropy@grantsmanagement.com
Web site: http://www.grantsmanagement.com
Fax: 617-426-7172

The Tanne Foundation offers one-time fellowship awards intended to recognize prior achievement and enrich the recipient's artistic life. Awards are made to individual artists who have demonstrated exceptional talent and creativity. The Foundation supports artistic endeavors in culturally underserved communities and underappreciated forms of artistic expression. Write for additional information.

Available to: No restrictions
Deadline: Inquire
Apply to: Michelle Jenney, Administrator, above address

Mark Taper Forum
Center Theatre Group/New Work Festival
135 North Grand Avenue
Los Angeles, CA 90012

Ⓓ The Forum encourages playwrights to send submission queries, with a short description of a play and 5 to 10 sample pages, so that the Forum can determine whether to request the entire manuscript for possible production or development. Allow six to eight weeks for a response. Unsolicited scripts will not be read. There are no restrictions as to format or subject matter. Cover letter should mention whether the play should be considered for the *New Work Festival*. Plays given a festival workshop or reading must be unproduced and unpublished. For all submissions, include SASE for a response and, if needed, the return of submitted materials.

Available to: No restrictions
Deadline: None for general submissions; New Work Festival submissions accepted January 1–April 30
Apply to: Pier Carlo Talenti, Literary Associate, above address

John Templeton Foundation
Five Radnor Corporate Center, Suite 100
100 Matsonford Road
Radnor, PA 19087
E-mail: book-rfp@templeton.org
Web site: http://www.templeton.org

Ⓝ The *Exemplary Papers in Humility Theology Program* has previously awarded $3,000 for outstanding papers and $1,500 for exemplary papers, 3,000 to 10,000 words in length, on one of the following three topics: theology and the natural sciences, religion and the medical sciences, and religion and the human behavioral sciences. Papers must have been accepted for publication or published in a peer-reviewed scholarly journal or another comparably selective publication. The program is currently being redesigned. Visit the Web site for updated information.

Available to: No restrictions
Deadline: Inquire
Apply to: Above address

Tennessee Arts Commission
401 Charlotte Avenue
Nashville, TN 37243-0780
Web site: http://www.arts.state.tn.us
Fax: 615-741-8559

Ⓜ The Tennessee Arts Commission offers a writing fellowship of $2,500 to writers of poetry and prose on a rotating basis. Write for additional information and guidelines.

Available to: Tennessee residents
Deadline: January 2001 for prose; January 2002 for poetry (inquire for exact dates)
Apply to: Above address

Tennessee Writers Alliance
PO Box 120396
Nashville, TN 37212

Ⓜ   The *Tennessee Writers Alliance Literary Awards* offer a first prize of $500, a second prize of $250, and a third prize of $100 for works of short fiction, poetry, and nonfiction. The entry fee is $10 for members of the Alliance and $15 for nonmembers.

Available to: U.S. poets and writers
Deadline: June 30
Apply to: Literary Awards, above address

Texas Institute of Letters
Center for the Study of the Southwest
Flowers Hall 327
Southwest Texas State University
San Marcos, TX 78666
E-mail: mb13@swt.edu
Web site: http://www.english.swt.edu/css/TIL/index.htm

The Texas Institute of Letters gives the following literary awards every March for books by Texas authors or on Texas subjects published during the preceding calendar year. Send SASE for guidelines and names and addresses of judges before submitting.

Ⓒ   The *Book Publishers of Texas Award* of $250, for the best book published for children or young people.

Ⓕ   The *Brazos Bookstore Short Story Award* of $750, for the best short story.

Ⓝ   The *Carr P. Collins Award* of $5,000, for the best book of nonfiction (generally for belletristic work).

Ⓣ   The *Soeurette Diehl Fraser Translation Award* of $1,000, for the best translation of a book into English.

Ⓝ   The *Friends of the Dallas Public Library Award* of $1,000, for the book that contributes most significantly to knowledge (generally for scholarly work).

Ⓙ Ⓝ The *O. Henry Award* of $1,000, for the best nonfiction writing in a magazine or Sunday newspaper supplement.

Ⓕ   The *Jesse H. Jones Award* of $6,000, for the best book of fiction.

Ⓟ   The *Natalie Ornish Poetry Award* of $1,000, for the best book of poetry.

Ⓕ   The *Steven Turner Award* of $1,000, for the best first book of fiction.

Ⓙ   The *Stanley Walker Award* of $1,000, for the best work of journalism appearing in a daily newspaper; the with emphasis is on literary merit.

Available to: Texas authors or books on a Texas subject
Deadline: First working day in January
Apply to: Mark Busby, Secretary-Treasurer, above address

Thanks Be to Grandmother Winifred Foundation
PO Box 1449
Wainscott, NY 11975

Grants of up to $5,000 are offered to women at least fifty-four years of age to develop and implement projects, programs, or policies that empower and enrich one or more aspects of the cultural, economic, educational, ethnic, mental, physical, professional, racial, sexual, social, or spiritual well-being of women. Send an SASE for additional information and application instructions.

Available to: See above
Deadline: March 21 and September 21
Apply to: Above address

Theatre Communications Group
355 Lexington Avenue, 4th floor
New York, NY 10017
E-mail: grants@tcg.org
Web site: http://www.tcg.org
Fax: 212-983-4847

Ⓓ *Extended Collaboration Grants* are designed to enable writers to collaborate with other artists for a period beyond a sponsoring theater's normal pre-production and rehearsal schedule. Grants of $5,000 each are awarded to support playwrights working with directors, designers, composers, actors, and other artists, to develop projects proposed by the sponsoring theater. Artistic directors of TCG constituent theaters must apply on behalf of the artists. Write, e-mail, or visit the Web site for guidelines and application materials.

Available to: See above
Deadline: Inquire
Apply to: Extended Collaboration Grants, above address

Ⓓ The *National Theatre Artist Residency Program* awards some ten to fourteen grants of $50,000 or $100,000 to accomplished theater artists who have created a significant body of work and the theaters with high artistic standards and the organizational capacity to provide substantial support services to artists. Funds are to be used for compensation and residence expenses for one or two artists, working singly or in collaboration, during discrete periods devoted exclusively to residence-related activities and totaling at least six full months over a two-year period. Proposals must be developed jointly by playwrights and institutions. Write, e-mail, or visit the Web site for guidelines and application.

Available to: No restrictions
Deadline: December 1 for intent-to-apply cards; December 15 for completed applications
Apply to: National Theatre Artist Residency Program, above address

Ⓓ Ⓡ The *NEA/TCG Theatre Residency Program for Playwrights* awards $25,000 to each of several playwrights (twelve in 1998) to create new works in residence at a host not-for-profit professional theater. Host theaters receive the $5,000 Seagram/Universal Residency Award to help them support the resident playwright's work. Playwrights must have had at least one play published or produced within the last five years; theaters must have high artistic standards, a history of developing new works, and a minimum operating budget of $150,000 in the most recently completed fiscal year. A total of six months (not necessarily consecutive) must be dedicated to the development of a new work with the host theater. Write, e-mail, or visit the Web site for guidelines and application materials.

Available to: U.S. citizens or permanent residents
Deadline: May 30 for Intent to Apply cards; June 15 for applications
Apply to: NEA/TCG Theatre Residency Program for Playwrights, above address

Theatre Conspiracy
10091 McGregor Boulevard
Fort Myers, FL 33919
E-mail: theatreconspiracy@prodigy.net
Web site: http://pages.prodigy.net/theatreconspiracy
Fax: 941-936-0510

Ⓓ The *Theatre Conspiracy Annual New Play Contest* awards $500 and production for an unproduced full-length play with a cast limit of six and simple production demands (no musicals). There is a $10 entry fee. Send SASE or e-mail for guidelines.

Available to: No restrictions
Deadline: January 31
Apply to: New Play Contest, above address

Thorngate Road
Illinois State University
Department of English
Campus Box 4240
Normal, IL 61790-4240
E-mail: jmelled@ilstu.edu
Fax: 309-438-5414

Ⓟ The *Frank O'Hara Award Chapbook Competition* offers $500, publication, and 25 copies for poetry, prose poems, and cross-genre texts by gay, lesbian, bisexual, and transgendered authors. Submissions are limited to 16 single- or double-spaced pages of text. There is a $15 reading fee per entry. Send SASE for guidelines.

Available to: Gay, lesbian, bisexual, and transgendered authors
Deadline: February 1
Apply to: Jim Elledge, Frank O'Hara Award Chapbook Competition, above address

Thunderbird Films
214 Riverside Drive #112
New York, NY 10025
E-mail: estannard@dekker.com
Web site: http://home.att.net/~thunderbirdfilms

Ⓢ The *Thunderbird Films Annual Screenplay Competition* offers $500 and a possible production option for a feature-length screenplay. There is a $35 entry fee. Send SASE, e-mail, or visit the Web site for details.

Available to: No restrictions
Deadline: March 30
Apply to: Screenplay Competition, above address

James Thurber Residency Program
Thurber House
77 Jefferson Avenue
Columbus, OH 42315
Web site: http://www.thurberhouse.org

Ⓡ The *James Thurber Residency Program* selects journalists, novelists, poets, and playwrights to spend a season living, writing, and teaching at Thurber House. Each writer will receive a stipend and accommodations in Thurber's boyhood home. The majority of the writer's time is reserved for the writer's own work, but there are responsibilities, as follows: The *James Thurber Journalist-in-Residence* teaches a class at Ohio State University School of Journalism and coaches staff writing for reporters at *The Columbus Dispatch*. Candidates should have experience in reporting, feature writing, reviewing, or other areas of journalism, as well as significant publications; experience as a teacher or writing coach is helpful. The stipend is $5,000 per quarter, available for one or two quarters. The *James Thurber Playwright-in-Residence* teaches a playwriting class in the OSU theater department.

Candidates should have had at least one play published and/or produced by a significant company and show aptitude for teaching. The stipend is $5,000. The *James Thurber Writer-in-Residence* teaches a class in creative writing at OSU and offers a public reading and a workshop for writers in the community. Candidates should have published at least one book with a major publisher (fiction, nonfiction, or poetry) and should have some teaching experience. The stipend is $5,000. For application, send a vita and a letter of interest.

Available to: See above
Deadline: December 15
Apply to: Michael J. Rosen, Literary Director, above address

tnr—the new renaissance
26 Heath Road #11
Arlington, MA 02174-3645

Ⓕ Ⓟ *the new renaissance* has two award programs, each covering work published in a three-issue volume of the magazine (about every eighteen to twenty-two months). The *Louise E. Reynolds Memorial Fiction Award* offers a first prize of $500, a second of $250, and a third of $100. The *tnr Poetry Award* offers a first prize of $250, a second of $125, and a third of $50. The $15 entry fee for nonsubscribers pays for either two back issues of the magazine or a current issue (writer's choice); the entry fee for subscribers is $10. Send SASE for guidelines.

Available to: No restrictions; poetry submissions not accepted in 2000
Deadline: Fiction submissions accepted January 1–June 30 and September 1–October 31; in 2001, both fiction and poetry accepted during these periods
Apply to: Above address

Towson University
8000 York Road
Towson, MD 21252-0001

Ⓜ The *Towson University Prize for Literature* of $1,500 is offered annually for a single book or book-length manuscript of fiction, poetry, drama, or creative nonfiction by a Maryland writer. The prize, supported by a grant from the Alice & Franklin Cooley Endowment, is given on the basis of aesthetic excellence. If published, the book must have appeared within three years before the year of nomination. If unpublished, the book must have been accepted by a publisher. Nomination forms are required.

Available to: Maryland residents under age forty
Deadline: May 15
Apply to: Dean, College of Liberal Arts, above address

Harry S. Truman Library Institute
Harry S. Truman Library
U.S. Highway 24 and Delaware
Independence, MO 64050-1798

The Institute offers several awards and research grants to scholars and graduate students to encourage study of the history of the Truman administration and the public career of Harry Truman and to promote the use of the Library as a national center for historical scholarship. Prospective applicants should write to the Committee on Research and Education at the above address for current information.

Ⓝ The *Harry S. Truman Book Award* of $1,000 is given biennially for the best book written within the previous two years dealing primarily and substantially with an aspect of U.S. history between April 12, 1945, and January 20, 1953, or with the public career of Harry Truman. Three copies of each book should be submitted to the Secretary of the Institute.

Available to: No restrictions
Deadline: January 20 in even-numbered years
Apply to: Secretary, above address

Truman State University Press
100 East Normal Street
Kirksville, MO 63501-4221
E-mail: tsup@truman.edu
Web site: http://www2.truman.edu/tsup
Fax: 660-785-4180 or 4181

Ⓟ   The *T. S. Eliot Prize* annually awards $1,500 and publication by Truman State University Press for the best collection of contemporary poetry in English. Manuscripts should be 64 to 96 pages of original poetry. There is a reading fee of $25. All entrants will receive a copy of the winning book. Send SASE, fax, or e-mail for guidelines, or visit the Web site.

Available to: No restrictions
Deadline: October 31
Apply to: T. S. Eliot Prize, above address

Trustus Theatre
Box 11721
Columbia, SC 29211
E-mail: Trustus88@aol.com
Web site: http://www.trustus.org
Fax: 803-771-9153

Ⓓ   The *Trustus Playwrights' Festival* awards $750 ($250 upon selection/staged reading, $500 upon production after one-year development period) plus paid travel and accommodations for a full-length play. Cast limit is eight. Submissions must not have been produced professionally. Send SASE for guidelines and application.

Available to: No restrictions
Deadline: January 1–March 1
Apply to: Trustus Playwrights' Festival, above address

Tulsa Library Trust
400 Civic Center
Tulsa, OK 74103
Web site: http://www.tulsalibrary.org/trust

[IN]   The *Peggy V. Helmerich Distinguished Author Award* of $20,000 is given to a nationally acclaimed writer for a body of work. There is no application process. *By Internal Nomination Only.*

Tupelo Press
Great River Arts Institute
PO Box 639
Walpole, NH 03680
E-mail: editors@tupelopress.org
Web site: http://www.greatriverarts.org or http://www.tupelopress.org
Fax: 603-756-4308

Ⓕ   The *Tupelo Press Award for the Best Novel-Length Fiction* offers $3,000, publication under a standard royalty contract, and an invitation to read at the Great River Arts Institute for a fiction manuscript of at leat 50,000 words by a U.S. citizen. There is a $20 entry fee. Send SASE, e-mail, or visit the Web site for further information and entry form.

Available to: U.S. citizens
Deadlines: Submissions must be postmarked March 1—June 15, 2000; inquire for 2001
Apply to: Fiction Award, above address

Ⓟ   The *Tupelo Press Poetry Award* offers a first prize of $3,000 and a second prize of $1,000 for an unpublished, full-length collection of poetry by poets who have not yet published a collection, excluding translations, self-published books, or chapbooks of no more than 48 pages. Both prizewinners will be published by Tupelo Press and invited to read at the Great River Arts Institute. Manuscripts must be at least 48 pages. There is a $20 entry fee. Send SASE for guidelines.

Available to: U.S. citizens
Deadline: January 15, 2000; inquire for 2001
Apply to: Poetry Award, above address

Ucross Foundation
30 Big Red Lane
Clearmont, WY 82834
E-mail: ucross@wyoming.com
Fax: 307-737-2322

®   The Ucross Foundation, located in the foothills of the Big Horn Mountains, offers residences of two weeks to two months (average stay six weeks) to writers and other creative artists. There is no charge for room, board, or studio space.

Available to: No restrictions
Deadlines: March 1 for fall; October 1 for spring
Apply to: Residency Program, above address

Ukiah Players Theatre
1041 Low Gap Road
Ukiah, CA 95482

Ⓓ   The *New American Comedy Festival* selects two entries from an open competition to receive staged readings in the spring. Of those two plays, one will be chosen for a workshop and given full production the following season. The workshop consists of seven days of developmental script work with a professional dramaturg, director, and local cast. Playwright's travel, lodging, and daily expenses are covered by the Theatre during this time. Write for guidelines and application.

Available to: No restrictions
Deadline: November 30
Apply to: New American Comedy Festival, above address

Unicorn Theatre
3828 Main Street
Kansas City, MO 64111

Ⓓ   The *National Playwrights' Award* gives an annual $1,000 first prize and production to an American playwright for a previously unproduced work (no musicals, one-acts, or historical plays). Send SASE for guidelines.

Available to: No restrictions
Deadline: April 30
Apply to: Herman Wilson, Literary Assistant, above address

Unitarian Universalist Association
25 Beacon Street
Boston, MA 02108
E-mail: pfrevert@uua.org
Web site: http://www.uua.org
Fax: 617-367-3237

Ⓜ   The *Frederic G. Melcher Book Award* consists of $1,000 and a citation for a book of fiction, nonfiction, drama, or poetry published in the year preceding the award that has contributed significantly to religious liberalism. Books must be nominated by the Melcher Book Award Committee or the publisher.

Available to: No restrictions
Deadline: January 31
Apply to: Patricia Frevert, UUA Staff Liaison, above address

United Daughters of the Confederacy
328 North Boulevard
Richmond, VA 23220-4057

Ⓝ The *Mrs. Simon Baruch University Award* is offered as a grant-in-aid for publication of an unpublished book or monograph dealing with southern history in or near the period of the Confederacy. One award of $2,000 and one of $500 are given biennially.

Available to: Graduate students or recipients of master's, doctoral, or other advanced degree within the last fifteen years
Deadline: May 1 in even-numbered years
Apply to: Chairman of the Committee, Mrs. Simon Baruch University Award, above address

UNITED KINGDOM
Boardman Tasker Charitable Trust
14 Pine Lodge
Dairyground Road
Bramhall
Stockport, Cheshire SK7 2HS
England

Ⓜ The *Boardman Tasker Prize* of £2,000 is awarded annually to "a book which has made an outstanding contribution to mountain literature." Eligible books must have been published or distributed in the United Kingdom for the first time between November 1 and October 31 of the prize year and must be submitted by publishers. Entries may be fiction, nonfiction, poetry, or drama concerned with a mountain environment and must be written in English, either initially or in translation. Publishers should submit four copies of each eligible book, or page-proofs if necessary, with a required entry form for each title. Write for additional information and forms.

Available to: No restrictions
Deadline: August 1
Apply to: Above address

UNITED KINGDOM
British Centre for Literary Translation
University of East Anglia
Norwich NR4 7TJ
England
E-mail: c.c.wilson@uea.ac.uk
Fax: 44-1603-592785

Ⓣ The BCLT, in conjunction with the British Comparative Literature Association, awards a first prize of £350 and a second prize of £150 for the best literary translation from any language into English. Poetry, fiction, or literary prose, from any period, is eligible. Write for complete rules and entry form.

Available to: No restrictions
Deadline: February 28
Apply to: BCLT/BCLA Translation Competition, above address

UNITED KINGDOM
Forward Publishing
c/o Colman Getty Public Relations
Carrington House
126–130 Regent Street
London W1R 5FE
England
E-mail: pr@colmangettypr.co.uk

Ⓟ The *Forward Poetry Prizes* are awarded annually for the best poetry published in the United Kingdom or the Republic of Ireland. A £10,000 prize is given for the best collection of poetry published in the preceding year; £5,000 is given for the best first collection of poetry; and £1,000 is given for the best individual poem to appear in a newspaper, periodical, or magazine. The winning individual poem and selected poems from the winning collections will be published in *The Forward Book of Poetry*, an anthology of the year's best verse. Entries must be submitted by editors of books or periodicals published in the United Kingdom or the Republic of Ireland; entries from poets are not accepted. Editors may nominate up to four poems or collections. For the 2000 prize, collections must have been published between October 1, 1999, and September 30, 2000; individual poems between June 1, 1999, and April 30, 2000. Write for guidelines.

Available to: No restrictions
Deadline: May (inquire for exact date)
Apply to: Forward Poetry Prize Administrator, above address

UNITED KINGDOM
International Retreat for Writers at Hawthornden Castle
Lasswade
Midlothian EH18 1EG
Scotland

® The retreat offers residences of four weeks for five published creative writers (novelists, poets, playwrights) at a time. Residences, which include room and board, are scheduled in spring, summer, and fall. Write for further information and application.

Available to: Published writers
Deadline: September 30 for the coming year
Apply to: Above address

UNITED KINGDOM
Orange Prize for Fiction
c/o Book Trust
45 East Hill
London SW18 2QZ
England
E-mail: sandra@booktrust.org.uk

Ⓕ The *Orange Prize for Fiction* annually awards £30,000 for the best novel written in English by a woman of any nationality and published in the United Kingdom. Short story collections and/or novellas are not eligible. Entries must be published in the United Kingdom between April 1 and the following March 31; they may have been previously published elsewhere. Publishers only may submit up to three full-length novels per bona fide imprint; publishers may submit a list of up to five other titles which must be accompanied by a justification of not more than 250 words. Books being published between the deadline and March 31 may be submitted as bound proofs. Write or e-mail for additional information and entry form.

Available to: Women writers
Deadline: Early January (inquire for exact date)
Apply to: Orange Prize for Fiction, above address

UNITED KINGDOM
Reuters Foundation
85 Fleet Street
London EC4P 4AJ
England
Web site: http://www.foundation.reuters.com

Ⓙ Reuters awards two annual *Fellowships in Medical Journalism*, tenable at the universities of Oxford, England, and Columbia, New York, to English-speaking, mid-career journalists for research and study relating to medical matters. The award at Oxford is for one term (mid-April to mid-July) within the Reuters Foundation Programme for International Journalists at Green College; the award at Columbia is for one semester starting in January at the Graduate School of Journalism in Manhattan. The fellowship covers travel expenses, tuition fees, and a monthly living allowance. Write or visit the Web site for further information and application.

Available to: No restrictions
Deadline: September 15 for Columbia fellowship; October 31 for Oxford
Apply to: The Director, above address

Ⓙ The *Reuters-IUCN Media Awards,* which recognize excellence in professional reporting on the environment and sustainable development, seek to enhance public awareness and foster a dialogue between journalists and environmental/development experts that will encourage informative and high-quality reporting based on sound scientific data. Candidates for the awards may submit published articles on environmental management, environmental degradation, nature conservation, sustainable use of natural resources, public and private investment, and social, economic, and development topics relevant to the environment. Winners of the regional awards will be invited to participate in a Reuters Foundation environmental journalism workshop. The global award winner will receive a three-month Reuters Foundation Fellowship at Oxford. All awards cover travel, accommodations, and living costs for the duration of the respective course. Write or visit the Web site for additional information.

Available to: No restrictions
Deadline: Inquire (generally August)
Apply to: U.S. journalists should write to: IUCN–U.S. Office, 1400 16th Street, NW, Suite 502, Washington, DC 20036; residents of other countries should contact Reuters, IUCN or the Web site for addresses of other regional offices

Ⓙ The *Reuters Oxford University Fellowships* provide a three-month study opportunity at the Reuters Foundation Programme at Green College, Oxford, for established journalists from the United States. The fellowship is open to American writers and broadcasters, including specialists in economic, environmental, medical, and scientific subjects. It covers travel expenses, tuition fees, and a monthly living allowance. Write or visit the Web site for further information and application.

Available to: U.S. journalists
Deadline: February 28
Apply to: The Director, Reuters Foundation, above address

UNITED KINGDOM
Royal Society of Literature of the United Kingdom
One Hyde Park Gardens
London W2 2LT
England
Fax: 44-171-402-0199

Ⓜ The *Heinemann Award for Literature* is given "primarily to reward those classes of literature which are less remunerative; namely, poetry, criticism, biography, history, etc.," and "to encourage the production of works of real merit." Submitted works must have been written originally in English. The amount of the award in 1998, for books published in 1998, was £5,000. Nominations may be made only by publishers.

Available to: No restrictions
Deadline: December 15
Apply to: Above address

Ⓕ The *Winifred Holtby Prize* of £10,000 is given for the best regional novel of the year written in English by a writer of British or Irish nationality, or a citizen of the Commonwealth. If it is judged there is no novel of sufficient merit, the prize may be awarded to an author of a literary work of nonfiction or poetry concerning a regional subject. Nominations may be made only by publishers.

Available to: See above
Deadline: December 15
Apply to: Winifred Holtby Prize, above address

UNITED KINGDOM
Stand Magazine
179 Wingrove Road
Newcastle-upon-Tyne NE4 9DA
England

Ⓕ Ⓟ *Stand Magazine's Short Story Competition* and *Poetry Competition* each offer first and second prizes of £1,500 and £500, respectively, for the best short stories and poems submitted. Send SASE to the U.S. address below for guidelines and entry form.

Available to: No restrictions
Deadline: Short story submissions accepted January 1–June 30; poetry, July 1–December 31
Apply to: David Latane, English Department, Virginia Commonwealth University, Richmond, VA 23284-2005

UNITED KINGDOM
Translators Association
84 Drayton Gardens
London SW10 9SB
England
E-mail: authorsoc@writers.org.uk
Web site: http://www.writers.org.uk/society
Fax: 44-0171-373-5768

The following prizes are given for translations published in the United Kingdom by a British publisher, except for the Vondel Prize, given for a translation that may have been published in the United States, and the Teixeira-Gomes Prize, for which unpublished translations are eligible. Translators may be of any nationality. For each prize, publishers should submit three copies of the translation and three copies (photocopies allowed) of the original to Dorothy Wright at the above address. Entry forms are not required. There is no limit on the number of submissions. For further information, contact Dorothy Wright.

Ⓣ The *John Florio Prize* of £1,000, awarded biennially for the best translation of a twentieth-century Italian work of literary merit and general interest.

Available to: No restrictions
Deadline: December 31, 2001, for books published in 2000 and 2001
Apply to: John Florio Prize, above address

Ⓣ The *Scott Moncrieff Prize* of £1,000, awarded annually for the best translation of a full-length French work of literary merit and general interest. The original must have been published in the last 150 years.

Available to: No restrictions
Deadline: December 31 for books published that year
Apply to: Scott Moncrieff Prize, above address

Ⓣ The *Sasakawa Prize* of £2,000, awarded every five years for the best translation of a full-length Japanese work of literary merit and general interest from any period.

Available to: No restrictions
Deadline: Inquire
Apply to: Sasakawa Prize, above address

Ⓣ The *Schlegel-Tieck Prize* of £2,200, awarded annually for the best translation of a twentieth-century German work of literary merit and general interest.

Available to: No restrictions
Deadline: December 31 for books published that year
Apply to: Schlegel-Tieck Prize, above address

Ⓣ The *Bernard Shaw Prize* of £1,000, awarded triennially for the best translation into English of a Swedish work of literary merit in any genre.

Available to: No restrictions
Deadline: December 31, 2002, for books published 2000–2002
Apply to: Bernard Shaw Prize, above address

ⓣ The *Teixeira-Gomes Prize* of £1,000, awarded triennially for the best translation into English of a Portuguese work by a Portuguese national. Unpublished translations are eligible.

> Available to: No restrictions
> Deadline: December 31, 2000, for books published 1998–2000
> Apply to: Teixeira-Gomes Prize, above address

ⓣ The *Premio Valle Inclan* of £1,000, awarded annually for the best translation of a Spanish work of literary merit and general interest from any period and from anywhere in the world.

> Available to: No restrictions
> Deadline: December 31 for books published that year
> Apply to: Premio Valle Inclan, above address

ⓣ The *Vondel Translation Prize* of £2,000, awarded triennially for a translation into English of a Dutch or Flemish work of literary merit and general interest. The translation must have been published first in the United Kingdom or the United States.

> Available to: No restrictions
> Deadline: December 31, 2001, for books published 1999–2001
> Apply to: Vondel Translation Prize, above address

UNITED KINGDOM
University of Cambridge
Corpus Christi College
Cambridge CB2 1RH
England

Research scholarships are available annually in all subjects to students of any nationality not eligible for United Kingdom state grants who hold a first-class honors degree or the equivalent. Excellent English is essential. Students must register for a postgraduate research degree (Ph.D.) at the university. Duration of the award is three years, subject to satisfactory progress. The value of the award in 1999–2000 was £6,252 per annum. Scholarships are normally awarded in collaboration with the Cambridge Overseas Trust and Cambridge Commonwealth Trust.

> Available to: See above
> Deadline: March 30
> Apply to: Tutor for Advanced Students, above address

UNITED KINGDOM
University of East Anglia
School of English and American Studies
Norwich NR4 7TJ
United Kingdom
E-mail: striker@uea.ac.uk
Web site: http://www.uea.ac.uk/eas/intro/prizes/wong/intro

ⓕ The *David T. K. Wong Fellowship* annually awards £25,000 to a writer of a work of fiction in English—either a novel or a collection of short stories—that deals seriously with an aspect of life in the Far East (Brunei, Cambodia, China, Hong Kong, Indonesia, Japan, Korea, Laos, Macao, Malaysia, Mongolia, Myanmar, the Philippines, Singapore, Taiwan, Thailand, Vietnam). The recipient is expected to spend a year at the University of East Anglia. The award is open to both new and established writers of any age, nationality, sex, religion, or political persuasion. Write for further information and application.

> Available to: No restrictions
> Deadline: October 31
> Apply to: David T. K. Wong Fellowship, above address

UNITED KINGDOM
University of Edinburgh
South Bridge
Edinburgh EH8 9YL
Scotland
E-mail: A.McKelvie@ed.ac.uk
Fax: 44-131-650-2253

Ⓕ Ⓝ The *James Tait Black Memorial Prizes*, of £3,000 each, are awarded annually to the best novel and the best biographical work published in Britain in the twelve-month period before the submission deadline. The awards are judged by the Professor of English Literature at the University. Books must originate with a British publisher, and must be submitted only by publishers; books by previous winners will not be considered. Winners are announced in December.

Available to: See above
Deadline: September 30
Apply to: University of Edinburgh, Department of English Literature, David Hume Tower, George Square, Edinburgh EH8 9JX, Scotland

UNITED KINGDOM
Wiener Library Unlimited
4 Devonshire Street
London W1N 2BH
England
Fax: 44-171-436-6428

Ⓝ The *Fraenkel Prize in Contemporary History* is given for outstanding unpublished works in one of the fields of interest of the Wiener Library. These include Central European and Jewish history in the twentieth century; the Second World War; fascism and totalitarianism; political violence; and racism. Two awards are offered: one for $5,000, which is open to all entrants with manuscripts between 50,000 and 150,000 words; the other for $3,000, which is open to entrants who have yet to publish a major work and whose manuscripts are between 25,000 and 100,000 words. Candidates should specify which prize they are applying for. Contact the Library for additional information.

Available to: No restrictions
Deadline: May 10, 2000; inquire for 2001
Apply to: Administrative Secretary, Fraenkel Prize, above address

United Methodist Communications
Public Media Division
PO Box 320
Nashville, TN 37202
E-mail: scholarships@umcom.umc.org
Web site: http://www.umc.org
Fax: 615-742-5404

Ⓙ The $2,500 *Leonard M. Perryman Communications Scholarship for Ethnic Minority Students* is offered yearly in recognition of Perryman, a journalist for the United Methodist Church for nearly thirty years. The scholarship is intended to aid ethnic minority college students (juniors or seniors) who intend to pursue a career in religious communication and are attending an accredited institution of higher education. The scholarship enables the recipient to continue media studies (audiovisual, electronic, or print) and seeks to promote excellence in communications among minority students. Write for guidelines and application.

Available to: U.S. ethnic minority undergraduates
Deadline: February 15
Apply to: Scholarship Committee, above address

Ⓙ The *Stoody–West Fellowship in Religious Journalism* of $6,000 is offered annually in recognition of the professional competence and inspired service of Drs. Ralph Stoody and Arthur

West. The grant assists a Christian engaged in religious journalism (audiovisual, electronic, or print) or planning to enter this field in doing graduate study at an accredited school or department of journalism. Write for guidelines and application.

Available to: Christian journalists with an undergraduate degree
Deadline: February 15
Apply to: Scholarship Committee, above address

United States Civil War Center
Louisiana State University
Raphael Semmes Drive
Baton Rouge, LA 70803
E-mail: lwood@lsu.edu
Web site: http://www.cwc.lsu.edu
Fax: 504-388-4876

Ⓝ The *Peter Seaborg Award for Civil War Nonfiction* offers an annual prize of $5,000 to the best nonfiction Civil War book that takes a unique approach, such as an interdisciplinary study or examination of an unusual facet of the war. Nominations for the award should be made by publishers and agents, though self-nominated books are eligible. Six copies of the nominated book should be submitted to the Center. Write, e-mail, or visit the Web site for additional information.

Available to: No restrictions
Deadline: Inquire
Apply to: Peter Seaborg Award, above address

Ⓕ The *Michael Shaara Award for Excellence in Civil War Fiction* offers an annual prize of $1,000 to the best Civil War novel or series of short stories published each year. Nominations should be made by the publisher; authors and critics may also nominate. Send five copies of the nominated work to the Center; copies become its property. Write, e-mail, or visit the Web site for additional information.

Available to: No restrictions
Deadline: December 31
Apply to: Michael Shaara Award, above address

United States Holocaust Memorial Museum
Center for Advanced Holocaust Studies
100 Raoul Wallenberg Place, SW
Washington, DC 20024-2150
E-mail: rtaft@ushmm.org
Web site: http://www.ushmm.org
Fax: 202-479-9726

The *Center for Advanced Holocaust Studies Fellowships* support research and writing projects for which the Museum's archival and other resources are critical. Awards are made in a variety of fields to qualified Ph.D. candidates preparing dissertations at accredited American universities, postdoctoral researchers with recent degrees from accredited American universities, and senior scholars from accredited academic and research institutions worldwide. A monthly stipend of $3,000 is offered for a semester or an academic year. Write, e-mail, or visit the Web site for further information.

Available to: See above
Deadline: November 15
Apply to: Renée Taft, Visiting Scholar Programs, above address

The *Center for Advanced Holocaust Studies Postdissertation Award* is given to encourage the work of exceptional new scholars in the area of Holocaust and genocide studies. The award, which consists of a residence fellowship at the Museum for one semester or more and a stipend up to $15,000, provides an opportunity for a recent Ph.D. recipient to convert his or her dissertation into a monograph or to research a new Holocaust-related topic. Applicants must be nominated by the chair of their dissertation committee and have the concurrence of the chair or the department in which the dissertation was prepared. Nominees must have completed defense of their dissertation no more than one year before nomination. Write, e-mail, or visit the Web site for further information.

Available to: See above
Deadline: December 15 and June 15
Apply to: Renée Taft, Visiting Scholar Programs, above address

The *Miles Lerman Center for the Study of Jewish Resistance Research Fellowship* is designed to encourage exploration of aspects of Jewish resistance including, but not limited to, partisan activity, rebellions in camps and ghettos, sabotage and espionage, document forgery, underground hiding and rescue, and the impact of resistance. Applicants must be Ph.D. candidates preparing dissertations at accredited American universities, postdoctoral researchers with recent degrees, or senior scholars from accredited academic and research institutions worldwide. Fellows receive a monthly stipend of $3,000 for a semester or a full academic year. Write, e-mail, or visit the Web site for further information.

Available to: See above
Deadline: November 15
Apply to: Renée Taft, Visiting Scholar Programs, above address

The *Pearl Resnick Postdoctoral Fellowship* offers promising young scholars who have received a Ph.D. or equivalent degree within the last ten years an academic year in residence at the Center for Advanced Holocaust Studies. Fellows are provided with a monthly stipend of $4,000 as well as up to $3,500 to cover travel expenses for them and accompanying family members (spouse and dependent children). Write, e-mail, or visit the Web site for further information and application.

Available to: See above
Deadline: November 15
Apply to: Renée Taft, Visiting Scholar Programs, above address

Approximately six *Charles H. Revson Foundation Fellowships for Archival Research* are offered each year to Ph.D. recipients or advanced Ph.D. candidates. Those with equivalent terminal degrees or recognized professional status will also be considered. Proposals that use new archival acquisitions of the Museum (e.g., from Ukraine, Croatia, France, Bulgaria, Italy, Romania, Spain, and the Netherlands) and proposals for research on the fate of Roma and Sinti (Gypsies), Jehovah's Witnesses, Poles, and other groups targeted by the Nazis and their allies and collaborators are of particular interest. Fellows receive a monthly stipend of $3,000 for a three-to-five-month residence. Write, e-mail, or visit the Web site for further information and application.

Available to: See above
Deadline: November 15
Apply to: Renée Taft, Visiting Scholar Programs, above address

The *Joyce and Arthur Schechter Fellowship* supports scholarly research in residence at the Museum. Applicants must hold a Ph.D. or be an advanced Ph.D. candidate by the application deadline. Candidates with equivalent terminal degrees or recognized professional status will be considered. Fellows receive up to $5,000 for a six-week-to-three-month residence. Write, e-mail, or visit the Web site for further information and application.

Available to: See above
Deadline: November 15
Apply to: Renée Taft, Visiting Scholar Programs, above address

United States Institute of Peace
1200 17th Street, NW, 2nd floor
Washington, DC 20036-3011
E-mail: jrprogram@usip.org
Web site: http://www.usip.org

® The *Jennings Randolph Program for International Peace* offers fellowships to outstanding professionals and scholars who wish to "undertake research and other kinds of communication that will improve understanding and skills on the part of policymakers and the public regarding important problems of international peace and conflict management." Fellows work in residence at the Institute; they receive a stipend (amount keyed to income earned in the twelve months before the fellowship), health benefits if needed, and support for appropriate project costs. The program works closely with the Institute toward publishing the results of fellows' research. Write for further information and application.

Available to: No restrictions
Deadline: Inquire
Apply to: Jennings Randolph Program for International Peace, above address

United States Naval Institute
291 Wood Road
Annapolis, MD 21402
E-mail: kclarke@usni.org
Web site: http://www.usni.org

Ⓝ The *Vincent Astor Memorial Leadership Essay Contest* annually recognizes essays of up to 3,500 words that address topics of leadership in the sea services. Offered are a first prize of $1,500, a second of $1,000, and two third prizes of $500. Winning essays are published in *Proceedings* magazine. Send SASE for rules.

Available to: Junior officers and officer trainees of the U.S. Navy, Marine Corps, and Coast Guard
Deadline: February 1
Apply to: Vincent Astor Memorial Leadership Essay Contest, Proceedings, above address

Ⓝ The *Arleigh Burke Essay Contest* annually recognizes original, unpublished essays of up to 3,500 words that address "the advancement of professional, literary, and scientific knowledge in the naval and maritime services, and the advancement of the knowledge of sea power." First prize is $3,000, first honorable mention $2,000, and second honorable mention $1,000. Winning essays are published in *Proceedings*. Send SASE for rules.

Available to: U.S. citizens
Deadline: December 1
Apply to: Arleigh Burke Essay Contest, above address

Ⓝ The *Coast Guard Essay Contest* annually recognizes essays that discuss current issues and new directions for the Coast Guard. First prize is $1,000, second $750, and third $500. Winning essays are published in *Proceedings*. Send SASE for rules.

Available to: U.S. citizens
Deadline: June 1
Apply to: Coast Guard Essay Contest, above address

Ⓝ The *Enlisted Essay Contest* annually recognizes essays of up to 2,500 words that concern the mission of the U.S. Naval Institute: the advancement of professional, literary, and scientific knowledge in the naval and maritime services, and the advancement of the knowledge of sea power. First prize is $1,000, second $750, and third $500. Winning essays are published in *Proceedings*. Send SASE for rules.

Available to: Enlisted personnel, including active, reserve, and retired
Deadline: September 1
Apply to: Enlisted Essay Contest

Ⓝ The *International Navies Essay Contest* annually recognizes essays about strategic, geographic, and cultural influences on individual or regional navies, their commitments and capabilities, and relationships with other navies. First prize is $1,000, second $750, and third $500. Winning essays are published in *Proceedings*. Send SASE for rules.

Available to: U.S. citizens
Deadline: August 1
Apply to: International Navies Essay Contest, above address

(N) The *Marine Corps Essay Contest* annually recognizes essays that discuss current issues and new directions for the Marine Corps. First prize is $1,000, second $750, and third $500. Winning essays are published in *Proceedings*. Send SASE for rules.

Available to: U.S. citizens
Deadline: May 1
Apply to: Marine Corps Essay Contest, above address

(N) The *Colin L. Powell Joint Warfighting Essay Contest* annually recognizes essays of up to 3,000 words about combat readiness in a joint context (key issues involving two or more services). Essays may be heavy in uni-service detail, but must have joint application in terms of tactics, strategy, weaponry, combat training, force structure, doctrine, operations, and organization for combat, or interoperability of hardware, software, and procedures. First prize is $2,500, second $2,000, and third $1,000. Winning entries are published in *Proceedings* magazine. Send SASE for rules.

Available to: U.S. citizens
Deadline: April 1
Apply to: Colin L. Powell Joint Warfighting Essay Contest, above address

United States Trotting Association
United States Harness Writers' Association
750 Michigan Avenue
Columbus, OH 43215
E-mail: jpawlak@ustrotting.com
Web site: http://www.ustrotting.com
Fax: 614-228-1385

(J) The *John Hervey Awards for Writing Excellence* and *Broadcasters Awards* are available to writers of stories and productions with harness racing as a focus. The contest is not limited to USHWA members. Awards of $500 (first place), $250 (second), and $100 (third) are given in each of four categories: newspaper, magazine, television program, and television feature. Winners are announced in March.

Available to: No restrictions
Deadline: December
Apply to: John Pawlak, Hervey/Broadcasters Awards Administrator, above address

University of Akron Press
374B Bierce Library
Akron, OH 44325-1703
E-mail: press@uakron.edu
Web site: http://www.uakron.edu/uapress/poetryprize.html
Fax: 330-972-5132

(P) The *Akron Poetry Prize* awards $1,000 and publication by the University of Akron Press for a collection of poems written in English, from 60 to 100 pages. Nonwinning manuscripts may be considered for publication in the series. There is a $20 reading fee. Send SASE, e-mail, or fax for guidelines, or visit the Web site.

Available to: No restrictions
Deadline: Submissions accepted May 15–June 30
Apply to: Akron Poetry Prize, above address

University of Alabama
Department of Theatre and Dance
Box 870239
Tuscaloosa, AL 35487-0239
E-mail: pcastagn@woodsquad.as.ua.edu
Web site: http://www.as.ua.edu/theatre
Fax: 205-348-9048

(D) *Janusfest* is a competitive festival in which two or three playwrights are chosen to take part in a workshop of their plays. Playwrights receive financial support, including stipends, travel funds, and payment of other expenses. Send SASE, e-mail, or visit the Web site for further information.

Available to: No restrictions
Deadline: November 1
Apply to: Janusfest, above address

(D) The *New Playwrights' Program* provides financial support, including stipends, travel funds, and other funding, for the development of new plays. The process varies from project to project but usually entails readings and workshops, with an emphasis toward production. Generally, the playwright will be invited to attend at various steps in the process, and may be asked to conduct a master class with MFA playwriting students. Send SASE, e-mail, or visit the Web site for further information.

Available to: No restrictions
Deadline: Submissions accepted August 15–April 15
Apply to: New Playwrights' Program, above address

University of Alabama in Huntsville
Department of English
Huntsville, AL 35899

(F) The *H. E. Francis Award*, co-sponsored by the university and the Ruth Hindman Foundation, offers $1,000 and publication to the best unpublished short story, not exceeding 5,000 words. Two honorable mentions will also receive publication. There is a $15 submission fee. Write for guidelines.

Available to: No restrictions
Deadline: December 1
Apply to: Above address

University of Alaska Southeast Explorations
11120 Glacier Highway
Juneau, AK 99801-8761
Fax: 907-465-6404
E-mail: jfamp@uas.alaska.edu

(F) (P) The *Explorations Awards for Literature* annually give a first prize of $1,000 for poetry or prose, a second prize of $500 for the genre that does not win first, and two third prizes of $100 each for prose and poetry, and publication for all winners in *Explorations*, the literary magazine of the University of Alaska Southeast. Poets may submit up to five poems of no more than 60 lines each, with a $6 entry fee for one or two poems and $3 for each additional poem. Fiction writers may submit up to two short stories of no more than 3,000 words each, with a fee of $6 per story. Send SASE or e-mail for guidelines.

Available to: No restrictions
Deadline: May 15
Apply to: Art Petersen, Editor, above address

University of Arizona
Poetry Center
1216 North Cherry Avenue
Tucson, AZ 85719
E-mail: poetry@u.arizona.edu
Web site: http://www.coh.arizona.edu/poetry/default.html
Fax: 520-621-5566

(R) The Poetry Center provides a writer with a one-month summer residence (between June 1 and August 31) at the guest cottage of a historic adobe located two houses from the Center. A $500 stipend is included. Applicants should submit no more than 10 pages of poetry or 20 pages of fiction or literary nonfiction, along with a one-page résumé. There is a $10 reading fee. Send SASE, e-mail, or fax for guidelines.

Available to: Writers who have not published more than one full-length work
Deadline: Submissions accepted February 15–March 15
Apply to: Residency Program, above address

University of Arkansas Press
McIlroy House
201 Ozark Avenue
Fayetteville, AR 72701
E-mail: uaprinfo@cavern.uark.edu
Web site: www.uark.edu/~uaprinfo
Fax: 501-575-6044

(T) The *Arabic Translation Awards* are given annually to two book-length translations from Arabic, chosen from four genres: poetry, novel, short story collection, and nonfiction. Translations must be previously unpublished in book form, and all translation rights must be cleared for University of Arkansas Press publication. For each award, the original author (if still holding rights) receives $7,500 in lieu of royalties; the translator also receives $7,500. Winning manuscripts are published the following season by the Press. Send SASE, e-mail, or visit the Web site for guidelines.

Available to: No restrictions
Deadline: April 15
Apply to: University of Arkansas Press Award for Arabic Literature in Translation, Department of English, University of Arkansas, Fayetteville, AR 72701

University of California at Irvine
Department of Spanish and Portuguese
322 Humanities Hall
Irvine, CA 92697-5275

(M) The *Chicano/Latino Literary Contest* offers a $1,000 first prize plus publication by the University of California Press for a book-length manuscript by a Chicano or Latino writer in the genre specified for the year. The award is given for the short story in 2000, for poetry in 2001, for drama in 2002, and for the novel in 2003. A second prize of $500 and a third of $250 are also offered. The first-prize winner receives paid transportation to Irvine to receive the award. Submissions may be in English or Spanish. Send SASE for guidelines.

Available to: U.S. citizens or permanent residents
Deadline: May 15
Apply to: Chicano/Latino Literary Contest, above address

University of California, Los Angeles
William Andrews Clark Memorial Library
2520 Cimarron Street
Los Angeles, CA 90018
E-mail: clarkfel@humnet.ucla.edu
Web site: http://www.humnet.ucla.edu/humnet/clarklib
Fax: 213-732-8744

The Clark Library and the Center for Seventeenth- & Eighteenth-Century Studies offer a limited number of resident fellowships to postdoctoral scholars with research projects that require work in any area of the Clark's collections. Awards are for periods of one to three months in residence. Write or visit the Web site for additional information and application.

Available to: See above
Deadline: March 15
Apply to: Fellowship Coordinator, Center for Seventeenth- & Eighteenth-Century Studies, 310 Royce Hall, UCLA, 405 Hilgard Avenue, Los Angeles, CA 90095-1404

The *Ahmanson–Getty Postdoctoral Fellowships* are part of a theme-based resident fellowship program, established with the support of the Ahmanson Foundation of Los Angeles and the J. Paul Getty Trust, designed to encourage the participation of junior scholars in the Center's core programs. The major theme for a given year is announced the preceding fall; for 2000–2001, the theme is "Culture and Authority in the Baroque." Scholars who have received their Ph.D. in the last six years and are engaged in research pertaining to the announced theme are eligible. Fellows are expected to make a substantive contribution to the Center's workshops and seminars. Awards are for two consecutive academic quarters in residence at the Clark. The stipend is $18,400 for two quarters. Write or visit the Web site for additional information and application.

Available to: See above
Deadline: March 15
Apply to: Fellowship Coordinator, Center for Seventeenth- & Eighteenth-Century Studies, 310 Royce Hall, UCLA, 405 Hilgard Avenue, Los Angeles, CA 90095–1404

University of Chicago
Harriet Monroe Poetry Award
Division of Humanities
1050 East 59th Street
Chicago, IL 60637

[IN] The *Harriet Monroe Poetry Award* of $1,000 is awarded periodically to U.S. poets of notable achievement and special promise. The president of the university regularly chooses poets from various sections of the U.S. to sit on the selection committee, which gives preference to poets of progressive rather than academic tendencies. *By Internal Nomination Only.*

University of Evansville
Department of English
1800 Lincoln Avenue
Evansville, IN 47722

(P) The *Richard Wilbur Award* offers $1,000 and publication by the University of Evansville Press for a book-length poetry manuscript, 50 to 100 pages in length, by a U.S. poet. There is a $20 entry fee. Send SASE for guidelines.

Available to: U.S. poets
Deadline: December (inquire for exact date)
Apply to: Richard Wilbur Award, above address

University of Georgia Press
330 Research Drive, Suite B-100
Athens, GA 30602-4901
Fax: 706-369-6131

(F) The *Flannery O'Connor Award for Short Fiction* offers $1,000 plus publication under a standard book contract for collections of original short fiction in English, by published or unpublished writers. Two winners are selected annually. Stories that have been published in magazines or anthologies may be included; stories that have been published in a book-length collection written solely by the author may not.. Submissions should be accompanied by a $15 handling fee. Manuscripts are not returned. Send SASE for guidelines.

Available to: No restrictions
Deadline: Submissions accepted April 1–May 31
Apply to: Flannery O'Connor Award for Short Fiction, above address

University of Hawai'i
2530 Dole Street, Sakamaki A-203
Honolulu, HI 96822-2383

(J) The *Asia Fellowships* provide a mid-career opportunity for American journalists to broaden their knowledge and understanding of Asian cultures and institutions through advanced study, and thus be better able to report and interpret developments relating to Asia and its people. Up to five fellows are selected to spend an academic year at the University of

Hawai'i. Fellows are provided with airfare to and from Hawaii and a stipend of $27,000, to be paid in ten monthly installments. After a successful completion of the academic year, fellows are invited to undertake a study trip to Asia, partially funded by the program. Write for further information and application.

Available to: Mid-career U.S. journalists
Deadline: March 15
Apply to: Asia Fellowships, above address

University of Hawaii at Manoa
Kumu Kahua Theatre
46 Merchant Street
Honolulu, HI 96813
Fax: 808-536-4226

(D) The *Kumu Kahua Playwriting Contest* annually awards $500 for a full-length play set in Hawaii and dealing with some aspect of the Hawaii experience. The contest also awards $400 for a full-length play set in or dealing with Hawaii, the Pacific islands, the Pacific Rim, or the Pacific/Asian experience. An award of $200 is offered for plays on any topic of any length by a Hawaii resident. Reading and/or production is possible for winning submissions. Write for guidelines before submitting.

Available to: See above
Deadline: January 1
Apply to: Kumu Kahua Playwriting Contest, above address

University of Iowa Press
University of Iowa
100 Kuhl House
Iowa City, IA 52242-1000
Fax: 319-335-2055

(P) Two *Iowa Poetry Prizes* are given annually for unpublished poetry manuscripts by poets who have published at least one full-length book of poems with a print run of at least 500 copies. The Press publishes the two prizewinning books every year. Write for guidelines before submitting.

Available to: See above
Deadline: Submissions accepted during May
Apply to: Iowa Poetry Prizes, above address

(F) The *Iowa Short Fiction Award* and the *John Simmons Short Fiction Award* are offered for book-length collections of short fiction by writers who have not published a book of prose. The Press publishes the two prizewinning books every year.

Available to: No restrictions
Deadline: Submissions accepted August 1–September 30
Apply to: Iowa Short Fiction Awards, Iowa Writers' Workshop, 102 Dey House, Iowa City, IA 52242

University of Kansas
University Theatre
317 Murphy Hall
Lawrence, KS 66045
Fax: 913-864-3381

(D) The *Great Plains Play Contest* annually awards a first prize of $2,000, production, and $500 for travel and housing costs, for a full-length play, musical, or opera for adult and young audiences that deals with a historical or contemporary aspect of the Great Plains. Second prize is $500. Submissions must not have been produced professionally.

Available to: No restrictions
Deadline: September 1
Apply to: Great Plains Play Contest, above address

University of Massachusetts
Department of Theater
112 Fine Arts Center
Amherst, MA 01003
E-mail: lmburns@english.umass.edu

Ⓓ *New Works for a New World* offers four playwrights a two-week development residence with actors, director, and dramaturg, culminating in a staged reading. Special interest is given to work by writers of color and work that reflects "the diversity of American culture." Selected playwrights receive an honorarium of $1,500, plus paid travel and housing. Send SASE for guidelines.

Available to: See above
Deadline: Inquire
Apply to: New Works for a New World, above address

University of Massachusetts Press
PO Box 429
Amherst, MA 01004
Web site: http://www.umass.edu/umpress
Fax: 413-545-1226

Ⓟ The *Juniper Prize* is granted for an original manuscript of poems, in odd-numbered years for a first book collection and in even-numbered years for a subsequent collection. In the first-book category, manuscripts are accepted from writers whose poems may have appeared in literary journals or anthologies but have not been published in book form. In the subsequent-book category, manuscripts are considered only from authors who have had at least one full-length book or chapbook of poetry published or accepted for publication. In both cases, the winning manuscript will be published by University of Massachusetts Press and the poet awarded $1,000. There is an entry fee of $10. For additional information, fax or write the above address.

Available to: Anyone except University of Massachusetts employees and students, and previous prize recipients
Deadline: September 30
Apply to: Juniper Prize, University of Massachusetts Press, c/o Mail Room, University of Massachusetts, Amherst, MA 01003

University of Michigan
Mike and Mary Wallace House
620 Oxford Road
Ann Arbor, MI 48104-2635

Ⓙ The *Livingston Awards for Young Journalists* offer three $10,000 prizes for the best local, national, and international reporting in any print or broadcast medium.

Available to: Journalists under thirty-five
Deadline: February 1
Apply to: Livingston Awards, above address

Ⓙ The *Mike Wallace Fellowship in Investigative Reporting*, the *Burton R. Benjamin Fellowship in Broadcast Journalism*, the *Knight Fellowships in Specialty Reporting*, the *Sports Reporting Fellowship*, the *Public Policy Journalism Fellowships*, the *Daniel B. Burke Fellowship*, the *Time-Warner Fellowship*, and the *Ford Transportation Technology Fellowship* are available to full-time employees (freelancers included) of any print or broadcast medium with at least five years' experience. Each fellowship carries a $40,000 stipend plus tuition.

Available to: See above
Deadline: February 1
Apply to: Michigan Journalism Fellows, above address, for information

University of Michigan Press
PO Box 1104
Ann Arbor, MI 48106-1104

IN The *University of Michigan Press Book Award* of $1,000 is given annually for the work, written or edited by a member of the University of Michigan teaching and research staff, including emeritus members, that has most distinguished the Press's list. *By Internal Nomination Only.*

University of Missouri
School of Journalism
Neff Hall
Columbia, MO 65211
Web site: http://www.missouri.edu/~jschool/lifestylejournalism.html

J The *Missouri Lifestyle Journalism Awards* (formerly the J. C. Penney Missouri Newspaper Awards) are available to writers, editors, and reporters for daily and weekly newspapers. Winners are chosen in the following categories: single-story and series; consumer affairs; fashion and design; multiculturalism; arts/entertainment; food/nutrition; health/fitness; and feature. Fifteen $1,000 awards are given annually. Send SASE or visit the Web site for further information.

Available to: See above
Deadline: January 31
Apply to: Director, Missouri Lifestyle Journalism Awards, above address

University of Nebraska–Kearney Theatre
Kearney, NE 68849-5260
Fax: 308-865-8405

D The *Great Platte River Playwrights' Festival* offers a $500 first prize plus full production and paid travel and housing to attend rehearsals, for an unproduced, unpublished full-length play. A second prize of $300 and a third of $200 are also offered. Submission of works-in-progress for possible development is encouraged. Write for further information.

Available to: No restrictions
Deadline: April 1
Apply to: Great Platte River Playwrights' Festival, above address

University of Nebraska Press
312 North 14th Street
Lincoln, NE 68588-0484
Fax: 402-472-0308

N The *North American Indian Prose Award* offers a cash advance of $1,000 and publication by the University of Nebraska Press for a book-length work of biography, autobiography, history, literary criticism, or essays by an author of North American Indian descent. Send SASE for guidelines.

Available to: North American Indian writers
Deadline: July 1
Apply to: North American Indian Prose Award, above address

University of Nevada
Department of Theatre
4505 Maryland Parkway
Box 455036
Las Vegas, NV 89154-5036

D The *Morton R. Sarett Memorial Award* biennially offers $3,000 and production for an original, innovative full-length play in English that has not been produced. The winning playwright will be provided with travel and housing to attend rehearsals and the opening performance. Send SASE for guidelines and application.

Available to: No restrictions
Deadline: December 2001 (inquire for exact date)
Apply to: Morton R. Sarett Memorial Award, above address

University of New Hampshire
Department of Theatre and Dance/TRY
Paul Creative Arts Center
30 College Road
Durham, NH 03824-3538
E-mail: kstaten@cisunix.unh.edu
Web site: http://www.unh.edu/theatre-dance
Fax: 603-862-0298

© Ⓓ The *Anna Zornio Memorial Children's Theatre Playwriting Award* every four years offers up to $1,000 plus production for an unpublished play or musical for young audiences that has not been produced professionally. Plays, preferably with a single or unit set, should be not more than one hour long. The next award will be announced on January 31, 2002. Write for guidelines.

Available to: U.S. or Canadian resident
Deadline: September 1, 2001
Apply to: Anna Zornio Playwriting Award, above address

University of New Mexico
English Department
Albuquerque, NM 87131

Ⓕ The *Premio Aztlán* of $2,000 is given annually to honor a book of fiction by a Chicano or Chicana writer who has published no more than two books. The prize includes an invitation to give a reading at the University of New Mexico. Writers or publishers should submit five copies of a work published during the calendar year. Send SASE for guidelines.

Available to: Chicano or Chicana fiction writers
Deadline: December 1
Apply to: Above address

University of North Texas Press
PO Box 311336
Denton, TX 76203-1336
Web site: http://www.unt.edu/untpress
Fax: 940-565-4590

Ⓟ The *Vassar Miller Prize in Poetry* consists of $1,000 and publication by University of North Texas Press of an original, book-length poetry manuscript of 50 to 80 pages. There is a $20 handling fee, payable to the Press. Send SASE for guidelines.

Available to: No restrictions
Deadline: November 30
Apply to: Scott Cairns, Series Editor, Vassar Miller Prize in Poetry, c/o English Department, Tate Hall 107, University of Missouri, Columbia, MO 65211

University of Notre Dame
Department of English
Notre Dame, IN 46556
E-mail: english.righter.1@nd.edu
Web site: http://www.nd.edu/~english/creatwrit/writinfo.html

Ⓕ Ⓟ The *Ernest Sandeen Prize in Poetry* and the *Richard Sullivan Prize in Fiction* each award $1,000 and publication by the University of Notre Dame Press of a book-length manuscript of, respectively, poetry and short fiction. Entrants must have published at least one book of poetry or short fiction. The Sandeen Prize is offered in odd-numbered years, the Sullivan Prize in even-numbered years. Send SASE for guidelines.

Available to: No restrictions
Deadline: August 31, 2000, for the Sullivan; August 31, 2001 for the Sandeen
Apply to: Sandeen Prize or Sullivan Prize, Director of Creative Writing, Department of English, University of Notre Dame, Notre Dame, IN 46556

University of Pittsburgh Press
3347 Forbes Avenue
Pittsburgh, PA 15261
Web site: http://www.pitt.edu/~press

(F) The *Drue Heinz Literature Prize*, given annually, consists of a cash award of $10,000 and publication of a collection of short fiction by University of Pittsburgh Press under a standard royalty contract. Send SASE or visit the Web site for guidelines before submitting.

Available to: Writers who have published a book-length collection of short fiction or a minimum of three short stories or novellas in commercial magazines or literary journals of national distribution
Deadline: Submissions must be postmarked May 1–June 30
Apply to: Drue Heinz Literature Prize, above address

(P) The *Agnes Lynch Starrett Prize*, given annually, consists of a cash award of $5,000 and publication of a first book of poetry by University of Pittsburgh Press under a standard royalty contract. There is a $20 reading fee. Send SASE or visit the Web site for guidelines before submitting.

Available to: Anyone who has not published a full-length book of poetry
Deadline: Submissions must be postmarked March 1–April 30
Apply to: Agnes Lynch Starrett Poetry Prize, above address

University of Rochester
Susan B. Anthony Institute for Gender and Women's Studies
Lattimore Hall, Room 538
Rochester, NY 14627-0434
Web site: http://www.rochester.edu/college/wst

(F) The *Janet Heidinger Kafka Prize* is awarded annually to a woman U.S. citizen for the best published book-length work of prose fiction (novel, short story collection, experimental writing). Works submitted must have been published within the previous twelve months; collections of short stories must have been assembled for the first time, or at least one-third of the material must have been previously unpublished. The prize consists of a cash award, which varies according to funding. Entries may be submitted only by publishers, who should write for guidelines.

Available to: See above
Deadline: February 28
Apply to: Janet Heidinger Kafka Prize, above address

University of Southern California
Professional Writing Program
WPH 404
Los Angeles, CA 90089-4034

(P) The *Ann Stanford Poetry Prize* awards $1,000 (first place), $200 (second), and $100 (third) for previously unpublished poems. Poets may submit up to five poems, with a $10 reading fee. Winning entries are published in *Southern California Anthology*. Send SASE for contest rules. All entrants will receive an issue of the anthology.

Available to: No restrictions
Deadline: April 15
Apply to: Ann Stanford Poetry Prize, above address

University of Texas. *See* Dobie-Paisano Project

University of Virginia Creative Writing Program
English Department, 219 Bryan Hall
Charlottesville, VA 22903
E-mail: LRS9E@virginia.edu
Web site: http://www.engl.virginia.edu/

The Graduate Writing Program offers several *Henry Hoyns Fellowships* to first-year MFA students. Fellows must be enrolled as candidates for the MFA degree. Write for further information and application guidelines.

Available to: See above
Deadline: January 1
Apply to: Above address

University of Wisconsin Press
2537 Daniels Street
Madison, WI 53704

Ⓟ The *Brittingham Prize in Poetry* and the *Felix Pollak Prize in Poetry*, each consisting of a cash award of $1,000 and publication by University of Wisconsin Press, are awarded annually to the best book-length manuscripts of original poetry (50 to 80 pages). A $20 reading fee must accompany each manuscript. Send SASE for guidelines.

Available to: No restrictions
Deadline: Submissions accepted September 1–October 1
Apply to: Ronald Wallace, Series Editor, above address

Unterberg Poetry Center of the 92nd Street Y
1395 Lexington Avenue
New York, NY 10128
Web site: www.92ndsty.org

Ⓟ The *"Discovery"/The Nation Poetry Contest: Joan Leiman Jacobson Poetry Prizes* are offered to four poets who have not published a book of poems (chapbooks and self-published books included). Each award consists of a $300 cash prize, a reading at the Poetry Center, and publication in *The Nation*. Four identical sets of a stapled, numbered 10-page manuscript should be submitted. Poems must be original and in English (no translations), and the manuscript should not exceed 500 lines. Personal identification must appear only in a single, separate cover letter, not on the poems; the cover letter must include name, address, and day and evening telephone numbers. Biographical information is not necessary. There is a $5 entry fee; do not send cash. For guidelines, send SASE to the above address.

Available to: See above
Deadline: Submissions accepted during January
Apply to: "Discovery"/The Nation, above address

Urban Stages/Playwrights Preview Productions
17 East 47th Street
New York, NY 10017
E-mail: UrbanStage@aol.com
Web site: http://www.mint.net/urbanstages
Fax: 212-421-1387

Ⓓ The *Emerging Playwright Award* offers $500, production, and paid travel to attend rehearsals for full-length plays and one-acts that have not been produced in New York City. Submissions by minority playwrights and plays with ethnically diverse casts are encouraged. Write for guidelines.

Available to: No restrictions
Deadline: Ongoing
Apply to: Emerging Playwright Award, above address

Utah Arts Council
617 East South Temple Street
Salt Lake City, UT 84102
E-mail: glebeda@arts.state.ut.us
Web site: http://www.dced.state.ut.us/arts
Fax: 801-236-7556

Ⓜ The *Utah Original Writing Competition* offers a $5,000 prize that will go directly to a publisher to assist in the publication and promotion of a book by a Utah writer. The winner is selected from among four book-length works in categories alternating yearly: novel, short fiction or poetry collection, biography/autobiography or general nonfiction, and juvenile or young adult book. The Council also offers prizes of up to $1,000 for novels, book-length collections of poems, individual poems, and short stories by Utah residents. Write for further information and guidelines.

Available to: Utah residents
Deadline: Last Friday in June
Apply to: Literary Competition Division, above address

Utah State University Press
Logan, UT 84322-7800
Web site: http://www.usu.edu/~usupress

Ⓟ The *May Swenson Poetry Award* offers $1,000, publication by Utah State University Press, and royalties for a poetry collection. Poets may submit manuscripts of 50 to 100 pages, along with a $20 reading fee, which covers a copy of the winning book. Send SASE for guidelines or visit the Web site.

Available to: No restrictions
Deadline: September 30
Apply to: May Swenson Poetry Award, above address

The Valley Players
Box 441
Waitsfield, VT 05673-0441

Ⓓ The *Vermont Playwrights Award* annually offers $1,000 and probable production for an unproduced, unpublished full-length play by a resident of Maine, New Hampshire, or Vermont. Plays should be suitable for a community group and have moderate production demands. Send SASE for guidelines.

Available to: Maine, New Hampshire or Vermont playwrights
Deadline: February 1
Apply to: Vermont Playwrights Award, above address

Vermont Arts Council
136 State Street, Drawer 33
Montpelier, VT 05633-6001
E-mail: info@arts.vca.state.vt.us
Web site: http://www.state.vt.us/vermont-arts
Fax: 802-828-3363

Ⓜ The *Opportunity Grants Program* makes funds available to individual Vermont artists for the creation of new work and artistic development. Grant amounts for new work range from $750 to $7,000; for development from $250 to $750. Write, e-mail, or visit the Web site for additional information and application materials.

Available to: Vermont residents
Deadline: Inquire
Apply to: Opportunity Grants, above address

Vermont Studio Center
Box 613
Johnson, VT 05656
E-mail: VSCVT@pwshift.com
Web site: http://www.vermontstudiocenter.com
Fax: 802-635-2730

® The Vermont Studio Center offers four-to-twelve-week residences year-round for writers and artists. Each of the twelve one-month periods features two visiting writers whose work falls into one of three genres: poetry, fiction, or nonfiction. Each writer gives a reading and a literary craft talk, and is available for conferences with residents in his/her genre. A number of full fellowships based on merit are awarded each year and cover all residence fees. In addition, *Vermont Studio Center Grants*, which include *Residency Grants* and *Work-Exchange Grants*, are awarded to those able to document financial need. VSC Grants cover part of the cost of the residence. There is a $25 application fee. Write, e-mail, or visit the Web site for additional information and application.

Available to: Emerging and mid-career writers
Deadline: September 30, February 15, and June 15 for full fellowships; ongoing for VSC Grants
Apply to: VSC Writers Program, Admissions Committee, above address

Verse
English Department
Plymouth State College
Plymouth, NH 03264
Web site: http://www.versemag.org

℗ The *Verse Prize* awards $1,000 plus publication by Verse Press for a book of poetry by a published or unpublished poet writing in English. There is a $20 entry fee. Send SASE or visit the Web site for guidelines.

Available to: No restrictions
Deadline: February 28
Apply to: Verse Prize, above address

Very Special Arts
1300 Connecticut Avenue, NW, Suite 700
Washington, DC 20036
E-mail: playwright@vsarts.org
Web site: http://www.vsarts.org

Ⓓ The *Playwright Discovery Award* is given for original one-acts by disabled students that address an aspect of disability. One script in each of two age categories—twenty-one and under, and twenty-two and above—is selected for professional production at the John F. Kennedy Center for the Performing Arts. Winners in both categories receive an expenses-paid trip to Washington to see the production or staged reading. The winner in the younger category receives $500; the winner in the older category receives $2,500. Write, e-mail, or visit the Web site for guidelines and application.

Available to: Disabled U.S. citizens or permanent residents
Deadline: April 30
Apply to: Above address

Veterans of Foreign Wars National Headquarters
Voice of Democracy Program
406 West 34th Street
Kansas City, MO 64111

Ⓝ The annual *Voice of Democracy Audio Essay Competition* awards fifty-six national scholarships, totaling more than $100,000, to high school students in grades 9 through 12 for tape-recorded essays, 3 to 5 minutes in length, on an announced theme. For more information, check with a high school counselor or contact a local VFW post.

Available to: High school students
Deadline: November 1
Apply to: High school counselor or local VFW Post

Villa Montalvo
PO Box 158
Saratoga, CA 95071
E-mail: kfunk@villamontalvo.org
Web site: http://www.villamontalvo.org
Fax: 408-961-5850

®   The *Artist Residency Program* awards artists, composers, and writers one-to-three-month residences at the 1912 Villa Montalvo in the foothills of the Santa Cruz Mountains. Writers are given fully equipped apartments with private kitchen; residents must provide their own food, supplies, and funds for living expenses. The program aims for "an ethnically diverse and international community of arts which will broaden artistic perspectives and catalyze dialogue." Send SASE, e-mail, or visit the Web site for information and application materials.

Available to: No restrictions
Deadlines: September 1 for April–May residences; March 1 for October–March
Apply to: Kathryn Funk, Artist Residency Program Director, above address

℗ ®   The *Villa Montalvo Biennial Poetry Competition* awards $1,000 and a one-month residence at Villa Montalvo for unpublished original poems. A $500 second prize and $300 third prize are offered also. Send SASE for guidelines.

Available to: California, Nevada, Oregon, and Washington State residents
Deadline: October 1, 2001
Apply to: Villa Montalvo Biennial Poetry Competition, above address

Virginia Center for the Creative Arts
Box VCCA
Sweet Briar, VA 24595
E-mail: vcca@vcca.com
Web site: http://www.vcca.com
Fax: 804-946-7239

®   The Virginia Center for the Creative Arts accepts applications from professional writers, visual artists, and composers for residences ranging from two weeks to two months. The Center is located in Amherst County, one hour south of Charlottesville. A standard daily fee of $30 covers private studio, bedroom, and three meals. Financial assistance is available for qualified applicants with demonstrated need. Write, e-mail, or visit the Web site for more information.

Available to: No restrictions
Deadline: January 15 for June–September residences; May 15 for October–January; September 15 for February–May
Apply to: Admissions, above address

Virginia College Stores Association
c/o Judy Sawyer
The Macon Bookshop
Randolph-Macon Woman's College
Lynchburg, VA 24503
E-mail: jsawyer@rmwc.edu

The *Virginia College Stores Association Book Award* annually offers $500 to an author residing in Virginia whose work possesses "outstanding literary, social, and intellectual merit." Books published within the calendar year may be submitted. Write or e-mail for guidelines prior to submitting.

Available to: Virginia authors
Deadline: December 15
Apply to: Book Award, above address

Virginia Commonwealth University
Department of English
PO Box 842005
Richmond, VA 23284-2005
E-mail: eng_grad@vcu.edu
Web site: http://www.has.vcu.edu/eng/grad/Levis_Prize.htm

(P)   The *Levis Reading Prize* offers an honorarium of $1,000 and an expenses-paid trip to Richmond for a public reading, to the author of a first or second book of poetry published during the calendar year. Poet or publisher should submit one copy of a book at least 48 pages long. Send SASE, e-mail, or visit the Web site for guidelines.

Available to: No restrictions
Deadline: January 15
Apply to: Levis Reading Prize, above address

Virginia Quarterly Review
One West Range
Charlottesville, VA 22903

(F) (P)   The *Emily Clark Balch Awards*, each $500, are given annually to the best short story and best poem published in *Virginia Quarterly Review* during the calendar year. The editors consider only those stories and poems which have been accepted and published.

Available to: U.S. citizens
Deadline: Submissions accepted year-round
Apply to: Above address

Visiting Writers Program
Knapp Hall
State University of New York at Farmingdale
Farmingdale, NY 11735
E-mail: brownml@snyfarva.cc.farmingdale.edu
Web site: http://www.farmingdale.edu/campuspages/artssciences/englishhumanities/paward.html

(P)   The *Paumanok Poetry Award* offers $1,000 plus paid expenses for a reading as part of the SUNY Farmingdale Visiting Writers Program series. Two runners-up receive $500 plus paid expenses for a reading in the series. To enter the competition, send five to seven poems (published or unpublished), a one-paragraph biography, a $12 reading fee, and SASE. Write for further information.

Available to: No restrictions
Deadline: September 15
Apply to: Above address

Ludwig Vogelstein Foundation
PO Box 277
Hancock, ME 04640

The Ludwig Vogelstein Foundation gives up to fifty grants to individuals in the arts and humanities, on the basis of merit and need. Grants are awarded for specific projects; no scholarships, graduate or undergraduate support, or faculty subsidies are offered. Send #10 SASE for instructions and information on deadlines.

Available to: Artists and writers
Deadline: Inquire
Apply to: Above address

Wagner College
Department of Theatre and Speech
One Campus Road
Staten Island, NY 10301
E-mail: lterry@wagner.edu

Ⓓ The *Stanley Drama Award* of $2,000 is given for an original full-length play, musical, or one-act sequence that has not been produced professionally or received trade book publication. Only one submission per playwright will be considered. Plays entered previously in the competition may not be resubmitted; previous award winners may not reapply. There is a $25 reading fee. Send SASE for required application form.

Available to: No restrictions
Deadline: October 1
Apply to: Stanley Drama Award, above address

Lila Wallace–Reader's Digest Fund
Two Park Avenue, 23rd floor
New York, NY 10016
Web site: http://www.lilawallace.org

ⒾⓃ The *Lila Wallace–Reader's Digest Writer's Awards* seek to enable writers of demonstrated talent and exceptional promise to devote significant time to their writing for up to three years and, during the period of the award, to encourage them to develop meaningful interactions with a broader public through affiliation with a community agency. Writers receive $35,000 per year for three years; their affiliated organizations receive a modest grant to defray the direct costs of managing the affiliation. The final round of the program will begin in 2000. There is no application process. *By Internal Nomination Only.*

Edward Lewis Wallant Book Award
c/o Dr. and Mrs. Irving Waltman
3 Brighton Road
West Hartford, CT 06117

Ⓕ The *Edward Lewis Wallant Book Award* is presented annually for a novel or collection of short stories significant to American Jews. Work must have been published during the calendar year. A $500 prize and a citation are awarded.

Available to: American writers
Deadline: December 31
Apply to: Above address

Washington Center for Politics & Journalism
PO Box 15201
Washington, DC 20003-0201
E-mail: pol-jrn@wcpj.org
Web site: http://www.wcpj.org
Fax: 800-858-8365

Ⓙ The *Politics & Journalism Semester* brings about a dozen undergraduate or graduate journalists whose career goal is political reporting to Washington each semester. Two sixteen-week courses for the students are held each year, from September to December and from February to May. Students receive a stipend of $2,500 to assist with the cost of relocating to and living in Washington for four months; in return, they must work full-time for the news bureaus to which they are assigned. Write, e-mail, or visit the Web site for additional information and application.

Available to: Undergraduates (at least second-term juniors), recent graduates (within one year), and graduate students
Deadline: Inquire
Apply to: Participating schools of communication and journalism; or Politics & Journalism Semester, above address

Washington Independent Writers (WIW)
220 Woodward Building
733 15th Street, NW
Washington, DC 20005
E-mail: washwriter@aol.com
Web site: http://www.washwriter.org

© The *Joan G. Sugarman Children's Book Award* of $1,000 is given to the author of a published work of fiction or nonfiction geared to children ages one through fifteen. Write for guidelines.

Available to: Washington, D.C., Maryland, and Virginia residents
Deadline: January 31
Apply to: Book Award, above address

The Washington Post
1150 15th Street, NW
Washington, DC 20071-7301
Fax: 202-334-5231

Ⓙ The *Washington Post Summer News Program* offers a paid twelve-week internship for junior or senior college students and graduate students enrolled in a degree program who have some experience in journalism. Selected interns work full-time as reporters, copy editors, photographers, or artists. For summer 1999, the weekly salary was approximately $790. Write for additional information and application.

Available to: See above
Deadline: November 1
Apply to: Summer News Program, above address

Washington State Arts Commission. *See* **Artist Trust**

Water-Stone
Graduate Liberal Studies Program
Hamline University
1536 Hewitt Avenue
St. Paul, MN 55104-1284

Ⓟ The *Jane Kenyon Poetry Prize* biennially offers a first prize of $500, a second of $300, and a third of $200, plus publication in *Water-Stone,* for an original, unpublished poem. Poets may submit up to three poems, 10 pages total. The $10 entry fee covers a one-year subscription to the review. If entry fees exceed costs of the contest, the remainder will go to the magazine and to a Jane Kenyon Poetry Scholarship for students in Hamline University's MFA program. Send SASE for guidelines.

Available to: No restrictions
Deadline: Submissions accepted September 15–December 15, 2000
Apply to: Poetry Prize, above address

Ⓕ Ⓝ The *Brenda Ueland Prose Prize* biennially offers two prizes of $500 each, plus publication in *Water-Stone,* for a piece of original, unpublished fiction and creative nonfiction with a maximum length of 5,000 words. Excerpts from longer works are eligible if they can stand on their own. There is a $10 entry fee, which covers a one-year subscription to the review. Send SASE for guidelines.

Available to: No restrictions
Deadline: Submissions accepted September 15–December 15, 2001
Apply to: Prose Prize, above address

Frank Waters Foundation
PO Box 1127
Taos, NM 87571
E-mail: fwaters@laplaza.org
Web site: http://www.taoswolf.com/frankwaters

(F)   The *Frank Waters Voices of the Southwest Writing Award* offers $2,000 plus publication for a novel whose focus is the "non-urban West," by a writer from Arizona, Colorado, Nevada, New Mexico, Texas, or Utah. Send SASE or e-mail for guidelines.

Available to: See above
Deadline: December 1, 2000; inquire for 2001
Apply to: Voices of the Southwest, above address

Thomas J. Watson Foundation
293 South Main Street
Providence, RI 02903
E-mail: WatsonFoundation@Brown.edu
Web site: http://www.WatsonFellowship.org
Fax: 401-274-1954

The *Thomas J. Watson Fellowship Program* is designed to give exceptional college graduates the freedom to engage in a year of independent study and travel abroad. The Foundation provides fellows an opportunity for "a focused and disciplined *Wanderjahr* of their own devising—to thoroughly explore a particular interest, to test their aspirations and abilities, to view their lives and American society in greater perspective and, concomitantly, to develop a more informed sense of international concern." The fellowship provides a grant of $22,000 to each recipient; fellows whose spouse or dependent child(ren) will accompany them may be eligible for a grant of $31,000. Fellows are required to maintain contact with the Foundation during their year abroad, to send quarterly progress reports, and at fellowship's end, to submit a report and an accounting of the funds. Graduating seniors at participating institutions are eligible for nomination by their institution. Write or visit the Web site for additional information, including list of participating institutions, and application procedures.

Available to: See above
Deadline: Early November (inquire for exact date)
Apply to: Thomas J. Watson Fellowship Program, above address

Wesleyan Writers Conference
Wesleyan University
Middletown, CT 06459-0094
Fax: 860-685-2441
E-mail: agreene@wesleyan.edu
Web site: http://www.wesleyan.edu/writing/conferen.html

(M)   The Wesleyan Writers Conference, staffed by award-winning writers, offers full and partial scholarships to conference participants. Scholarships include the *Joan and John Jakobson Scholarships*, open to writers of fiction, nonfiction, and poetry, and the *Jon Davidoff Scholarships for Journalists*. Teaching fellowships, including the *Barach Fellowship*, are also awarded. Fellowship candidates should have completed a book-length manuscript. Write for further information and guidelines.

Available to: No restrictions
Deadline: April 12, 2000; inquire for 2001
Apply to: Fellowship and Scholarship Committee, above address

West Coast Ensemble
Box 38728
Los Angeles, CA 90038
Fax: 323-876-8916

Ⓓ The *Full-Length Play Competition* awards $500 and production (and royalties on any performance beyond an eight-week run) for an unproduced, unpublished full-length play. The play must not have been produced previously in southern California; playwrights seeking a second production of a play produced elsewhere are welcome to submit.

Ⓓ The *Musical Stairs Competition* selects five finalist musicals for presentation in a workshop staged-reading format, with the winner receiving a fully staged production and a prize of $500. Write for information.

Available to: No restrictions
Deadline: December 31 for full-length plays; June 30 for musicals
Apply to: Above address (specifying competition)

West Virginia Commission on the Arts
The Cultural Center
1900 Kanawha Boulevard East
Charleston, WV 25305-0300
E-mail: mccomas@wvlc.wvnet.edu
Web site: http://www.wvlc.wvnet.edu/culture/arts.html

Ⓜ Fellowship awards of $3,500 are given in alternating years to West Virginia poets, playwrights, and fiction and nonfiction writers. Write, e-mail, or visit the Web site for further information.

Available to: West Virginia residents
Deadline: September 1
Apply to: Above address

Western History Association
University of New Mexico
1060 Mesa Vista Hall
Albuquerque, NM 87131-1181
E-mail: wha@unm.edu
Web site: http://www.unm.edu/~wha/
Fax: 505-277-6023

Ⓝ The *Robert G. Athearn Book Award* is offered in even-numbered years for a published book on the twentieth century that has a copyright date no more than two years old. The Association awards $500 to the author and $500 to the publisher. Write, e-mail, or visit the Web site for list of award committee members.

Available to: No restrictions
Deadline: June 1, 2000
Apply to: Above address

Ⓝ The *Caughey Western History Association Prize* annually offers $2,500 to the author of the most outstanding book on the history of the American West. Publishers should submit nominations for books published in the previous calendar year to each member of the award committee. Write, e-mail, or visit the Web site for list of committee members.

Available to: No restrictions
Deadline: July 1
Apply to: Above address

The *Huntington Library–Western History Association Martin Ridge Fellowship for Study in Western History Award* offers $2,000 and a one-month fellowship at the Huntington Library to Ph.D. recipients or doctoral students in western history. Applicants should send a two-to-three-page description of their project, specifying the materials they plan to consult at the Huntington and indicating progress to date on the project, as well as a brief curriculum vitae, to each member of the award committee. Recipients of the fellowship are expected to be in continuous residence at the Huntington for one month. Write, e-mail, or visit the Web site for list of award committee members.

Available to: See above
Deadline: September 1
Apply to: Above address

The *Sara Jackson Award* offers $500 annually to support graduate student research in western history. Preference will be given to African-American and other minority students. Write for additional application information, and for list of award committee members.

Available to: Graduate students
Deadline: July 31
Apply to: Above address

Ⓝ The *W. Turrentine Jackson Award* biennially awards $1,000 to a beginning professional historian for a first book on any aspect of the American West. Publishers should submit books published in the two years before the award deadline to each member of the award committee. Write, e-mail, or visit the Web site for list of committee members.

Available to: No restrictions
Deadline: July 1, 2001
Apply to: Above address

The *Rundell Graduate Student Award* annually offers $1,000 to a doctoral candidate who has completed comprehensive Ph.D. examinations and is in the process of researching a dissertation topic in western history. Write, e-mail, or visit the Web site for additional application information.

Available to: Doctoral candidates
Deadline: July 31
Apply to: Above address

The Western History Association offers several other awards with lesser monetary stipends for articles and research work on western history. Contact the Association for further information.

Whetstone
Barrington Area Arts Council
PO Box 1266
Barrington, IL 60011

Ⓜ The *Whetstone Prize* is given for the best poem, fiction, or creative nonfiction accepted for publication in *Whetstone*, an annual literary journal published by the Barrington Area Arts Council. Winning writers receive a cash award (usually $500 to a single author). Send $5 for a sample copy and guidelines.

Available to: No restrictions
Deadline: Submissions accepted year-round
Apply to: Whetstone Prize, above address

White Eagle Coffee Store Press
PO Box 383
Fox River Grove, IL 60021-0383
E-mail: wecspress@aol.com
Web site: http://members.aol.com/wecspress

Ⓕ The *A. E. Coppard Prize for Long Fiction* annually recognizes the author of a long story with $500, chapbook publication, and 25 copies of the published book. Fiction writers may submit unpublished stories, from 8,000 to 14,000 words, with a $15 entry fee; for additional manuscripts in the same envelope, $5 each. Writers from any country may apply, but all submitted work must be in English. All entrants receive a copy of the prizewinning chapbook. Send SASE for guidelines.

Available to: No restrictions
Deadline: December 15
Apply to: A. E. Coppard Prize for Long Fiction, above address

White Pine Press
PO Box 236
Buffalo, NY 14201
E-mail: wpine@whitepine.org
Fax: 716-842-0158

(P)   The *White Pine Press Poetry Prize* offers $1,000 and publication by the Press for a book-length collection of poems by a U.S. author. Poets may submit original typed manuscripts of up to 100 pages. Poems may have been published in periodicals or in limited-edition chapbooks. There is a $20 reading fee. Send SASE for notification of results; manuscripts will not be returned.

     Available to: U.S. citizens
     Deadline: Submissions accepted July 15–December 1
     Apply to: White Pine Press Poetry Prize, above address

Mrs. Giles Whiting Foundation
1133 Avenue of the Americas, 22nd floor
New York, NY 10036-6710

[IN]   Ten *Whiting Writers' Awards*, of $30,000 each, are given in recognition of the quality of current and past writing and in anticipation of outstanding future work. The program places special emphasis on exceptionally promising emerging talent. *By Internal Nomination Only*.

Wichita Falls Backdoor Players
Box 896
Wichita Falls, TX 76307
E-mail: backdoor@wf.net
Fax: 940-322-8167

(D)   The *Annual Backdoor Theatre New Play Project* offers a $500 honorarium and travel and housing for a five-week development program that includes rehearsals and a workshop production with a minimum of six performances. Submitted work must be professionally unproduced. Write or e-mail for additional information.

     Available to: No restrictions; playwrights from Texas and surrounding region preferred
     Deadline: March 15
     Apply to: New Play Project, above address

Elie Wiesel Foundation for Humanity
380 Madison Avenue, 20th floor
New York, NY 10017
E-mail: info@eliewieselfoundation.org
Web site: http://www.eliewieselfoundation.org
Fax: 212-490-6006

(N)   The *Elie Wiesel Prize in Ethics Essay Contest* awards a first prize of $5,000, a second of $2,500, and a third of $1,500 for an essay of 3,000 to 4,000 words on one of three suggested topics, which change yearly. Applicants must be full-time registered junior and senior undergraduates at an accredited four-year college or university in the United States. Essays must be reviewed by a professor at the applicant's school and submitted with a faculty sponsor form. Write, e-mail, or visit the Web site for additional information and application materials.

     Available to: See above
     Deadline: January (inquire for exact date)
     Apply to: Elie Wiesel Prize in Ethics, above address

Tennessee Williams/New Orleans Literary Festival
5500 Prytania Street, Suite 217
New Orleans, LA 70115
E-mail: twfest@gnofn.org
Web site: http://www.sparkie.gnofn.org/~twfest
Fax: 504-529-2430

Ⓓ The *Tennessee Williams/New Orleans Literary Festival One-Act Play Competition* offers a cash prize of $1,000, a reading of the winning play at the festival, and a full production during the following year's festival. Only professionally unproduced, unpublished one-act plays on an American subject are eligible. There is a $15 entry fee. Send SASE for information.

Available to: No restrictions
Deadline: December 1
Apply to: Tennessee Williams/New Orleans Literary Festival, One-Act Play Contest, c/o Creative Writing Workshop, University of New Orleans–Lakefront, New Orleans, LA 70148

Woodrow Wilson International Center for Scholars
Fellowship Office
One Woodrow Wilson Plaza
Washington, DC 20004-3027
E-mail: fellowships@wwic.si.edu
Web site: http://www.wwics.si.edu
Fax: 202-691-4009

The Woodrow Wilson Center awards some twenty residential fellowships annually to individuals with outstanding project proposals in a broad range of the social sciences and humanities, on national and/or international topics that intersect with questions of public policy. Applicants must hold a doctorate or have equivalent professional accomplishments. Fellows are provided offices, access to the Library of Congress, computers or manuscript-typing services, and research assistants. Fellowships are normally for an academic year, though a few are available for shorter periods with a minimum of four months. The average yearly stipend is approximately $43,000. The Center pays travel expenses and 75 percent of health insurance premiums for fellows and immediate dependents. Write, e-mail, or visit the Web site for additional information and application materials.

Available to: No restrictions
Deadline: October 1
Apply to: Above address

Wind Publications
PO Box 24548
Lexington, KY 40524
Web site: http://www.wind.org/publications.htm

Ⓟ The *Allen Tate Memorial Award* offers $500 and publication in *Wind* magazine for a single poem, previously unpublished, of up to 100 lines. The entry fee is $2 per poem.

Available to: No restrictions
Deadline: June 30
Apply to: Allen Tate Memorial Award, above address

Ⓕ The *Wind Magazine Short Story Competition* awards $500 and publication for a short story of up to 5,000 words. The entry fee is $10 per story.

Available to: No restrictions
Deadline: April 30
Apply to: Short Story Competition, above address

Wisconsin Arts Board
101 East Wilson Street, 1st floor
Madison, WI 53702
E-mail: artsboard@arts.state.wi.us
Web site: http://www.arts.state.wi.us
Fax: 608-267-0380

Ⓜ The Wisconsin Arts Board offers eight fellowships, of $8,000 each, in fiction, poetry, essay/ criticism, and drama to Wisconsin residents. Full-time degree-credit students are not eligible. Write for application form.

Available to: Wisconsin residents
Deadline: September 15 in even-numbered years
Apply to: Above address

Wisconsin Institute for Creative Writing
University of Wisconsin
Department of English
600 North Park Street
Madison, WI 53706
Web site: http://polyglot.lss.wisc.edu/english

Ⓕ Ⓟ The *Jay C. and Ruth Halls, Carl Djerassi, Diane Middlebrook, Carol Houck Smith, Anastasia C. Hoffman,* and *James McCreight Fellowships* offer an academic year in Madison as artists-in-residence at the University of Wisconsin to six new writers working on a first book of poetry or fiction. Fellows will teach one introductory creative writing workshop per semester and give one public reading from work in progress. The fellowship pays $23,000 for the academic year. Write for application guidelines.

Available to: Poets and fiction writers with an MA, MFA, or equivalent degree in creative writing who have not yet published a book
Deadline: Applications accepted in February
Apply to: Jesse Lee Kercheval, Director, above address

The Thomas Wolfe Society
c/o Dr. James Clark, Jr.
807 Gardner Street
Raleigh, NC 27607

The *Thomas Wolfe Student Essay Prize* offers $500 to an undergraduate or graduate student for an essay related to Wolfe or his works. The winner will be invited to deliver the winning essay at the annual meeting of the Society. Submissions should be in English, 8 to 15 double-spaced, typed pages.

Available to: No restrictions
Deadline: January 15
Apply to: Thomas Wolfe Student Essay Prize, above address

Carter G. Woodson Institute for Afro-American and African Studies
University of Virginia
108 Minor Hall
Charlottesville, VA 22903
Web site: http://www.virginia.edu/~woodson
Fax: 804-924-8820

The *Carter G. Woodson Institute Predoctoral and Postdoctoral Residential Research Fellowships* are awarded to eligible scholars whose work focuses on race, ethnicity, and society in Africa and the Atlantic world (broadly defined as the African Diaspora). Predoctoral fellowships, covering two years, carry an annual stipend of $15,000. Postdoctoral fellowships, covering one year, carry a stipend of $25,000. Fellows whose projects are selected for publication in the University Press of Virginia series Studies of Race, Ethnicity, and Society in Africa and the Atlantic World are eligible for up to $3,000 in editorial assistance. Fellows must be in residence at the university for the duration of the award period and are expected to make periodic presentations of their work to the Woodson fellows and the larger academic community. Write or visit the Web site for additional information.

Available to: No restrictions
Deadline: December 1
Apply to: Selection Committee, Residential Research Fellowships, above address

Word Works
Box 42164
Washington, DC 20015
E-mail: wordworks@shirenet.com

(P) The *Washington Prize* awards $1,500 and publication by Word Works for an unpublished volume of original poetry of outstanding literary merit by a living American poet. Send SASE for guidelines and application procedures.

Available to: U.S. citizens
Deadline: Submissions accepted February 1–March 1
Apply to: Washington Prize, above address

World Hunger Year
505 Eighth Avenue, 21st floor
New York, NY 10018-6582
E-mail: whyawards@aol.com
Web site: http://www.worldhungeryear.org

(J) The *Harry Chapin Media Awards* are given to "encourage better and more extensive reporting on issues broadly related to hunger and poverty" and to "honor the media for excellence in impacting hunger, poverty, and self-reliance." Awards of $2,500 each are given for the year's best journalism in the following categories: books, broadcast media, periodicals, newspapers, and photojournalism. Write, e-mail, or visit the Web site for further information and guidelines.

Available to: No restrictions
Deadline: February 15
Apply to: Harry Chapin Media Awards, above address

World Literature Today
University of Oklahoma
110 Monnet Hall
Norman, OK 73019-4033
Web site: http://www.ou.edu/wordlit/

[IN] The *Neustadt International Prize for Literature* is given to honor a life's work, or to direct attention to an outstanding writer whose literary career is still in progress. Political and geographic considerations do not enter into the selection, made by an international jury. One prize of $40,000 is given in even-numbered years. *By Internal Nomination Only.*

Writers Colony at Dairy Hollow
515 Spring Street
Eureka Springs, AR 72632
E-mail: director@writerscolony.org
Web site: http://www.writerscolony.org

(R) Residences of four to twelve weeks are available at Dairy Hollow, located in the Ozark Mountains. Residents are provided with private living/work space and meals (breakfast and lunch are self-service; dinner is served in an inn dining room five nights a week). The actual cost per resident per day is $125, and each resident is asked to contribute; however, demonstrable talent, self-discipline, and achievement are the only criteria for a residence. For every thirty days' residence, each writer is asked to contribute one day of community service within the region. There is a $35 application fee. Write, e-mail, or visit the Web site for application.

Available to: No restrictions
Deadline: September 30 for spring–midsummer residence; December 31 for midsummer–fall; April 30 for winter
Apply to: Above address

The Writers Community
YMCA of the USA
101 North Wacker Drive
Chicago, IL 60606

Ⓜ The Writers Community of the YMCA National Writer's Voice funds semester-long residences at select YMCA Writer's Voice centers nationwide to established poets, fiction writers, nonfiction writers, playwrights, and children's book authors. Residents teach a master-level workshop and give a public reading. In 1999, writers received $5,500 each. Each center selects a local writer according to its own guidelines; centers should be contacted directly for application information.

Available to: Accomplished writers with teaching experience and interest
Deadline: Inquire at Writer's Voice centers
Apply to: Above address for a list of nationwide center addresses

Writers' Conferences & Centers
c/o Associated Writing Programs
Tallwood House, MSN 1E3
George Mason University
Fairfax, VA 22030
Web site: http://www.awpwriter.org

Writers' Conferences & Centers conducts an annual competition to provide scholarships for emerging writers who wish to attend a writers' conference. Two scholarships of $500 each will be awarded and applied to the fees of any of the member conferences of WC&C, an association of conferences, colonies, and festivals for writers. There is a $10 reading fee for each manuscript submitted. Send SASE or visit the Web site for guidelines.

Available to: No restrictions
Deadline: Submissions must be postmarked in January or February
Apply to: WC&C Scholarship Program, PO Box 386, Amherst, MA 01004, attn: Michael Pettit

Writer's Digest
1507 Dana Avenue
Cincinnati, OH 45207
E-mail: competitions@fwpubs.com
Web site: http://www.writersdigest.com

Ⓜ The *National Self-Publishing Awards* offer a grand prize of $1,000 and promotion in *Publishers Weekly* and *Writer's Digest* for a book self-published in the current calendar year. Books may be submitted in one of eight categories: reference, inspirational, life stories, cookbooks, children's and young adult books, fiction, nonfiction, and poetry. The grand-prize winner is chosen from among the eight categories; winners in the other seven each receive $300. Eligible are books for which the author paid the full cost of publication in an edition of at least 500 copies. There is a $95 reading fee per book. Send SASE or visit the Web site for an application and guidelines.

Available to: No restrictions
Deadline: December 15
Apply to: National Self-Publishing Awards, above address

Ⓜ The *Writer's Digest Annual Writing Competition* offers more than $25,000 in prizes. Original unpublished manuscripts may be entered in the following categories: personal essay/

memoir, feature article, literary/mainstream short story, genre short story, rhyming poetry, nonrhyming poetry, stage play, television/movie script, children's fiction, and inspirational writing. The first-place winner in each category receives $750, $100 worth of Writer's Digest books, and a manuscript critique and marketing advice. Second- through tenth-place winners receive cash prizes. There is a $10 entry fee. Write, e-mail, or visit the Web site for rules and entry form.

Available to: No restrictions
Deadline: May 31
Apply to: Writing Competition, above address

The Writer's Voice of the West Side YMCA
5 West 63rd Street
New York, NY 10023
Web site: http://users.aol.com/wtrsvoice/files/WVintro.html

Ⓜ The *Capricorn Novel Award*, the *Capricorn Poetry Award*, and the *Capricorn Nonfiction Award* each annually offer a $2,000 honorarium and a reading at The Writer's Voice to an emerging novelist, poet, and nonfiction writer, respectively, over age forty. No more than half of any entry may have been previously published. There is a $20 entry fee. Send SASE or visit the Web site for guidelines.

Ⓜ The *New Voice Poetry Award*, the *New Voice Fiction Award*, and the *New Voice Nonfiction Award* are given annually to current and previous students of the Writer's Voice. Each award consists of a $250 honorarium, a featured reading, and a weeklong fellowship at Ledig House International Writers' Colony in Omi, New York. Submissions must not have been previously published. There is a $5 entry fee. Send SASE or visit the Web site for guidelines.

Ⓜ The *Open Voice Poetry Award*, the *Open Voice Scott Sommer Fiction Award*, and the *Open Voice Nonfiction Award* are given to published and unpublished writers who have not previously read at The Writer's Voice. Each award consists of a $1,000 honorarium and a reading at The Writer's Voice. Submissions must not have been previously published. There is a $15 application fee. Send SASE or visit the Web site for guidelines.

Available to: See above
Deadline: December 31
Apply to: Capricorn Award, Open Voice Award, or New Voice Award (specify genre for all), above address

Writers at Work
PO Box 1146
Centerville, UT 84014-5146
Web site: http://www.ihi-env.com/watw.html

Ⓜ Writers at Work sponsors a fellowship competition in fiction (short stories or novel excerpts), literary nonfiction, and poetry. The first prize in each category consists of $1,500, publication in *Quarterly West*, a featured reading, and tuition to the afternoon session at the Writers at Work summer conference in Park City, Utah. Second-place winners each receive $500 and tuition to the afternoon session at the conference. Eligible are writers who have not published a book-length volume of original work. Fiction and literary nonfiction submissions should not exceed 20 pages; poetry may be 6 poems not exceeding 10 pages total. Only unpublished work will be considered. A $12 reading fee and two SASEs are also requested. Send a copy of the manuscript with cover letter including name, address, phone number, and title; title only should appear on the manuscript. Manuscripts are not returned.

Available to: See above
Deadline: March 15
Apply to: Fellowship Competition, above address

WritersBlok
3409 Mariana Court
Loveland, CO 80537
Web site: webster@writersblok.com
Web site: http://www.writersblok.com/contest.html
Fax: 970-461-0820

Ⓕ The *WritersBlok Short Story Contest* offers prizes of $1,000, $250, and $75 for unpublished short stories up to 15,000 words. Winners are published and featured on BookLocker.com, and they collect 80 percent of sales profits. There is a $25 entry fee; additional entries are $5 each. Send SASE, e-mail, or visit the Web site for guidelines.

Available to: No restrictions
Deadline: March 31, 2000; inquire for 2001
Apply to: Short Story Contest, above address

Helene Wurlitzer Foundation of New Mexico
Box 1891
Taos, NM 87571
Fax: 505-758-2559

Ⓡ Residences in Taos, with free housing and utilities, are available from April 1 through September 30, and on a limited basis from October through March. Residents must provide their own food. Families are not accepted. Residences are currently booked through 2002; however, the Foundation does occasionally receive cancellations. Write or fax request for application.

Available to: No restrictions
Deadline: None
Apply to: Above address

Wyoming Council on the Arts
2320 Capitol Avenue
Cheyenne, WY 82002
E-mail: mshay@missc.state.wy.us
Web site: http://spacr.state.wy.us/cr/arts

Ⓜ Up to four *Literary Fellowships* of $2,000 each are offered annually to writers who are legal residents of Wyoming, at least eighteen years old, and not full-time students.

Available to: See above
Deadline: July 15
Apply to: Above address

Ⓜ The *Neltje Blanchan Award*, given to a Wyoming writer whose work, in any genre, is inspired by nature, and the *Frank Nelson Doubleday Memorial Award*, given to a Wyoming woman writer in any creative genre, each carry a cash prize of $1,000. Applicants must submit up to 25 pages of prose or 10 of poetry, either published or unpublished. Write for guidelines.

Available to: Wyoming residents
Deadline: May 15
Apply to: Blanchan Award or Doubleday Award, above address

Xeric Foundation
PMB 214
351 Pleasant Street
Northampton, MA 01060

Grants of up to $5,000 are offered to assist book creators with some of the costs of self-publishing (physical production and distribution, printing, color separation, solicitation, shipping). Grants are not intended to support an artist/writer fully through the process of self-publishing, but rather to encourage creators to learn from the experience of working toward such a goal. Write for additional information and application.

Available to: U.S. and Canadian residents
Deadline: January 31 and July 31
Apply to: Above address

Yaddo
Box 395
Saratoga Springs, NY 12866
E-mail: chwait@aol.com
Web site: www.yaddo.org
Fax: 518-584-1312

® Invitations are extended to writers of any nationality who have published work of high artistic merit and are currently engaged in another project, and to unpublished writers working at professional levels in their fields, to spend one to two months at Yaddo, a working community for writers, visual artists, composers, choreographers, performance artists, and film and video artists. Samples of work must be submitted, together with application form, letters of recommendation, and application fee of $20. Applicants are judged on their artistic merit and professional promise. Awards include room, board, and studio. Up to $1,000 in financial aid is available for writers who might otherwise be unable to accept an invitation to visit. There are no limitations on how the funds are used (child care, travel expenses, rent, etc.). Yaddo is open year-round, except for a short period in early September, and accommodates up to thirty-five artists at a time. Write for additional information and application form. Inquiries are accepted by e-mail but no forms will be transmitted or applications accepted by e-mail.

Available to: See above
Deadlines: January 15 for residences starting mid-May of the same year through February of the following year; August 1 for residences starting late October of the same year through May of the following year
Apply to: Admissions Committee, above address

Yale University Library
Beinecke Rare Book and Manuscript Library
1603A Yale Station
New Haven, CT 06520

IN The *Bollingen Prize* of $50,000 is awarded biennially to the American poet whose work represents the highest achievement in the field of American poetry, on the basis of a review of publications during the previous two years. The next award will be given in February 2001. *By Internal Nomination Only.*

Yale University Press
PO Box 209040
New Haven, CT 06520-9040
Web site: http://www.yale.edu/yup/poetry.html

℗ Yale University Press publishes one new book of poetry annually as part of the *Yale Series of Younger Poets*. Selection is made through a competition open to any U.S. citizen under age forty who has not previously published a volume of poetry. The author receives royalties. Manuscripts should be 48 to 64 pages in length. An application fee of $15 is required. Send SASE for submission guidelines.

Available to: See above
Deadline: Submissions accepted in February
Apply to: Editor, Yale Series of Younger Poets, above address

Young Adult Library Services Association
American Library Association
50 East Huron Street
Chicago, IL 60611
E-mail: yalsa@ala.org
Web site: http://www.ala.org/yalsa

© The *Margaret A. Edwards Award*, co-sponsored by *School Library Journal*, honors an author's lifetime achievement for writing books that have been popular with teenagers over a period of time. The award consists of a $1,000 cash prize and a citation at the ALA Annual Conference. Nominations may be submitted by teenagers and young adult librarians. Write or e-mail for nomination forms.

Available to: No restrictions
Deadline: June 1
Apply to: Margaret A. Edwards Award, above address

Young Playwrights, Inc.
321 West 44th Street, Suite 906
New York, NY 10036
E-mail: writeaplay@aol.com
Web site: http://www.youngplaywrights.org
Fax: 212-307-1454

Ⓓ The *Young Playwrights Festival National Playwriting Competition* is an annual contest open to writers aged eighteen and under. Winning plays receive professional production in New York City, and royalties. There are no restrictions on the subject, style, form, or length of plays submitted. Adaptations of works by others, screenplays, and musicals are not accepted. The e-mail address is for inquiries only.

Available to: See above
Deadline: December 1
Apply to: Young Playwrights Festival, above address

Zoetrope: All-Story
1350 Avenue of the Americas, 24th floor
New York, NY 10019
Web site: http://www.zoetrope-stories.com

Ⓕ The *Sam Adams Short Story Contest* annually awards a full scholarship, with round-trip airfare, to the weeklong Zoetrope Short Story Writers Workshop at Francis Ford Coppola's Blancaneaux Lodge in Belize, Central America, to the writer of an unpublished short story of up to 5,000 words. Send SASE or visit the Web site for guidelines.

Available to: No restrictions
Deadline: April 15
Apply to: Sam Adams Short Story Contest, above address

Ⓕ The *Zoetrope Short Fiction Contest* annually offers a first prize of $1,000, a second of $500, and a third of $250 for an unpublished short story of up to 5,000 words. Send SASE for guidelines. E-mail and fax submissions are not accepted.

Available to: No restrictions
Deadline: October 1
Apply to: Zoetrope Short Fiction Contest, above address

Zone 3
Susan Wallace, Managing Editor
Austin Peay State University
PO Box 4565
Clarksville, TN 37044

Ⓟ The *Rainmaker Awards in Poetry* offer a first prize of $500 and publication in *Zone 3* for an original unpublished poem. A second prize of $300 and a third of $100 are also given. Poets may submit up to three poems. The entry fee of $8 covers a year's subscription to *Zone 3*.

Available to: No restrictions
Deadline: January 1
Apply to: Rainmaker Awards in Poetry, above address

APPENDIX: STATE ARTS COUNCILS

Below, listed state by state, is relevant information for contacting state arts councils throughout the United States (including the District of Columbia, Puerto Rico, and the U. S. Virgin Islands). Literature programs vary from state to state. To be eligible for funding, writers must be residents of the state to which they are applying.

Alabama State Council on the Arts
Randy Shoults, Literature Program Manager
201 Monroe Street
Montgomery, AL 36130-1800
334-242-4076
E-mail: randy@arts.state.al.us
Web site: http://www.arts.state.al.us
Fax: 334-240-3269

Alaska State Council on the Arts
Shannon Planchon, Grants Administrator
411 West 4th Avenue, Suite 1E
Anchorage, AK 99501-2343
907-269-6610
E-mail: info@aksca.org
Web site: http://www.aksca.org
Fax: 907-269-6601

Arizona Commission on the Arts
Jill Bernstein, Literature Director
417 West Roosevelt
Phoenix, AZ 85003
602-255-5882
E-mail: general@ArizonaArts.org
Web site: http://az.arts.asu.edu/artscomm
Fax: 602-256-0282

Arkansas Arts Council
James E. Mitchell, Executive Director
1500 Tower Building
323 Center Street
Little Rock, AR 72201
501-324-9766
E-mail: info@dah.state.ar.us
Web site: http://www.arkansasarts.com
Fax: 501-324-9154

California Arts Council
Ray Tatar, Literature Administrator
1300 I Street, Suite 930
Sacramento, CA 95814
916-322-6555
E-mail: cac@cwo.com
Web site: http://www.cac.ca.gov
Fax: 916-322-6575

Colorado Council on the Arts and Humanities
Fran Holden, Executive Director
750 Pennsylvania Street
Denver, CO 80203
303-894-2617
E-mail: coloarts@artswire.org
Web site: http://www.coloarts.state.co.us
Fax: 303-894-2615

Connecticut Commission on the Arts
John Ostrout, Executive Director
755 Main Street
1 Financial Plaza
Hartford, CT 06103
860-566-4770
E-mail: jostrout@cslib.org
Web site: http://www.cslnet.ctstateu.edu/cca
Fax: 860-566-6462

Delaware Division of the Arts
Peggy Amsterdam, Executive Director
Carvel State Office Building
820 North French Street
Wilmington, DE 19801
302-577-8278
E-mail: delarts@artswire.org
Web site: http://www.artsdel.org
Fax: 302-577-6561

District of Columbia Commission on the Arts and Humanities
Anthony Gittens, Executive Director
410 8th Street, NW, 5th floor
Washington, DC 20004
202-724-5613
E-mail: dccah@erols.com
Web site: http://www.capaccess.org/ane/dccah
Fax: 202-727-4135

Florida Division of Cultural Affairs
Peg Richardson, Executive Director
Department of State
The Capitol
Tallahassee, FL 32399-0250
850-487-2980
E-mail: dalborn@mail.dos.state.fl.us
Web site: http://www.dos.state.fl.us/dca
Fax: 850-922-5259

Georgia Council for the Arts
Caroline Leake, Executive Director
530 Means Street, NW, Suite 115
Atlanta, GA 30318
404-651-7920
E-mail: info@arts-ga.com
Web site: http://www.artswire.org/Artswire/
    nasaa/new/nasaa/gateway/GA.html
Fax: 404-651-7922

Hawaii State Foundation on Culture and the Arts
Holly Richards, Executive Director
44 Merchant Street
Honolulu, HI 96813
808-586-0300
E-mail: sfca@sfca.state.hi.us
Web site: http://www.state.hi.us/sfca
Fax: 808-586-0308

Idaho Commission on the Arts
Cort Conley, Literature Director
PO Box 83720
Boise, ID 83720-0008
208-334-2119
E-mail: cconley@ica.state.id.us
Web site: http://www.state.id.us/arts
Fax: 208-334-2488

Illinois Arts Council
Richard Gage, Director of Communication Arts
    Program
James R. Thompson Center
100 West Randolph, Suite 10-500
Chicago, IL 60601
312-814-6750
E-mail: info@arts.state.il.us
Web site: http://www.state.il.us/agency/ica
Fax: 312-814-1471

Indiana Arts Commission
Dorothy Ilgen, Executive Director
402 West Washington, Room W072
Indianapolis, IN 46204-2741
317-232-1268
E-mail: arts@state.in.us
Web site: http://www.state.in.us/iac
Fax: 317-232-5595

Iowa Arts Council
Bruce Williams, Individual Artists Program
Capitol Complex
600 East Locust
Des Moines, IA 50319-0290
Web site: http://www.artswire.org/nasaa/
    new/nasaa/gateway/IA.html
515-281-4451
Fax: 515-242-6498

Kansas Arts Commission
David Wilson, Executive Director
Jayhawk Tower
700 Jackson, Suite 1004
Topeka, KS 66603
785-296-3335
Web site: http://www.nasaa-arts.org/new/
    nasaa/gateway/KS.html
Fax: 785-296-4989

Kentucky Arts Council
Gerri Combs, Executive Director
Old Capitol Annex
300 West Broadway
Frankfort, KY 40601
502-564-3757
E-mail: kyarts@mail.state.ky.us
Web site: http://www.kyarts.org
Fax: 502-564-2839

Louisiana Division of the Arts
James Borders, Executive Director
PO Box 44247
Baton Rouge, LA 70804-4247
225-342-8180
E-mail: arts@crt.state.la.us
Web site: http://www.crt.state.la.us/arts
Fax: 225-342-8173

Maine State Arts Commission
Alden C. Wilson, Executive Director
55 Capitol Street
25 State House Station
Augusta, ME 04333-0025
207-287-2724
E-mail: alden.wilson@state.me.us
Web site: http://www.mainearts.com
Fax: 207-287-2335

Maryland State Arts Council
Pamela Dunne, Program Director
601 North Howard Street
Baltimore, MD 21201
410-767-6555
E-mail: pdunne@mdbusiness.state.md.us
Web site: http://www.msac.org
Fax: 410-333-1062

Massachusetts Cultural Council
Michael Brady, Program Officer
120 Boylston Street, 2nd Floor
Boston, MA 02116-4600
617-727-3668
E-mail: web@art.state.ma.us
Web site: http://www.massculturalcouncil.org
Fax: 617-727-0044

Michigan Council for Arts and Cultural Affairs
Betty Boone, Executive Director
525 West Ottawa
PO Box 30705
Lansing, MI 48909
517-241-3973
Web site: http://www.cis.state.mi.us/arts
Fax: 517-241-3979
Also:
ArtServe Michigan
Mark Packer, Program Director
17515 West Nine Mile Road, Suite 250
Southfield, MI 48075
248-557-8288
Web site: http://www.artservemichigan.org
Fax: 248-557-8581

Minnesota State Arts Board
Robert C. Booker, Executive Director
400 Sibley Street, Suite 200
Saint Paul, MN 55101-1928
651-215-1600
E-mail: msab@state.mn.us
Web site: http://www.arts.state.mn.us
Fax: 651-215-1602

Mississippi Arts Commission
Tim Hedgepeth, Program Administrator/Arts
239 North Lamar Street, Suite 207
Jackson, MS 39201
601-359-6030
E-mail: vlindsay@arts.state.ms.ud
Web site: http://www.arts.state.ms.us
Fax: 601-359-6008

Missouri Arts Council
Floa Maria Garcia, Executive Director
Wainwright State Office Complex
111 North Seventh Street, Suite 105
Saint Louis, MO 63101-2188
314-340-6845
E-mail: fgarcia@mail.state.mo.us
Web site: http://www.missouriartscouncil.org
Fax: 314-340-7215

Montana Arts Council
Arlynn Fishbaugh, Executive Director
PO Box 202201
Helena, MT 59620-2201
406-444-6430
E-mail: mac@state.mt.us
Web site: http://www.mt.gov/art
Fax: 406-444-6548

Nebraska Arts Council
Jennifer S. Clark, Executive Director
3838 Davenport
Omaha, NE 68131-2329
402-595-2122
E-mail: nacart@synergy.net
Web site: http://www.gps.K12.ne.us/
   nac_web_site/nac.htm
Fax: 402-595-2334

Nevada Arts Council
Susan Boskoff, Executive Director
602 North Curry Street
Carson City, NV 89703
775-687-6680
E-mail: dmla@clan.lib.nv.us
Web site: http://www.dmla.clan.lib.nv.us
Fax: 702-687-6688

New Hampshire State Council on the Arts
Audrey V. Sylvester, Artist Services
  Coordinator
40 North Main Street
Concord, NH 03301-4974
603-271-2789
E-mail: asylvester@nharts.state.nh.us
Web site: http://www.state.nh.us/nharts
Fax: 603-271-3584

New Jersey State Council on the Arts
Barbara Russo, Executive Director
20 West State Street
PO Box 306
Trenton, NJ 08625-0306
609-292-6130
E-mail: barbara@arts.sos.state.nj.us
Web site: http://www.njartscouncil.org
Fax: 609-989-1440

New Mexico Arts
Margaret Brommelsiek, Executive Director
PO Box 1450
Santa Fe, NM 87501-1450
505-827-6490
E-mail: NMAegrants@lvr.state.nm.us
Web site: http://www.artsnet.org/nma
Fax: 505-827-6043

New York State Council on the Arts
Kathleen Masterson, Literature Program
915 Broadway, 8th floor
New York, NY 10010
212-387-7000
E-mail: kmasterson@nysca.org
Web site: http://www.nysca.org
Fax: 212-387-7164
Also:
New York Foundation for the Arts
Theodore S. Berger, Executive Director
155 Avenue of the Americas, 14th floor
New York, NY 10013-1507
212-366-6900
E-mail: nyfaweb@nyfa.org
Web site: http://www.nyfa.org
Fax: 212-366-1778

North Carolina Arts Council
Debbie McGill, Literature Director
Department of Cultural Resources
Raleigh, NC 27699-4632
919-733-2821
E-mail: debbie.mcgill@ncmail.net
Web site: http://www.ncarts.org
Fax: 919-733-4834

North Dakota Council on the Arts
Daphne Ghorbani, Executive Director
418 East Broadway, Suite 70
Bismarck, ND 58501-4086
701-328-3954
E-mail: dghorban@state.nd.us
Web site: http://www.state.nd.us/arts
Fax: 701-328-3963

Ohio Arts Council
Ken Emerick, Individual Artist Fellowship
  Coordinator
727 East Main Street
Columbus, OH 43205-1796
614-466-2613
E-mail: kemerick@oac.state.oh.us
Web site: http://www.oac.state.oh.us
Fax: 614-466-4494

Oklahoma Arts Council
Betty Price, Executive Director
PO Box 52001-2001
Oklahoma City, OK 73152-2001
405-521-2931
E-mail: okarts@arts.state.ok.us
Web site: http://www.state.ok.us/~arts
Fax: 405-521-6418

Oregon Arts Commission
Michael Faison, Assistant Director
775 Summer Street, NE
Salem, OR 97301-1284
503-986-0082
E-mail: michael.b.faison@state.or.us
Web site: http://art.econ.state.or.us
Fax: 503-986-0260

Pennsylvania Council on the Arts
Philip Horn, Executive Director
Finance Building, Room 216
Harrisburg, PA 17120
717-787-6883
E-mail: phorn@state.pa.us
Web site: http://artsnet.heinz.cmu.edu/pca
Fax: 717-783-2538

Rhode Island State Council on the Arts
Randall Rosenbaum, Executive Director
95 Cedar Street, Suite 103
Providence, RI 02903-1034
401-222-3880
E-mail: info@risca.state.ri.us
Web site: http://www.risca.state.ri.us
Fax: 401-521-1351

South Carolina Arts Commission
Sara June Goldstein, Program Director for
  Literary Arts
1800 Gervais Street
Columbia, SC 29201
803-734-8696
E-mail: goldsta@arts.state.sc.us
Web site: http://www.state.sc.us/arts
Fax: 803-734-8526

South Dakota Arts Council
Dennis Holub, Executive Director
800 Governors Drive
Pierre, SD 57501-2294
605-773-3131
E-mail: sdac@stlib.state.sd.us
Web site: http://www.state.sd.us/state/
  executive/deca/sdarts/sdarts.htm
Fax: 605-773-6962

Tennessee Arts Commission
Alice Swanson, Director, Literary Arts
Citizens Plaza
401 Charlotte Avenue
Nashville, TN 37243-0780
615-741-1701
Web site: http://www.arts.state.tn.us
Fax: 615-741-8559

Texas Commission on the Arts
John Paul Batiste, Executive Director
PO Box 13406
Capitol Station
Austin, TX 78711-3406
512-463-5535
E-mail: jbatiste@arts.state.tx.us
Web site: http://www.arts.state.tx.us
Fax: 512-475-2699

Utah Arts Council
Guy Lebeda, Literary Coordinator
617 East South Temple Street
Salt Lake City, UT 84102-1177
801-236-7555
E-mail: glebeda@arts.state.ut.us
Web site: http://www.dced.state.ut.us/arts
Fax: 801-236-7556

Vermont Arts Council
Michele Bailey, Artist Grants Coordinator
136 State Street, Drawer 33
Montpelier, VT 05633-6001
802-828-3291
E-mail: info@arts.vca.state.vt.us
Web site: http://www.state.vt.us/vermont-
arts
Fax: 802-828-3363

Virginia Commission for the Arts
Peggy J. Baggett, Executive Director
223 Governor Street
Richmond, VA 23219-2010
804-225-3132
E-mail: vacomm@artswire.org
Web site: http://www.artswire.org/~vacomm
Fax: 804-255-4327

Washington State Arts Commission
Kris Tucker, Executive Director
PO Box 42675
Olympia, WA 98504-2675
360-753-3860
E-mail: krist@wsac.wa.gov
Web site: http://www.wa.gov/art
Fax: 360-586-5351

West Virginia Commission on the Arts
Richard Ressmeyer, Executive Director
The Cultural Center
1900 Kanawha Boulevard East
Charleston, WV 25305-0300
304-558-0240
E-mail: richard.ressmeyer@wvculture.org
Web site: www.wvculture.org
Fax: 304-558-2779

Wisconsin Arts Board
Mark Fraire, Grant Programs and Services
  Specialist
101 East Wilson Street, 1st Floor
Madison, WI 53702
608-266-0190
E-mail: mark.fraire@arts.state.wi.us
Web site: http://www.arts.state.wi.us
Fax: 608-267-0380

Wyoming Council on the Arts
John G. Coe, Executive Director
2320 Capitol Avenue
Cheyenne, WY 82002
307-777-7742
E-mail: rbovee@state.wy.us
Web site: http://commerce.state.wy.us/cr/arts
Fax: 307-777-5499

PUERTO RICO

Institute of Puerto Rican Culture
Jose Ramon de la Torre, Executive Director
PO Box 9024184
San Juan, PR 00902-4184
787-725-5137
Web site: http://www.nasaa-arts.org/new/
  nasaa/gateway/PR.html
Fax: 787-724-8393

U. S. VIRGIN ISLANDS

Virgin Islands Council on the Arts
John Jowers, Executive Director
41-42 Norre Gade
PO Box 103
St. Thomas, VI 00804
340-774-5984
E-mail: vicouncil@islands.vi
Web site: http://www.nasaa-arts.org/new/
  nasaa/gateway/VI.html
Fax: 340-774-6206

INDEX OF AWARDS

AAAS Science Journalism Awards, 8

AAS-American Society for Eighteenth-Century Studies Fellowships, 7

AAS-National Endowment for the Humanities Fellowships, 7

AAS-Northeast Modern Language Association Fellowship, 8

Edward Abbey Short Fiction Award, 32

Abby Award, 9

ABC-Clio America: History and Life Award, 180

Academy Awards, 5

Acadia National Park Artist-in-Residence Program, 3

ACT/Hedgebrook Women Playwrights Festival, 1

Herbert Baxter Adams Prize, 10

Sam Adams Short Story Contest, 276

Aga Khan Prize for Fiction, 183

Age Studies Award, 87

Ahmanson-Getty Postdoctoral Fellowships, 251

AJL Sydney Taylor Book Award, 27

AJL Sydney Taylor Manuscript Award, 27

Akron Poetry Prize, 249

Nelson Algren Awards for Short Fiction, 53

Frances C. Allen Fellowship, 172

Alligator Juniper Writing Contest, 5

ALTA National Translation Award, 15

Ambassador Book Awards, 76

American Academy of Religion Research Grants Program, 7

American Awards for Literature, 62

American Awards for Literature International Award, 62

American Dreamer Script Competition, 9

American Historical Print Collectors Society Fellowship, 7

American Legion Fourth Estate Award, 13

American Literary Review Poetry Contest, 15

American Literary Review Short Fiction Contest, 15

American Poetry Review/Honickman First Book Prize, 16

American Poets Fund, 1

American Research Center in Egypt Fellowship Program, 17

American Shorts Contest, 81

Amy Foundation Writing Awards, 20

Anamnesis Poetry Chapbook Competition, 20

Anchorage Press Theatre for Youth Playwriting Award, 125

Anhinga Prize for Poetry, 20

Anisfield-Wolf Book Awards, 57

Annual Backdoor Theatre New Play Project, 268

Frank Annunzio Award, 55

Antarctic Artists & Writers Program, 160

Anthem Essay Contest, 205

APF Fellowships, 184

Apostle Islands National Lakeshore Artist-in-Residence Program, 21

APSA Congressional Fellowship Program, 16

Arabic Translation Awards, 251

Ariadne Press Fiction Prize, 22

Artists-in-Berlin Program, 86

Artists in Michigan Program, 24

Arts Education Projects Program, 69

Arts & Letters Prizes Competition, 23

Arts Lottery Grants, 44

Arts Recognition and Talent Search Program, 156

ArtsLink Collaborative Projects, 49

Arvon International Poetry Competition, 106

ASCAP-Deems Taylor Awards, 18

ASF Translation Prize, 17

Asia Fellowships, 252

Isaac Asimov Award for Undergraduate Excellence in Science Fiction and Fantasy Writing, 25

Associated Press Summer Minority Internship Program, 25

Vincent Astor Memorial Leadership Essay Contest, 248

ATA German Literary Translation Prize, 19

AT&T/East West Players New Voices Playwriting Competition, 74

Robert G. Athearn Book Award, 266

Atlanta Review International Poetry Competition, 28

Atlas Shrugged Essay Contest, 205

Auricle Award, 194

Aurora Borealis Prize for Outstanding Translation of Fiction Literature, 107

Aurora Borealis Prize for Outstanding Translation of Nonfiction Literature, 107

Austin Film Festival Screenwriters Competition, 29

Authors in the Park Short Story Contest, 30

Award of Merit Medal of the American Academy of Arts and Letters, 5

AWP Award Series, 25

AWP/Prague Summer Seminars Fellowships, 26

Backwaters Prize, 30

Bakeless Literary Publication Prizes, 40

Emily Clark Balch Awards, 262

Bananafish Short Story Contest, 31

Bancroft Prizes, 59

Barach Fellowship, 265

Roy Barker Playwriting Prize, 209

Barnard New Women Poets Prize, 32

Mrs. Simon Baruch University Award, 240

Whitman Bassow Award, 182

James K. Batten Award for Excellence in Civic Journalism, 191

John and Patricia Beatty Award, 42

George Louis Beer Prize, 11

Bellwether Prize, 162

Elinor Benedict Poetry Prize, 183

Burton R. Benjamin Fellowship in Broadcast Journalism, 254

Robert Spiers Benjamin Award, 182

George Bennett Fellowship, 192

Berlin Prize Fellowships, 6

Myrna Bernath Book Award, 221

Stuart L. Bernath Book Prize, 221

Best First Private Eye Novel Contest, 209

Albert J. Beveridge Award, 11

Albert J. Beveridge Grants, 10

Beverly Hills Theatre Guild Plays for Children's Theatre Competition, 34

Beyond Baroque Poetry Chapbook Contest, 35

Ray Allen Billington Prize, 180

Binational Commission (Fulbright) Scholarships, 68

Bingham Poetry Prize, 38

Worth Bingham Prize, 112

Binkley-Stephenson Award, 180

Paul Birdsall Prize, 11

Black Caucus of the American Library Association Literary Awards, 36

James Tait Black Memorial Prizes, 245

Susan Smith Blackburn Prize, 36

Neltje Blanchan Award, 274

Blethen Family Newspaper Internship Program for Minorities, 214

Bliss Prize Fellowship in Byzantine Studies, 72

Blue Lynx Poetry Prize, 137

Bluestem Award, 76

Boardman Tasker Prize, 240

James Boatwright III Prize for Poetry, 216

George Bogin Memorial Award, 198

Bollingen Prize, 275

Herbert Eugene Bolton Memorial Prize, 61

Book Publishers of Texas Award, 234

Border Playwrights Project, 37

Bordighera Bilingual Poetry Prize, 205

Robert Bosch Foundation Fellowship Program, 38

Boston Book Review Literary Awards, 38

Boston Globe-Horn Book Awards for Excellence in Children's Literature, 97

Boston Review Poetry Contest, 38

Boston Review Short Story Contest, 38

Stephen Botein Fellowship, 7

Boulevard Short Fiction Contest for Emerging Writers, 39

Paul Bowles Prize for Short Fiction, 80

Bill Boyd Library Literature Award, 14

Margery Davis Boyden Writing Residency, 189

Hal Boyle Award, 182

Michael Braude Award for Light Verse, 5

Brazos Bookstore Short Story Award, 234

James Henry Breasted Prize, 11

Philip Brett Award, 15

Frank S. and Elizabeth D. Brewer Prize, 18

Bright Hill Press Poetry Award, 40

BRIO (Bronx Recognizes Its Own) Fellowships, 40

British Council Prize, 174

Brittingham Prize in Poetry, 258

Broadcasters Awards, 249

Cleanth Brooks Medal for Distinguished Achievement in Southern Letters, 78

Bross Prize, 131

Heywood Broun Award, 172

John Carter Brown Library Research Fellowships, 41

John Nicholas Brown Prize, 141

Dorothy Brunsman Poetry Prize, 33

Bryan Family Foundation Award for Drama, 78

Bucknell Seminar for Younger Poets, 41

Metchie J. E. Budka Award, 130

Bunting Fellowship Program, 42

Arleigh Burke Essay Contest, 248

Daniel B. Burke Fellowship, 254

Arthur F. Burns Fellowship, 113

Business/Economic Reporting/William Brewster Styles Award, 212

Buxtehude Bulle, 86

Witter Bynner Award for Poetry, 6

Gerald Cable Book Award, 217

Maria Moors Cabot Prizes, 60

Pierre-François Caille Memorial Medal, 107

California Book Awards, 61

Campbell Corner Essay Prize, 44

Campbell Corner Poetry Prize, 44

Karel Capek Medal, 107

Capricorn Nonfiction Award, 273

Capricorn Novel Award, 273

Capricorn Poetry Award, 273

Carolina Novel Award, 31

Hayden Carruth Award for Emerging Poets, 62

Vernon Carstensen Award, 4

Rosalynn Carter Fellowships for Mental Health Journalism, 48

Thomas H. Carter Prize for the Essay, 216

Raymond Carver Short Story Contest, 99

Willa Cather Fiction Prize, 94

Caughey Western History Association Award, 266

Cave Canem Poetry Prize, 49

Center for Advanced Holocaust Studies Fellowships, 246

Center for Advanced Holocaust Studies Postdissertation Award, 246

Center for Book Arts Poetry Chapbook Competition, 50

Centrum Residencies, 52

Jane Chambers Playwriting Award, 125

Harry Chapin Media Awards, 271

Chekhov Award for Short Fiction, 64

Chelsea Award Competition, 52

Robert Chesley Award for Lesbian and Gay Playwriting, 202

Chesterfield Film Company/Writers' Film Project, 53

Chicago Literary Awards, 21

Chicago Reporter Minority Fellowship in Urban Journalism, 53

Chicano/Latino Literary Contest, 251

Children's Literature Association Research Fellowships and Scholarships, 54

Chinook Prize, 211

John Ciardi Lifetime Achievement Award in Poetry, 118

John Ciardi Prize for Poetry, 35

Cintas Fellowship Program, 55

City Arts Projects Program, 69

Evert Clark Award, 159

Mary Higgins Clark Mystery/Suspense Short Story Contest, 78

Clauder Competition for Excellence in Playwriting, 57

James L. Clifford Prize, 18

Coast Guard Essay Contest, 248

David Mark Cohen National Playwriting Award, 125

Morton N. Cohen Award, 147

Cohen Award in Poetry and Fiction, 196

Anna C. and Oliver Colburn Fellowship, 21

Carr P. Collins Awards, 234

Colorado Prize, 59

Betsy Colquitt Award for Poetry, 69

Christopher Columbus Screenplay Discovery Awards, 49

Commentary Award, 212

Common Wealth Awards, 60

Community Writers Association International Writing Competition, 61

Conch Republic Prize for Literature, 94

Bernard F. Conners Prize for Poetry, 183

Bob Considine Award, 182

James Fenimore Cooper Prize for Historical Fiction, 220

A. E. Coppard Prize for Long Fiction, 267

Albert B. Corey Prize in Canadian-American Relations, 11

Cornerstone Dramaturgy and Development Project, 190

John William Corrington Award for Literary Excellence, 50

Courage in Journalism Award, 115

Crab Orchard Award Series in Poetry, 64

Avery O. Craven Award, 180

Creative Nonfiction and Cultural Journalism Program, 45

Creative Writing Fellowships, 232

Crossing Boundaries Writing Awards, 114

Violet Crown Book Awards, 29

Ed Cunningham Memorial Award, 182

Cunningham Prize for Playwriting, 68

Merle Curti Award, 180

Cushwa Center for the Study of American Catholicism Publication Awards, 65

Cyclone Productions Screenwriters Project, 65

Dana Awards, 66

Dart Award, 143

Jon Davidoff Scholarships for Journalists, 265

Watson Davis and Helen Miles Davis Prize, 96

Dayton Playhouse FutureFest, 66

Marguerite de Angeli Prize, 31

Diane Decorah Memorial Award for Poetry, 162

Delacorte Press Prize for a First Young Adult Novel, 32

Cino del Duca World Prize, 106

Eben Demarest Fund, 67

Dexter Prize, 221

Martin Dibner Memorial Fellowship for Maine Writers Fund, 138

Alice Fay Di Castagnola Award, 198

James Dickey Prize for Poetry, 80

Annie Dillard Award for Nonfiction, 33

Joe and Laurie Dine Award, 182

Everett McKinley Dirksen Award for Distinguished Reporting of Congress, 159

Discover Great New Writers Award, 32

"Discovery"/The Nation Poetry Contest: Joan Leiman Jacobson Poetry Prizes, 258

Walt Disney Studios Fellowship Program, 69

Carl Djerassi Fellowship, 270

Djerassi Resident Artists Program, 70

Dobie-Paisano Writing Fellowships, 70

Milton Dorfman Poetry Prize, 209

David Dornstein Memorial Creative Writing Contest for Young Adult Writers, 58

Dorset Colony House Residences, 71

John Dos Passos Prize for Literature, 134

Frank Nelson Doubleday Award, 274

Frederick Douglass Book Prize, 88

Dow Jones Newspaper Fund Business Reporting Program, 71

DramaRama, 195

John H. Dunning Prize, 11

Jack Dyer Fiction Prize, 64

Eaton Literary Award, 74

Eckerd College Review Poetry Contest, 74

Editorial Writing/Walker Stone Award, 213

Editors' Book Award, 203

Editors' Prize Awards, 147

Editor's Prize (Spoon River Poetry Review), 228

Educator's Award, 67

Everett Edwards Award, 4

Margaret A. Edwards Award, 275

Alfred Einstein Award, 15

Einstein Institution Fellows Program, 75

Charles C. Eldredge Prize, 158

Electronic Arts Grant Program, 77

T. S. Eliot Award for Creative Writing, 103

T. S. Eliot Prize, 238

Sue Saniel Elkind Poetry Contest, 124

Ernest M. Eller Prize in Naval History, 162

Van Courtlandt Elliott Prize, 141

Emerging Playwright Award, 258

Ralph Waldo Emerson Award, 191

Verna Emery Poetry Competition, 203

Maurice English Poetry Award, 76

Enlisted Essay Contest, 248

Ensemble Studio Theatre/Alfred P. Sloan Foundation Science & Technology Project, 76

Environmental Reporting/Edward J. Meeman Award, 213

Kenan T. Erim Award, 22

Willard R. Espy Award, 77

Evans Biography Award, 151

Evans Handcart Prize, 151

Eve of St. Agnes Award in Poetry, 163

Evergreen Chronicles Novella Contest, 77

"Evil Companions" Literary Award, 59

Excellence in the Academy Awards, 155

Exemplary Papers in Humility Theology Program, 233

Explorations Awards for Literature, 250

Extended Collaboration Grants, 235

John K. Fairbank Prize in East Asian History, 11

Norma Farber First Book Award, 198

Joan Fassler Memorial Book Award, 27

Virginia Faulkner Award for Excellence in Writing, 200

William Faulkner Creative Writing Competition, 193

Herbert Feis Award, 11

Fellowship of the Academy of American Poets, 1

Fellowship's Award for Nonfiction, 78

Fellowships for College Teachers and Independent Scholars, 156

Fellowship's New Writing Award, 78

Fellowships for University Teachers, 156

Antonio Feltrinelli International Prize, 107

Shubert Fendrich Memorial Playwriting Contest, 193

Ferro-Grumley Awards, 202

Festival of Firsts Playwriting Competition, 231

Fiction Open, 89

Field Poetry Prize, 177

Final Draft International Screenwriting Competition, 78

First Series Awards for the Novel, Poetry, Short Fiction and Creative Nonfiction, 144

Robert L. Fish Memorial Award, 153

Fish Short Story Prize, 116

Fisk Fiction Prize, 38

F. Scott Fitzgerald Literary Conference Short Story Contest, 79

Florida Playwrights' Process, 80

Florida Review Editors' Awards, 80

John Florio Prize, 243

Folger Institute Consortium Funds, 81

Folger Library and National Endowment for the Humanities Fellowships, 81

Malcolm Forbes Award, 182

Ford Environmental Journalism Fellowships, 113

Ford Transportation Technology Fellowship, 254

Morris D. Forkosch Prize, 123

Morris O. Forkosch Prize, 11

49th Parallel Poetry Award, 33

Forward Poetry Prizes, 240

The Fountainhead Essay Contest, 205

Four Way Award Series in Poetry, 83

Four Way Intro Prize in Poetry, 83

Fourth Freedom Forum Playwriting Award, 125

Dixon Ryan Fox Manuscript Prize of the New York State Historical Association, 170

Fraenkel Prize in Contemporary History, 235

H. E. Francis Award, 250

Josette Frank Award, 31

Morton Frank Award, 182

Miles Franklin Award, 30

Soeurette Diehl Fraser Award, 234

French-American Foundation Journalism Fellowship Program, 83

French-American Foundation Translation Prize, 83

Friends of American Writers Literary Adult Awards, 83

Friends of American Writers Young People's Literature Award, 83

Friends of the Dallas Public Library Award, 234

Frost Medal, 198

Robert Frost Poetry Award, 84

Fulbright Scholar Program, 63

Full-Length Play Competition, 266

Fund for Investigative Journalism Prize, 84

Lewis Galantiere Prize, 19

John Gassner Memorial Playwriting Awards, 164

Christian Gauss Award, 191

Gay, Lesbian, Bisexual, and Transgendered Book Award, 14

John C. Geilfuss Fellowship, 229

Lionel Gelber Prize, 45

Georgia State University Review's Writing Contest, 85

German Marshall Fund of the United States Research Fellowships, 85

Leo Gershoy Award, 12

Gerty, Gerty, Gerty in the Arts, Arts, Arts Award, 150

Charles M. Getchell New Play Award, 224

Getty Grant Program Fellowships, 88

John Gilgun Poetry Award, 99

Brendan Gill Prize, 152

Allen Ginsberg Poetry Award, 184

Gival Press Chapbook Competition, 89

Robert H. Goddard Historical Essay Award Competition, 160

Goethe Prize, 87

Gold Medal of the American Academy of Arts and Letters, 6

Dick Goldensohn Fund, 90

Goldsmith Book Prize, 216

Goldsmith Prize for Investigative Reporting, 216

Goldsmith Research Awards, 216

Jeanne Charpiot Goodheart Prize for Fiction, 216

Goshen College Peace Playwriting Contest, 90

Louis Gottschalk Prize, 18

Graduate Scholarship Award, 161

Graduate Scholarship in Lesbian Studies, 161

James T. Grady-James H. Stack Award for Interpreting Chemistry for the Public, 9

Judy Grahn Award, 202

Grand Prix des Biennales, 110

Great Plains Play Contest, 253

Great Platte River Playwrights' Festival, 255

Paul Green Playwrights Prize, 174

Green Rose Prize in Poetry, 166

Greg Grummer Award in Poetry, 192

Andreas Gryphius Prize, 86

Guideposts Young Writers Contest, 91

John Guyon Literary Nonfiction Prize, 64

Gulf Coast Poetry and Short Story Prizes, 91

Friedrich Gundolf Prize, 87

Violet Reed Haas Poetry Prize, 219

Larry J. Hackman Research Residency Program, 170

Hackney Literary Awards, 35

Sarah Josepha Hale Award, 207

John Whitney Hall Book Prize, 26

Jay C. and Ruth Halls Fellowship, 270

Fannie Lou Hamer Award, 150

Hanes Prize for Poetry, 78

Hanks Chapbook Award, 82

Lorraine Hansberry Award, 125

O. B. Hardison, Jr., Poetry Prize, 81

Clarence H. Haring Prize, 12

Aurand Harris Children's Theatre Fellowships, 54

Aurand Harris Memorial Playwriting Competition, 165

Julie Harris Playwright Competition, 34

Haskins Medal, 142

Beatrice Hawley Award, 119

Ellis W. Hawley Prize, 180

John Hay Award, 182

Hayek Fund for Scholars, 104

Rear Admiral John D. Hayes Pre-Doctoral Fellowship, 163

Headwaters Literary Competition, 168

HEArt Quarterly Poetry and Short Fiction Contest, 93

Heartland Prizes, 53

Hugh M. Hefner First Amendment Awards, 194

Heinemann Award for Literature, 242

Heinz Awards, 93

Drue Heinz Literature Prize, 257

Senator John Heinz Fellowship in Environmental Reporting, 113

Peggy V. Helmerich Distinguished Author Award, 238

Hemingway Foundation/PEN Award, 189

Hemingway Research Grants, 127

Lorian Hemingway Short Story Competition, 94

Hendricks Manuscript Award, 84

O. Henry Award, 234

John Hervey Awards for Writing Excellence, 249

High School Journalism Teacher of the Year, 71

High School Playwriting Contest, 31

High School Workshop Writing Competition, 71

Highlights for Children Fiction Contest, 95

Highlights Foundation Scholarship Program, 95

Sidney Hillman Foundation Prize Awards, 95

Hillsdale Prize for Fiction, 78

Hispanic Playwrights Project, 224

History of Women in Science Prize, 96

Alfred Hodder Fellowship, 201

Anastasia C. Hoffman Fellowship, 270

Pearl Hogrefe Fellowship, 116

Winifred Holtby Prize, 242

Vice Admiral Edwin B. Hooper Research Grant, 163

Herbert Hoover Presidential Travel & Grant Program, 96

George A. and Eliza Gardner Howard Foundation, 97

Roy W. Howard National Reporting Competition, 213

Howells Medal of the American Academy of Arts and Letters, 6

Henry Hoyns Fellowships, 258

Hudson River Classics Annual Playwriting Contest, 98

Huggins-Quarles Awards, 181

Human Interest/Ernie Pyle Writing Award, 213

Humane Studies Fellowships, 104

Humanitas Prize, 98

Amy Louise Hunter Fellowship, 229

Huntington Library-Western History Association Martin Ridge Fellowship for Study in Western History Award, 266

Hurston/Wright Award, 99

ICARUS Poetry Competition, 99

ICIJ Award for Outstanding International Investigative Reporting, 114

ICJ-KKC Journalism Fellowship in Japan, 113

IHS Film & Fiction Scholarships, 104

IHS Young Communicators Fellowships, 104

Illinois Artstour Program, 101

Indiana Review Fiction Prize, 102

Inkwell Poetry Competition, 103

Inkwell Short Fiction Contest, 103

International Herald Tribune/Singapore Repertory Theatre International Playwriting Competition, 111

International Impac Dublin Literary Awards, 108

International League of Antiquarian Booksellers Bibliography Prize, 108

International Navies Essay Contest, 248

International Reading Association Children's Book Awards, 114

International Rainer Maria Rilke Prize for Poetry, 108

Iowa Award, 116

Iowa Poetry Prizes, 253

Iowa Short Fiction Award, 253

IRA Lee Bennett Hopkins Promising Poet Award, 114

Irish American Cultural Institute Literary Awards, 117

Irish Research Fund Grants, 117

Irish Times International Fiction Prize, 109

Irish Times Irish Literature Prizes, 109

Islamicist-in-Residence Program, 17

Isle Royale National Park Artist-in-Residence Program, 117

Italian Government Translation Prizes and Grants, 118

Jackpot Grants, 164

Joseph Henry Jackson Award, 116

Sara Jackson Award, 267

W. Turrentine Jackson Award, 267

Rona Jaffe Foundation Writers' Awards, 119

Joan and John Jakobson Scholarships, 265

Olivia James Traveling Fellowships, 22

J. Franklin Jameson Fellowship, 10

J. Franklin Jameson Prize, 12

Jamestown Prize, 179

Janusfest, 249

Japan-U.S. Friendship Commission Prize for the Translation of Japanese Literature, 125

Randall Jarrell Poetry Prize, 174

Jefferson Fellowship Program, 73

Jerome Foundation Travel and Study Grant Program, 121

Jerome Playwright-in-Residence Fellowships, 195

Jerusalem Prize, 109

Jewel Box Theatre Playwriting Award, 121

Jewish Caucus Prize, 161

Charles Johnson Awards for Fiction and Poetry, 102

James Jones First Novel Fellowship, 122

Jesse H. Jones Award, 234

Journalists in Europe Program, 109

Juniper Prize, 254

Janet Heidinger Kafka Prize, 257

Kaiser Media Fellowships in Health, 123

Kaiser Media Internships, 123

Kaiser/National Press Foundation Media Mini-Fellowships, 123

Barbara Karlin Grant, 221

Sue Kaufman Prize for First Fiction, 6

KC/ACTF College Musical Theater Award, 126

KC/ACTF Sí TV Playwriting Award, 126

Ezra Jack Keats/Kerlan Collection Memorial Fellowship, 54

Ezra Jack Keats New Writer Award, 73

Barbara Mandigo Kelly Peace Poetry Awards, 176

Joan Kelly Memorial Prize in Women's History, 12

Kennedy Library Research Grants, 127

Robert F. Kennedy Annual Book Award, 128

Robert F. Kennedy Journalism Awards for Outstanding Coverage of the Problems of the Disadvantaged, 128

Jane Kenyon Award, 165

Jane Kenyon Chapbook Award, 119

Jane Kenyon Poetry Prize, 264

Kestrel Writing Contest, 78

Donald E. Keyhoe Journalism Award, 85

Coretta Scott King Award, 14

Coretta Scott King/John Steptoe Award for New Talent, 14

Otto Kinkeldey Award, 16

Kiriyama Pacific Rim Book Prize, 51

Marc A. Klein Playwriting Award, 48

John S. Knight Fellowships, 229

Knight Fellowships in Specialty Reporting, 254

Knight International Press Fellowships, 113

Knight Science Journalism Fellowships, 141

Knight-Bagehot Fellowship Program in Economics and Business Journalism, 60

Knight-Ridder Internships for Native American Journalists, 129

Gregory Kolovakos Award, 185

Korean Literature Translation Award, 130

Koret Jewish Book Awards, 130

Lee Korf Playwriting Awards, 52

Katherine Singer Kovacs Prize, 147

Marjorie Kovler Research Fellowship, 127

Michael Kraus Research Grants, 10

Kress Fellowship in Egyptian Art and Architecture, 17

Kumu Kahua Playwriting Contest, 253

Harold Morton Landon Translation Award, 1

Dorothea Lange-Paul Taylor Prize, 50

James Laughlin Award, 1

Lawrence Foundation Award, 200

Lawrence Foundation Prize, 143

Ledge Annual Poetry Chapbook Competition, 131

Ledge Poetry Award, 131

Legacy Fellowship, 7

Leighton Studios for Independent Residencies, 45

Waldo G. Leland Prize, 12

Nikolaus Lenau Prize, 86

Richard W. Leopold Prize, 181

Miles Lerman Center for the Study of Jewish Resistance Research Fellowship, 247

Lerner-Scott Prize, 181

Lesbian Writers' Fund Awards, 28

Joseph Levenson Book Prizes, 26

Frank K. and Janet Levin Award, 57

Larry Levis Editor's Prize in Poetry, 147

Levis Poetry Prize, 83

Larry Levis Poetry Prize, 200

Levis Reading Prize, 262

Claudia Lewis Award, 31

Lloyd Lewis Fellowship in American History, 171

Lifetime Achievement Award, 165

Lifetime Achievement Awards for Literature, 162

Ruth Lilly Poetry Fellowships, 197

Ruth Lilly Poetry Prize, 197

Lincoln Prize, 56

Anne Spencer Lindbergh Prize in Children's Literature, 132

Astrid Lindgren Translation Prize, 107

Literal Latte Roy T. Ames Essay Awards, 133

Literal Latte Fiction and Poetry Awards, 133

Literal Latte Food Verse Contest, 133

Littleton-Griswold Prize, 12

Littleton-Griswold Research Grants, 10

Livingston Awards for Young Journalists, 254

Frances Locke Memorial Poetry Award, 35

Gerald Loeb Awards for Distinguished Business and Financial Journalism, 133

Los Angeles Public Library Literary Award, 135

Los Angeles Times Book Prizes, 135

Low-Budget Feature Project, 65

Amy Lowell Poetry Travelling Scholarship, 136

James Russell Lowell Prize, 147

J. Anthony Lukas Prize, 136

J. Anthony Lukas Work-in-Progress Award, 136

Hugh J. Luke Award, 200

Lullwater Prize for Poetry, 136

Audrey Lumsden-Kouvel Fellowship, 172

Lyndhurst Prize, 137

Mark Lynton History Prize, 136

Lyric Poetry Award, 198

Tom McAfee Discovery Feature in Poetry, 147

MacArthur Fellows Program, 137

Bobbi McCallum Memorial Scholarship, 214

Mary McCarthy Prize in Short Fiction, 211

John J. McCloy Fund, 138

James McCreight Fellowship, 270

MacDowell Colony Fellowships, 138

John H. McGinnis Memorial Award, 227

Tim McGinnis Memorial Award, 116

MacGuffin National Poet Hunt, 212

McKnight Artist Fellowships for Writers, 134

McKnight Fellowship, 195

McLaren Memorial Comedy Playwriting Competition, 144

Maclean-Hunter Endowment Award for Literary Nonfiction, 45

Naomi Long Madgett Poetry Award, 135

Madison Review/Chris O'Malley Fiction Award, 138

Madison Review/Phyllis Smart Young Prize in Poetry, 138

Magazine Internship Program, 19

Magellan Prize, 42

Malahat Review Long Poem Prize, 45

Malahat Review Novella Prize, 45

Malice Domestic Best First Novel Contest, 209

Manhattan Theatre Club Playwriting Fellowships, 139

Richard J. Margolis Award, 37

Marine Corps Essay Contest, 249

Beryl Markham Prize for Creative Nonfiction, 230

S. J. Marks Memorial Poetry Prize, 16

Marlboro Review Poetry Prize, 139

Helen and Howard R. Marraro Prize, 12

Howard R. Marraro Prize, 148

Lenore Marshall Poetry Prize, 2

Walter Rumsey Marvin Grant, 178

Maryland Author Award, 140

Master Artists-in-Residence Program, 28

Masters Literary Awards, 51

Mayor's Fellowships in the Arts, 55

Maxim Mazumdar New Play Competition, 5

Elise G. Mead Fellowship, 232

Lucille Medwick Memorial Award, 198

Frederic G. Melcher Book Award, 239

Mellon Postdoctoral Research Fellowship (American Antiquarian Society), 7

Mellon Postdoctoral Research Fellowship (Folger Shakespeare Library), 81

Mellon Postdoctoral Research Fellowship (Newberry Library), 171

Mentor Series Contest, 134

Horace Samuel & Marion Galbraith Merrill Travel Grants in Twentieth-Century American Political History, 181

Addison M. Metcalf Award in Literature, 6

James A. Michener Fellowship, 142

James A. Michener Memorial Prize, 142

James A. Michener Prize in Writing, 155

Michigan Author Award, 143

Diane Middlebrook Fellowship, 270

290

Midwest Theatre Network Original Play Competition/Rochester Playwright Festival, 144

Kenneth W. Mildenberger Prize, 148

Milkweed National Fiction Prize, 144

Milkweed Prize for Children's Literature, 145

Mill Mountain Theatre New Play Competition, 145

Jim Wayne Miller Prize in Poetry, 129

Llewellyn Miller Fund, 18

Vassar Miller Prize in Poetry, 256

C. Wright Mills Award, 222

Minnesota McKnight Fellowship for Interdisciplinary Artists, 106

Minnesota Literature Live Grants, 134

Minnesota Voices Project, 168

Minnesota Writers' Career Initiative Program, 134

Mississippi Review Prize in Fiction and Poetry, 146

Missouri Lifestyle Journalism Awards, 255

H. L. Mitchell Award, 225

Mitchell Prize for the History of Art, 110

Eric Mitchell Prize, 110

MLA Prize for a Distinguished Bibliography, 148

MLA Prize for a Distinguished Scholarly Edition, 148

MLA Prize for a First Book, 148

MLA Prize for Independent Scholars, 148

Monbusho Scholarships, 120

Scott Moncrieff Prize, 243

Harriet Monroe Poetry Award, 252

Monterey County Film Commission Screenwriting Competition, 151

Monticello College Foundation Fellowship for Women, 171

Jenny McKean Moore Writers Program, 85

Marianne Moore Poetry Prize, 94

Richard F. and Virginia P. Morgan Fellowship, 8

Felix Morley Journalism Competition, 105

Robert T. Morse Writers Award, 17

Samuel French Morse Poetry Prize, 175

Kathryn A. Morton Prize in Poetry, 211

Frank Luther Mott Kappa Tau Alpha Journalism and Mass Communication Research Award, 124

Mudfish Poetry Prize, 39

Edward R. Murrow Fellowship, 63

Musical Stairs Competition, 266

NABJ Summer Internships, 153

NABJ Scholarships, 153

NASA Fellowship, 10

George Jean Nathan Award for Dramatic Criticism, 63

National AIDS Fund CFDA-Vogue Initiative Award for Playwriting, 126

National Awards and Fellowships for Education Reporting, 74

National Book Awards, 154

National Children's Theatre Festival, 3

National Education Association Art of Teaching Prize, 155

National Education Association Democracy in Higher Education Prize, 155

National Education Association New Unionism in the Academy Prize, 155

National Education Association New Scholar Prize, 155

National Endowment for the Arts Fellowships in Creative Writing 155

National Endowment for the Arts Translation Project Grants, 156

National Endowment for the Humanities Fellowship (Newberry Library), 171

National Endowment for the Humanities Fellowships, 156

National Hispanic Playwriting Contest, 22

National Jesuit Book Award Competition, 27

National Jewish Book Awards, 121

National McKnight Fellowship for Interdisciplinary Artists, 106

National New Play Award, 99

National One-Act Playwriting Contest, 72

National Play Award, 159

National Playwrights' Award, 239

National Playwrights Conference, 179

National Poetry Competition, 122

National Poetry Series, 158

National Press Club Scholarship for Minorities in Journalism, 158

National Screenwriting Competition, 160

National Screenwriting Competition (Maui Writers Conference), 141

National Self-Publishing Awards, 272

National Sephardic Literary Contest, 118

National Society of Arts and Letters Literature Awards, 160

National Steinbeck Center Writing Competition, 161

National Student Playwriting Award, 126

National Ten-Minute Play Contest, 4

National Theatre Artist Residency Program, 235

National Youth Theatre Playwriting Competition, 102

NEA/TCG Theatre Residency Program for Playwrights, 235

Larry Neal Writers' Competition, 70

Nebraska Review Fiction and Poetry Prizes, 163

Negative Capability Short Fiction Award, 163

Howard Nemerov Sonnet Award, 82

Pablo Neruda Prize for Poetry, 173

Dr. Henry and Lilian Nesburn Award, 34

Frederic W. Ness Book Award, 26

Neustadt International Prize for Literature, 271

Allan Nevins Prize, 220

New American Comedy Festival, 239

New Century Writer Awards, 179

New Directors/New Works, 72

New England/New York Award, 119

New Harmony Project, 165

New Issues First Book of Poetry Prize, 166

New Jersey Council for the Humanities Book Award, 166

New Jersey Writers Project, 166

New Letters Creative Nonfiction Prize, 167

New Letters Fiction Prize, 167

New Letters Poetry Prize, 167

New Millennium Awards, 167

New Plays Festival, 57

New Playwrights' Program, 250

New Professional Theatre Writers Festival, 167

New Visions Award, 204

New Voice Fiction Award, 273

New Voice Nonfiction Award, 273

New Voice Poetry Award, 273

New Works for a New World, 254

New Writer Awards, 90

New York Foundation for the Arts Fellowships, 168

New York Public Library Helen Bernstein Book Award for Excellence in Journalism, 169

New York State Edith Wharton Citation of Merit, 170

New York State Walt Whitman Citation of Merit, 170

New York Stories Fiction Prize, 170

New York University Press Prizes for Fiction and Poetry, 171

The New Yorker Literary Awards, 171

New Yorkers Need to Know Prizes for Journalism, 171

Newberry-British Academy Fellowship for Study in Great Britain, 172

Newberry Library/American Antiquarian Society Short-term Fellowships, 172

John Newbery Medal, 28

Thomas Newcomen Book Award in Business History, 172

Don and Gee Nicholl Screenwriting Fellowships, 2

Lucius W. Nieman Fellowships for Journalists, 173

NLAPW Scholarship for Mature Women in Letters, 158

North American Authors and Fiction Writers Contest, 201

North American Indian Prose Award, 255

North American Native Authors First Book Awards, 162

Novel Writing Contest, 161

Eli N. Oboler Memorial Award, 14

Flannery O'Connor Award for Short Fiction, 252

Frank O'Connor Fiction Award, 69

Scott O'Dell Award for Historical Fiction, 177

Frank O'Hara Award Chapbook Competition, 236

Ohio State University Press/The Journal Award in Poetry, 178

Ohioana Award for Children's Literature/Alice Wood Memorial Award, 178

Ohioana Poetry Award/Helen and Laura Krout Memorial, 179

Louis Littlecoon Oliver Memorial Award for Short Fiction, 162

Omaha Prize, 30

Onassis International Prize, 110

Open Voice Nonfiction Award, 273

Open Voice Poetry Award, 273

Open Voice Scott Sommer Fiction Award, 273

Opportunity Grants Program, 259

Opus Magnum Discovery Awards, 49

Orange Prize for Fiction, 241

Oregon Book Awards, 133

Oregon Literary Fellowships, 133

Oregon Women Writers Fellowship, 133

Natalie Ornish Poetry Award, 234

Outstanding Children's Book Award, 165

Outstanding Dissertation of the Year Award, 115

Outstanding Emerging Writer Award, 165

Outstanding Work of Fiction Award, 165

Outstanding Work of Nonfiction Award, 165

Guy Owen Poetry Prize, 226

Frank Lawrence and Harriet Chappell Owsley Award, 225

William and Kingman Page Poetry Book Award, 200

Robert Troup Paine Prize, 92

Mildred and Albert Panowski Playwriting Award, 175

Francis Parkman Prize, 220

Passager Poetry Contest, 183

Kenneth Patchen Competition, 193

Paterson Fiction Prize, 184

Paterson Poetry Prize, 184

Paterson Prize for Books for Young People, 184

Paumanok Poetry Award, 262

Pavement Saw Press Transcontinental Poetry Award, 185

Ethel Payne Fellowships, 154

PeaceWriting International Writing Awards, 185

Pearl Poetry Prize, 185

William Peden Prize, 147

Louis Pelzer Memorial Award, 181

PEN/Martha Albrand Award for the Art of the Memoir, 186

PEN/Martha Albrand Award for First Nonfiction, 186

PEN/Architectural Digest Award for Literary Writing on the Visual Arts, 186

PEN/Book-of-the-Month Club Translation Prize, 186

PEN/Faulkner Award for Fiction, 189

PEN/Jerard Fund Award, 186

PEN/Norma Klein Award, 186

PEN/Malamud Award for Excellence in Short Fiction, 190

PEN/Nabokov Award, 187

PEN/Naylor Working Writer Fellowship, 187

PEN/Joyce Osterweil Award for Poetry, 187

PEN/Laura Pels Foundation Awards for Drama, 187

PEN/Spielvogel-Diamonstein Award for the Art of the Essay, 188

PEN/Voelcker Award for Poetry, 188

PEN Award for Poetry in Translation, 186

PEN Fund for Writers and Editors with AIDS, 188

PEN Center USA West Literary Awards, 188

PEN Writers Fund, 188

Peregrine Prize, 19

Leonard M. Perryman Communications Scholarship for Ethnic Minority Students, 245

Julia Peterkin Award, 62

Peterson Emerging Playwright Competition, 49

Kate B. and Hall J. Peterson Fellowships, 7

Pew Fellowships in the Arts, 191

Pfizer Award, 96

James D. Phelan Award, 116

Phi Beta Kappa Award in Science, 191

Philbrick Poetry Award, 201

Phillips Foundation Journalism Fellowship Program, 192

Robert J. Pickering Award for Playwriting Excellence, 58

Paul A. Pisk Prize, 16

Playboy College Fiction Contest, 194

Playhouse on the Square New Play Competition, 194

PlayLabs, 195

Plays for the 21st Century, 196

Playwright Discovery Award, 260

Playwrights First Award, 195

Pockets Fiction Writing Contest, 197

Poetry Center Book Award, 197

Poetry Center Prize, 57

Poetry Magazine Awards, 197

Poetry Open, 89

Poets & Writers Readings/Workshops Program, 199

Poets Out Loud Prize, 199

Renato Poggioli Award, 188

Forrest C. Pogue Prize, 75

Daniel A. Pollack-Harvard Review Prize, 92

Felix Pollak Prize in Poetry, 258

Politics & Journalism Semester, 263

Harriet and Leon Pomerance Fellowship, 22

Pope Foundation Journalism Awards, 200

Katherine Anne Porter Prize for Fiction, 173

Ezra Pound Poetry Award, 183

Colin L. Powell Joint Warfighting Essay Contest, 249

Premio Anual de Ensayo Literario Hispanoamericano Lya Kostakowsky, 108

Premio Aztlán, 256

Premio del Rey, 11

Premio Valle Inclan, 244

Presidio La Bahia Award, 222

Francesca Primus Prize, 68

Princess Grace Awards Playwright Fellowship, 201

PRISM international Short Fiction Contest, 47

Promising Playwright Award, 58

Public Policy Journalism Fellowships, 254

Public Service Reporting/Roy W. Howard Awards, 213

Pulitzer Prizes, 203

Pulliam Journalism Fellowships, 203

Pushcart Prize, 203

QPBC/Estés International Storyteller Prize, 204

Quarterly Review of Literature Poetry Book Awards, 204

Quarterly West Novella Competition, 204

QuickArt$, 100

Rainmaker Awards in Poetry, 276

Raiziss/de Palchi Translation Award, 2

A.K. Ramanujan Book Prize for Translation, 26

Jennings Randolph Program for International Peace, 247

James A. Rawley Prize, 181

Rea Award for the Short Story, 73

Rea Nonfiction Prize, 38

Red Rock Poetry Award, 206

Phillip D. Reed Memorial Award for Outstanding Writing on the Southern Environment, 225

Reese Fellowship, 8

Refined Savage Poetry Competition, 206

Regional Book Awards, 152

Arthur Rense Poetry Prize, 6

Renwick-Sumerwell Award for Short Fiction, 64

Pearl Resnick Postdoctoral Fellowship, 247

Reuters Fellowships in Medical Journalism, 241

Reuters-IUCN Media Awards, 241

Reuters Oxford University Fellowships, 241

Revson Fellows Program, 60

Charles H. Revson Foundation Fellowships for Archival Research, 247

Louise E. Reynolds Memorial Fiction Award, 237

Harold U. Ribalow Prize, 92

Mary Roberts Rinehart Fund, 207

River City Writing Awards in Fiction, 207

River Oak-Hemingway Foundation Short Story Contest, 208

River Oak Poetry Contest, 208

River Styx International Poetry Contest, 208

Summerfield G. Roberts Award, 222

Helen M. Robinson Award, 115

Robinson Jeffers Tor House Foundation Prize, 208

James Harvey Robinson Prize, 12

Rockefeller Foundation Fellowship in Gender Studies in Early Modern Europe, 172

Rocky Mountain Artists/Eccentric Book Competition, 94

Rocky Mountain National Park Artist-in-Residence Program, 209

Nicholas Roerich Poetry Prize, 230

Rome Fellowship in Literature, 6

Rome Prize Competition, 7

Lois and Richard Rosenthal New Play Prize, 55

Richard and Hilda Rosenthal Foundation Award, 6

Madeline Dane Ross Award, 182

Bruce Rossley Literary Award, 173

Philip Roth Residence in Creative Writing, 41

Pleasant T. Rowland Prize for Fiction, 196

Elliott Rudwick Prize, 181

William B. Ruggles Journalism Scholarship, 157

Juan Rulfo International Latin American and Caribbean Prize for Literature, 110

Rundell Graduate Student Award, 267

Cornelius Ryan Award, 182

Renee Sagiv Fiction Prize, 192

Salmon Run National Poetry Book Award, 210

Theodore Saloutos Award, 4

Salt Hill Journal Poetry Prize, 210

Salt Hill Journal Short Short Fiction Prize, 210

Janet and Maxwell Salter Award, 34

Benjamin Saltman Poetry Award, 206

Carl Sandburg Literary Awards, 84

Ernest Sandeen Prize in Poetry, 256

Sandstone Prize in Short Fiction, 178

Marjory Bartlett Sanger Award, 21

Morton R. Sarett Memorial Award, 255

Sasakawa Prize, 243

Barbara Savage "Miles from Nowhere" Memorial Award, 152

Say the Word National Poetry Competition, 75

Aldo and Jeanne Scaglione Prize for Comparative Literary Studies, 149

Aldo and Jeanne Scaglione Prize for French and Francophone Studies, 149

Aldo and Jeanne Scaglione Prize for Literary Translation, 149

Aldo and Jeanne Scaglione Prize for Studies in Germanic Languages and Literatures, 149

Aldo and Jeanne Scaglione Prize for Studies for Slavic Languages and Literatures, 149

Aldo and Jeanne Scaglione Prize in Italian Literary Studies, 148

Joyce and Arthur Schechter Fellowship, 247

Schlegel-Tieck Prize, 243

Arthur M. Schlesinger Jr. Research Fellowship, 127

Bernadette E. Schmitt Research Grants, 10

Scholars-in-Residence Program, 212

Scholars and Writers Fellowship Program, 169

Scholastic Writing Awards, 211

Henry and Ida Schuman Prize, 96

Abba P. Schwartz Research Fellowship, 127

Science in Society Journalism Awards, 154

Screenplay Discovery of the Year, 49

Ted Scripps Environmental Fellowship Program, 50

Peter Seaborg Award for Civil War Nonfiction, 246

Seattle Artist Program, 214

Serpentine Annual Short Story Contest, 215

Seventeen Magazine Fiction Contest, 215

Michael Shaara Award for Excellence in Civil War Fiction, 246

Mina P. Shaughnessy Prize, 150

Bernard Shaw Prize, 243

Frances Shaw Fellowship for Older Women Writers, 205

Philip Shehadi New Writers Award, 143

Shelley Memorial Award, 198

Jerome J. Shestack Poetry Prizes, 16

Randy Shilts Award, 202

Reva Shiner Full-Length Play Contest, 36

Short Grain Writing Contest, 45

Short Play Awards Program, 126

Short Play Festival, 135

Short Story Award for New Writers, 89

Mary Isabel Sibley Fellowship, 192

Siena College International Playwrights' Competition, 217

Dorothy Silver Playwriting Competition, 121

John Simmons Short Fiction Award, 253

Francis Butler Simpkins Award, 225

Inger Sjöberg Award, 17

Slapering Hol Press Chapbook Competition, 98

Slipstream Annual Poetry Chapbook Contest, 218

Bernice Slote Award, 200

Alice E. Smith Fellowship, 230

Elizabeth Simpson Smith Award, 52

Carol Houck Smith Fellowship, 270

Jean Kennedy Smith Playwriting Award for the Best Play Written on the Theme of Disability, 126

Peregrine Smith Poetry Competition, 218

John Ben Snow Foundation Prize, 174

John Ben Snow Prize, 232

Richard Snyder Poetry Award, 24

Society for the History of Technology Popular Book Prize, 222

Theodore C. Sorensen Research Fellowship, 127

Source Theatre Company Literary Prize, 223

South Carolina Fiction Project, 223

Southern Appalachian Playwrights' Conference, 225

Southern Playwrights Competition, 51

Southern Playwrights Competition (Jacksonville State University), 119

The Southern Review/Louisiana State University Short Fiction Award, 226

Sow's Ear Chapbook Competition, 227

Sow's Ear Poetry Competition, 227

Spanish Language Fellowships, 159

Special Award for Nonfiction, 116

Spencer Foundation Fellowship in the History of Education, 171

Sports Reporting Fellowship, 254

Spuyten Duyvil Book Award, 228

SQUARE magazine Screenwriting Award, 228

SQUARE magazine Television Award, 228

STAGE Festival of New Plays, 228

Stand Magazine's Short Story and Poetry Competition, 243

Ann Stanford Poetry Prize, 257

Edward Stanley Award for Poetry, 200

Stanley Drama Award, 263

Agnes Lynch Starrett Prize, 257

Wallace E. Stegner Fellowships, 229

Stoody-West Fellowship in Religious Journalism, 245

Stork Search, 131

Elizabeth Matchett Stover Memorial Award, 227

Flora Stieglitz Straus Award, 31

James Still Award for Writing, 78

Mildred and Harold Strauss Livings, 6

Strousse Award, 200

Snorri Sturluson Icelandic Fellowships, 100

Joan G. Sugarman Children's Book Award, 264

Richard Sullivan Prize in Fiction, 256

Summer Newsroom Internships, 214

Summer Resident Fellowship Program, 176

Hollis Summers Poetry Prize, 178

Sundance Institute Feature Film Program, 231

Sundance Theater Laboratory, 231

May Swenson Poetry Award, 259

Charles S. Sydnor Prize, 225

Amaury Talbot Fund Annual Prize, 111

Tamarack Award, 146

Tanning Prize, 2

Allen Tate Memorial Award, 269

Aiken Taylor Award for Modern American Poetry, 215

Marvin Taylor Playwriting Award, 217

Peter Taylor Prize for the Novel, 130

Teddy Book Award, 29

Teixeira-Gomes Prize, 244

Ten-Minute Play Festival, 126

Tennessee Writers Alliance Literary Awards, 234

Texas History Essay Contest, 223

Theatre Conspiracy Annual New Play Contest, 236

TheatreFest Regional Playwriting Contest, 150

Lowell Thomas Travel Journalist Awards, 220

Richard H. Thornton Writer-in-Residence, 137

Three Oaks Prize for Fiction, 230

Thunderbird Films Annual Screenplay Competition, 236

James Thurber Journalist-in-Residence, 236

James Thurber Playwright-in-Residence, 236

James Thurber Residency Program, 236

James Thurber Writer-in-Residence, 236

Reginald S. Tickner Writing Fellowship, 89

Time-Warner Fellowship, 254

tnr (the new renaissance) Poetry Award, 237

Lena-Miles Wever Todd Poetry Series, 196

Towngate Theatre Playwriting Competition, 177

Towson University Prize for Literature, 237

Joyce A. Tracy Fellowship, 8

Harry S. Truman Book Award, 237

Trustus Playwrights' Festival, 238

Kate Tufts Discovery Award, 56

Kingsley Tufts Poetry Award, 56

Tupelo Press Award for the Best Novel-Length Fiction, 238

Tupelo Press Poetry Award, 238

Frederick Jackson Turner Award, 182

Steven Turner Award, 234

Mark Twain Award for Short Fiction, 206

Mark Twain Comedy Playwriting Award, 126

2001 Writing Prize, 167

UBC Creative Writing Residency Prize in Stageplay, 47

Brenda Ueland Prose Prize, 264

UNESCO-Aschberg Bursaries for Artists, 112

UNESCO/Françoise Gallimard Prize, 112

UNESCO Prize for Children's and Young People's Literature in the Service of Tolerance, 111

United State/Japan Creative Artists' Program, 120

University of Michigan Press Book Award, 255

U.S. West TheatreFest, 68

USIA Fulbright, 105

Utah Original Writing Competition, 259

Van Lier Fellowships, 24

Daniel Varoujan Prize, 164

Vermont Playwrights Award, 259

Verse Prize, 260

Very Short Fiction Award, 89

Villa Montalvo Biennial Poetry Competition, 261

Virginia College Stores Association Book Award, 261

Visiting Davis Fellowships, 66

Visiting Fellowships for Historical Research by Creative and Performing Artists and Writers, 8

Voice of Democracy Audio Essay Competition, 260

Vondel Translation Prize, 244

Johann Heinrich Voss Prize for Translation, 87

Harold D. Vursell Memorial Award, 6

Lawrence Wade Journalism Fellowship, 95

Walden Residency Program, 226

Stanley Walker Award, 234

Mike Wallace Fellowship in Investigative Reporting, 254

Lila Wallace-Reader's Digest Writers' Awards, 263

Edward Lewis Wallant Book Award, 263

Chad Walsh Poetry Award, 33

Cornelia Carhart Ward Fellowship, 232

Theodore Ward Prize for Playwriting, 59

Robert Penn Warren Awards, 21

Robert Penn Warren Poetry Prize, 65

Robert Penn Warren Prize for Fiction, 78

Robert Penn Warren Prize for Fiction (The Southerner), 226

Bradford Washburn Award, 152

Washington Post/Children's Book Guild Nonfiction Award, 54

Washington Post Summer News Program, 264

Washington Prize, 271

Frank Waters Voices of the Southwest Writing Award, 265

Thomas J. Watson Fellowship Program, 265

"We Don't Need No Stinkin' Dramas" Playwriting Contest, 147

Weatherford Award, 33

Richard M. Weaver Award for Scholarly Letters, 103

Arthur Weinberg Fellowship for Independent Scholars, 172

Edward Weintal Prize for Diplomatic Reporting, 105

Wesley-Logan Prize, 12

Whetstone Prize, 267

White Pine Press Poetry Prize, 268

Bill Whitehead Award for Lifetime Achievement, 202

Whiting Writers' Awards, 268

Walt Whitman Award, 2

Stan and Tom Wick Poetry Prize, 128

Elie Wiesel Prize in Ethics Essay Contest, 268

Richard Wilbur Award, 252

Willamette Award in Fiction and Poetry, 56

Gertrude Johnson Williams Writing Contest, 122

Kemper and Leila Williams Prizes in Louisiana History, 96

Tennessee Williams/New Orleans Literary Festival One-Act Play Competition, 269

William Carlos Williams Award, 198

Wind Magazine Short Story Competition, 269

Robert H. Winner Memorial Award, 198

L. L. Winship/PEN New England Award, 189

Paul A. Witty Short Story Award, 115

Thomas Wolfe Fiction Prize, 175

Thomas Wolfe Student Essay Prize, 270

Tobias Wolff Award for Fiction, 33

David T. K. Wong Fellowship, 244

Charles B. Wood Award for Distinguished Writing, 48

Carter G. Woodson Institute Predoctoral and Postdoctoral Residential Research Fellowships, 270

World of Expression Scholarship Program, 34

Writer's Digest Annual Writing Competition, 272

Writers Exchange Program, 199

Writers of the Future Contest, 98

Writers on Site, 199

WritersBlok Short Story Contest, 274

Writing Awards in Physics and Astronomy, 13

Yale Series of Younger Poets, 275

Year-End-Series New Play Festival, 175

Lamar York Prize for Nonfiction, 52

Young Playwrights Festival National Playwriting Competition, 276

Yukon Pacific New Play Award, 200

Morton Dauwen Zabel Prize, 6

John C. Zacharis First Book Award, 196

Zoetrope Short Fiction Contest, 276

Charlotte Zolotow Award, 62

Anna Zornio Memorial Children's Theatre Playwriting Award, 256

INDEX OF ORGANIZATIONS

A Contemporary Theatre, 1
Academy of American Poets, 1
Academy of Motion Picture Arts and Sciences, 2
Acadia National Park, 3
The Actors' Fund of America, 3
Actors' Playhouse at the Miracle Theatre, 3
Actors Theatre of Louisville, 4
Agricultural History Society, 4
Alabama State Council on the Arts, 4
Alaska State Council on the Arts, 4
Edward F. Albee Foundation, 5
Alleyway Theatre, 5
Alligator Juniper, 5
American Academy of Arts and Letters, 5
American Academy in Berlin, 6
American Academy of Religion, 7
American Academy in Rome, 7
American Antiquarian Society, 7
American Association for the Advancement of Science, 8
American Association of University Women, 8
American Booksellers Association, 9
American Chemical Society, 9
American Council of Learned Societies, 9
American Dreamer Independent Filmworks, 9
American Historical Association, 10
American Institute of Indian Studies, 13
American Institute of Physics, 13
American Jewish Archives, 13
The American Legion, 13
American Library Association, 14
American Literary Review, 15
American Literary Translators Association, 15
American Musicological Society, 15
American Poetry Review, 16
American Political Science Association, 16
American Psychiatric Association, 17
American Research Center in Egypt, 17
American-Scandinavian Foundation, 17
American Society of Church History, 18
American Society of Composers, Authors, and Publishers, 18
American Society for Eighteenth-Century Studies, 18
American Society of Journalists and Authors Charitable Trust, 18
American Society of Magazine Editors, 19
American Translators Association, 19
Amherst Writers and Artists Press, 19

Amy Foundation, 20
Anamnesis Press, 20
Mary Anderson Center for the Arts, 20
Anhinga Press, 20
Another Chicago Magazine, 21
Anthology of New England Writers, 21
Apostle Islands National Lakeshore, 21
Archaeological Institute of America, 21
Ariadne Press, 22
Arizona Commission on the Arts, 22
Arizona Theatre Company, 22
Arrowhead Regional Arts Council, 23
Artist Trust, 23
Arts & Letters Journal of Contemporary Culture, 23
ArtServe Michigan, 24
Ashland Poetry Press, 24
Asian American Writers Workshop, 24
Asian Cultural Council, 25
Isaac Asimov Award, 25
Associated Press, 25
Associated Writing Programs, 25
Association of American Colleges and Universities, 26
Association for Asian Studies, 26
Association for the Care of Children's Health, 27
Association of Jesuit Colleges and Universities, 27
Association of Jewish Libraries, 27
Association for Library Services to Children, 28
Astraea National Lesbian Action Foundation, 28
Atlanta Review, 28
Atlantic Center for the Arts, 28
Austin Film Festival, 29
Austin Writers' League, 29
AUSTRALIA: Arts Management Pty, Ltd., 30
Authors League Fund, 30
Authors in the Park, 30
The Backwaters Press, 30
Baker's Plays, 31
bananafish, 31
Bank Street College of Education, 31
Banks Channel Books, 31
Bantam Doubleday Dell, 31
Barnard College, 32
Barnes & Noble, 32
The Bear Deluxe Magazine, 32
Bear Star Press, 33
Bellagio Study and Conference Center. *See*

Rockefeller Foundation
Bellingham Review, 33
The Beloit Poetry Journal, 33
Berea College, 33
Berkshire Conference of Women Historians, 34
Bertelsmann USA, 34
Beverly Hills Theatre Guild, 34
Beyond Baroque Literary/Arts Center, 35
Birmingham-Southern College, 35
The Bitter Oleander, 35
BkMk Press, 35
Black Caucus of the American Library
    Association, 36
Black Warrior Review, 36
Susan Smith Blackburn Prize, 36
Bloomington Playwrights Project, 36
Blue Mountain Center, 37
The Bogliasco Foundation, 37
Borderlands Theater, 37
Robert Bosch Foundation, 38
Boston Authors Club, 38
The Boston Book Review, 38
Boston Review, 38
Boulder Museum of Contemporary Art, 39
Boulevard, 39
Box Turtle Press, 39
Bread Loaf Writers' Conference, 39
Bright Hill Press, 40
Brody Arts Fund, 40
Bronx Council on the Arts, 40
John Carter Brown Library, 41
Bucknell University, 41
Mary Ingraham Bunting Institute at Radcliffe, 41
Bush Artist Fellows Program, 42
Buttonwood Press, 42
Witter Bynner Foundation for Poetry, 43
California Arts Council, 43
California Library Association, 43
Camargo Foundation, 44
Cambridge Arts Council, 44
Campbell Corner, 44
CANADA: Banff Centre for the Arts, 45
CANADA: Lionel Gelber Prize, 45
CANADA: Grain Magazine, 46
CANADA: Malahat Review, 46
CANADA: PRISM international, 46
CANADA: Saskatchewan Writers Guild, 47
CANADA: University of British Columbia, 47
Carnegie Fund for Authors, 48
Carolina Quarterly, 48
The Carter Center, 48
Case Western Reserve University, 48
Catawba College, 49

Cave Canem Foundation, 49
CCS Entertainment Group, 49
CEC International Partners, 49
Centenary College of Louisiana, 50
Center for Book Arts, 50
Center for Documentary Studies, 50
Center for Environmental Journalism, 50
Center for the Pacific Rim, 51
Center Press, 51
Center for Southern Studies, 51
Centrum, 52
Cerritos College, 52
Charlotte Writers Club, 52
Chattahoochee Review, 52
Chelsea Award Competition, 52
Chesterfield Film Company, 53
The Chicago Reporter, 53
Chicago Tribune, 53
Children's Book Guild of Washington, D.C., 54
Children's Literature Association, 54
Children's Literature Research Collections, 54
The Children's Theatre Foundation of
    American, 54
Christopher Columbus Fellowship
    Foundation, 55
Cincinnati Playhouse in the Park, 55
Cintas Foundation, 55
City of Atlanta Bureau of Cultural Affairs, 55
Civil War Institute, 56
Clackamas Literary Review, 56
Claremont Graduate University, 56
Clauder Competition for Excellence in
    Playwriting, 57
Cleveland Foundation, 57
Cleveland Public Theatre, 57
Cleveland State University, 57
Coalition for the Advancement of Jewish
    Education, 58
Coldwater Community Theater, 58
Colonial Players, 58
Colorado Council on the Arts and
    Humanities, 58
Colorado Review, 59
Columbia College, 59
Columbia University (Bancroft Prize
    Committee), 59
Columbia University (Graduate School of
    Journalism), 60
Columbia University (Charles H. Revson
    Fellows), 60
Common Wealth Awards, 60
Commonwealth Club of California, 61
Community Writers Association, 61
Conference on Latin American History, 61
Connecticut Commission on the Arts, 61

Contemporary Arts Educational Project, 62

Converse College, 62

Cooperative Children's Book Center, 62

Copper Canyon Press, 62

Cornell University, 63

Council on Foreign Relations, 63

Council for International Exchange of Scholars, 63

Crab Orchard Review, 64

Crane-Rogers Foundation. *See* Institute of Current World Affairs

The Crescent Review, 64

Cultural Arts Council of Houston/Harris County, 64

Cumberland Poetry Review, 65

Cushwa Center for the Study of American Catholicism, 65

Cyclone Productions, 65

Dana Awards, 66

Shelby Cullom Davis Center for Historical Studies, 66

Dayton Playhouse, 66

Delaware Division of the Arts, 66

Gladys Krieble Delmas Foundation, 67

Delta Kappa Gamma Society International, 67

Eben Demarest Trust, 67

DENMARK: Commission for Educational Exchange Between Denmark & the U.S.A., 68

Denver Center Theatre Company, 68

DePaul University, 68

descant, 69

Walt Disney Studios, 69

District of Columbia Commission on the Arts and Humanities, 69

Djerassi Resident Artists Program, 70

Dobie-Paisano Project, 70

DOMINICAN REPUBLIC: Altos de Chavon, 70

Dorland Mountain Arts Colony, 71

Dorset Colony, 71

Dow Jones Newspaper Fund, 71

Drama League of New York, 72

Dubuque Fine Arts Players, 72

Dumbarton Oaks, 72

Dungannon Foundation, 73

Earhart Foundation, 73

Early Childhood Resources and Information Center of the New York Public Library, 73

East-West Center, 73

East West Players, 74

Eaton Literary Agency, 74

Eckerd College Review, 74

Education Writers Association, 74

The Albert Einstein Institution, 75

Eisenhower Center for American Studies, 75

Ellipse Arts Center, 75

Emporia State University, 76

Maurice English Foundation for Poetry, 76

The English-Speaking Union, 76

The Ensemble Studio Theatre, 76

Willard R. Espy Literary Foundation, 77

Evergreen Chronicles, 77

Experimental Television Center, 77

Fairmont State College, 78

Family Circle, 78

Fellowship of Southern Writers, 78

Final Draft, 78

Fine Arts Work Center in Provincetown, 79

FINLAND: Finnish Literature Information Center, 79

F. Scott Fitzgerald Literary Conference, 79

Five Points, 80

Florida Division of Cultural Affairs, 80

Florida Playwrights' Process, 80

The Florida Review, 80

Florida Studio Theatre, 81

Folger Shakespeare Library, 81

Fontbonne College, 82

The Formalist, 82

Foundation for Contemporary Performance Art, 82

Foundation for Iranian Studies, 82

Four Way Books, 83

French-American Foundation, 83

Friends of American Writers, 83

Friends of the Chicago Public Library, 84

Friends of New Netherland, 84

Robert Frost Foundation, 84

Fund for Investigative Journalism, 84

Fund for UFO Research, 85

George Washington University, 85

Georgia State University Review, 85

German Marshall Fund of the United States, 85

GERMANY: Art Society (Künstlergilde), 86

GERMANY: Stadt Buxtehude, 86

GERMANY: DAAD (German Academic Exchange Service), 86

GERMANY: German Academy for Language and Literature, 87

GERMANY: Goethe Prize of the City of Frankfurt, 87

GERMANY: Institut für Europäische Geschichte, 87

Gerontological Society of America, 87

Getty Grant Program, 88

The Gilder Lehrman Center for the Study of Slavery, Resistance, and Abolition, 88

Gilman School, 89

Gival Press, 89

Glimmer Train Press, 89

Dick Goldensohn Fund Projects, 90

Goshen College, 90

Great Lakes Colleges Association, 90

Harry Frank Guggenheim Foundation, 90

John Simon Guggenheim Memorial Foundation, 91

Guideposts, 91

Gulf Coast, 91

Hadassah Magazine, 92

Hambidge Center, 92

The Harvard Review, 92

Harvard University Press, 92

Headlands Center for the Arts, 93

HEArt Quarterly, 93

Hedgebrook, 93

Heinz Family Foundation, 93

Helicon Nine Editions, 94

Hemingway Days Festival, 94

Hemingway Western Studies Center, 94

The Heritage Foundation, 95

Highlights for Children, 95

Sidney Hillman Foundation, 95

Historic New Orleans Collection, 96

History of Science Society, 96

Herbert Hoover Presidential Library Association, 96

The Horn Book, 97

George A. and Eliza Gardner Howard Foundation, 97

L. Ron Hubbard's Writers of the Future Contest, 98

Hudson River Classics, 98

Hudson Valley Writers' Center, 98

Humanitas Prize, 98

Humboldt State University (English Department), 99

Humboldt State University (Theatre Department), 99

Hurston/Wright Foundation, 99

Icarus, 99

ICARUS, 99

ICELAND: Ministry of Education, Science and Culture, 100

ICELAND: Sigurdur Nordal Institute, 100

Idaho Commission on the Arts, 100

Illinois Arts Council, 101

Illinois State University, 102

Indiana Review, 102

Indiana University-Purdue University of Indianapolis, 102

The Ingersoll Prizes, 103

Inkwell Magazine, 103

Institute on the Arts & Civic Dialogue, 103

Institute of Current World Affairs, 103

Institute for Humane Studies, 104

Institute of International Education, 105

Institute for the Study of Diplomacy, 105

Inter American Press Association Scholarship Fund, 105

Intermedia Arts, 106

INTERNATIONAL: Arvon Foundation, 106

INTERNATIONAL: Simone and Cino del Duca Foundation, 106

INTERNATIONAL: Fédération Internationale des Traducteurs, 107

INTERNATIONAL: Premio Feltrinelli, 107

INTERNATIONAL: Fundación Cultural Lya y Luis Cardoza y Aragón, 108

INTERNATIONAL: Impac, 108

INTERNATIONAL: International Academy of Poetry and Poetics, 108

INTERNATIONAL: International League of Antiquarian Booksellers, 108

INTERNATIONAL: The Irish Times Ltd., 109

INTERNATIONAL: Jerusalem International Book Fair, 109

INTERNATIONAL: Journalists in Europe Fund, 109

INTERNATIONAL: Maison Internationale de la Poésie, 110

INTERNATIONAL: The Mitchell Prizes, 110

INTERNATIONAL: Alexander S. Onassis Benefit Foundation, 110

INTERNATIONAL: Juan Rulfo Prize, 110

INTERNATIONAL: Singapore Repertory Theatre, 111

INTERNATIONAL: Amaury Talbot Fund, 111

INTERNATIONAL: UNESCO (Division of Creativity, Cultural Industries and Copyright), 111

INTERNATIONAL: UNESCO (International Fund for the Promotion of Culture), 112

INTERNATIONAL: UNESCO (Françoise Gallimard Prize), 112

International Center for Journalists, 112

International Consortium of Investigative Journalists, 114

International Quarterly, 114

International Reading Association, 114

International Research and Exchanges Board, 115

International Women's Media Foundation, 115

Intersection for the Arts, 116

The Iowa Review, 116

Iowa State University, 116

IRELAND: Fish Publishing, 116

IRELAND: Tyrone Guthrie Centre, 117

Irish American Cultural Institute, 117

Isle Royale National Park, 117

Italian Americana, 118

ITALY: Harvard University Center for Italian Renaissance Studies, 118

ITALY: Italian Cultural Institute, 118
Ivri-NASAWI, 118
Jacksonville State University, 119
Rona Jaffe Foundation, 119
Alice James Books, 119
JAPAN: Association of International Education, 120
JAPAN: The Japan Foundation, 120
JAPAN: Japan/U.S. Friendship Commission, 120
The Jerome Foundation, 121
Jewel Box Theatre, 121
Jewish Book Council, 121
Jewish Community Center of Cleveland, 121
The Lyndon Baines Johnson Foundation, 122
Johnson Publishing Company, 122
The Chester H. Jones Foundation, 122
James Jones Society, 122
Journal of the History of Ideas, 123
The Henry J. Kaiser Family Foundation, 123
Kalliope, a journal of women's art, 124
Kansas Arts Commission, 124
Kappa Tau Alpha, 124
Donald Keene Center of Japanese Culture, 125
The Kennedy Center, 125
John F. Kennedy Library Foundation, 127
Robert F. Kennedy Memorial Book & Journalism Awards, 128
Kent State University Press, 128
Kentucky Arts Council, 128
Kentucky Foundation for Women, 129
Kentucky Writers' Coalition, 129
Kiplinger Reporting Program, 129
Knight-Ridder Internships for Native American Journalists, 129
Knoxville Writers' Guild, 130
KOREA: Korean Culture and Arts Foundation, 130
The Koret Foundation, 130
Kosciuszko Foundation, 130
Lake Forest College, 131
Laughing Stork Press, 131
The Ledge, 131
Ledig House International Writers' Colony, 131
Leeway Foundation, 132
Lifebridge Foundation, 132
Lindbergh Foundation, 132
Literal Latte, 133
Literary Arts, 133
Gerald Loeb Awards, 133
The Loft Literary Center, 134
Longwood College, 134
Los Angeles Public Library, 135
Los Angeles Times Book Prizes, 135
Lotus Press, 135

Louisiana Division of the Arts, 135
Love Creek Productions, 135
Amy Lowell Poetry Travelling Scholarship, 136
Lukas Prize Project, 136
Lullwater Review, 136
Lynchburg College, 137
Lyndhurst Foundation, 137
Lynx House Press, 137
John D. and Catherine T. MacArthur Foundation, 137
John J. McCloy Fund, 138
MacDowell Colony, 138
The Madison Review, 138
Maine Community Foundation, 138
MAMMOTH press, 139
Manhattan Theatre Club, 139
Marin Arts Council, 139
Marlboro Review, 139
Maryland Library Association, 140
Maryland State Arts Council, 140
Massachusetts Cultural Council, 140
Massachusetts Institute of Technology, 141
Maui Writers Conference, 141
Medieval Academy of America, 141
MEXICO: U.S.-Mexico Fund for Culture, 142
Michener Center for Writers, 142
Michigan Council for the Arts. *See* ArtServe Michigan
Michigan Library Association, 143
Michigan Quarterly Review, 143
Michigan State University, 143
Middle East Report, 143
Midland Community Theatre, 144
Mid-List Press, 144
Midwest Theatre Network, 144
Milkweed Editions, 144
Mill Mountain Theatre, 145
Millay Colony for the Arts, 145
Milton Center, 145
Minnesota Monthly, 146
Minnesota State Arts Board, 146
Mississippi Arts Commission, 146
Mississippi Review, 146
The Missouri Review, 147
Mixed Blood Theatre Company, 147
Modern Language Association of America, 147
Money for Women/Barbara Deming Memorial Fund, 150
Montana Artist Refuge, 150
Montana Arts Council, 150
Montclair State University, 150
Monterey County Film Commission, 151
The Jenny McKean Moore Writers Program. *See* George Washington University

William Morris Society in the United States, 151

Mountain West Center for Regional Studies, 151

Mountaineers Books, 152

Mountains and Plains Booksellers Association, 152

Municipal Art Society of New York, 152

Museum of Science, 152

Mystery Writers of America, 153

National Arts Journalism Program, 153

National Association of Black Journalists, 153

National Association of Hispanic Journalists, 154

National Association of Science Writers, 154

National Book Awards, 154

National Council for the Social Studies, 155

National Education Association, 155

National Endowment for the Arts, 155

National Endowment for the Humanities, 156

National Foundation for Advancement in the Arts, 156

National Gallery of Art, 157

National Humanities Center, 157

National Institute for Labor Relations Research, 157

National League of American Pen Women, 158

National Museum of American Art, 158

National Poetry Series, 158

National Press Club, 158

National Press Foundation, 159

National Repertory Theatre Foundation, 159

National Science Foundation, 160

National Screenwriting Competition, 160

National Society of Arts and Letters, 160

National Space Club, 160

National Steinbeck Center, 161

National Women's Studies Association, 161

National Writers Association, 161

National Writers' United Service Organization, 162

Native American Journalists Association, 162

Native Writers' Circle of the Americas, 162

Naval Historical Center, 162

Nebraska Arts Council, 163

The Nebraska Review, 163

Negative Capability Magazine, 163

Nevada Arts Council, 164

New Dramatists, 164

New England Poetry Club, 164

New England Theatre Conference, 164

New Hampshire State Council on the Arts, 165

New Hampshire Writers and Publishers Project, 165

New Harmony Project, 165

New Issues Press, 166

New Jersey Council for the Humanities, 166

New Jersey State Council on the Arts, 166

New Letters Magazine, 167

New Millennium, 167

New Orleans Literary Festival. *See* Tennessee Williams/New Orleans Literary Festival

New Professional Theatre, 167

New Rivers Press, 168

New York Foundation for the Arts, 168

New York Mills Arts Retreat, 169

New York Public Library (Helen Bernstein Book Award), 169

New York Public Library (Center for Scholars and Writers), 169

New York State Archives Partnership Trust, 170

New York State Historical Association, 170

New York State Writers Institute, 170

New York Stories, 170

New York University Press, 171

The New Yorker, 171

New Yorkers Need to Know, 171

Newberry Library, 171

Newcomen Society in the United States, 172

Newspaper Guild, 172

Nieman Foundation, 173

Nimrod International Journal of Fiction & Poetry, 173

96 Inc., 173

Norcroft, 174

North American Conference on British Studies, 174

North Carolina Arts Council, 174

North Carolina Writers' Network, 174

Northeastern University, 175

Northern Kentucky University, 175

Northern Michigan University, 175

Northwood University, 176

NORWAY: Nordmanns-Forbundet, 176

NORWAY: NORLA-Norwegian Literature Abroad, 176

Nuclear Age Peace Foundation, 176

Oberlin College Press, 177

Scott O'Dell Award for Historical Fiction, 177

Oglebay Institute, 177

Ohio Arts Council, 177

Ohio State University Press, 178

Ohio University Press, 178

Ohioana Library Association, 178

Omicron World Entertainment, 179

Omohundro Institute of Early American History and Culture, 179

Eugene O'Neill Theater Center, 179

Oregon Arts Commission, 180

Organization of American Historians, 180

Orion Society, 182

Overseas Press Club of America, 182
Paintbrush, 183
The Paris Review, 183
Passager, 183
Passages North, 183
Passaic County Community College, 184
Alicia Patterson Foundation Fellowship
    Program, 184
Pavement Saw Press, 185
Pearl Editions, 185
PeaceWriting, 185
PEN American Center, 185
PEN Center USA West, 188
PEN New England, 189
PEN Northwest, 189
PEN/Faulkner Foundation, 189
Peninsula Community Foundation, 190
Pennsylvania Council on the Arts, 190
Penumbra Theatre Company, 190
Pew Center for Civic Journalism, 191
Pew Fellowships in the Arts, 191
Phi Beta Kappa, 191
Phillips Exeter Academy, 192
The Phillips Foundation, 192
Phoebe: A Journal of Literary Arts, 192
Pig Iron Press, 193
Pilgrim Project, 193
Pioneer Drama Service, 193
Pirate's Alley Faulkner Society, 193
Playboy Foundation, 194
Playboy Magazine, 194
Playhouse on the Square, 194
Plays on Tape, 194
The Playwright's Center, 195
Playwrights' Center of San Francisco, 195
Playwrights First, 195
The Playwrights' Theater, 196
Pleasant Company Publications, 196
Pleiades Press, 196
Ploughshares, 196
Pockets Magazine, 197
The Poetry Center & American Poetry
    Archives, 197
Poetry Magazine, 197
Poetry Society of America, 197
Poets Out Loud, 199
Poets & Writers, 199
Pope Foundation, 200
Potato Eyes Foundation, 200
Prairie Schooner, 200
Prince William Sound Community College, 200
Princess Grace Foundation-USA, 201
Princeton University, 201

Providence Anthenaeum, 201
PublishingOnline.com, 201
Publishing Triangle, 202
Puffin Foundation, 202
The Pulitzer Prizes, 203
Pulliam Journalism Fellowships, 203
Purdue University Press, 203
Pushcart Press, 203
Quality Paperback Book Club, 204
Quarterly Review of Literature, 204
Quarterly West, 204
Ragdale Foundation, 204
Sonia Raiziss-Giop Charitable Foundation, 205
Ayn Rand Institute, 205
Red Hen Press, 206
Red Rock Review, 206
The Refined Savage, 206
Rhode Island State Council on the Arts, 207
Richard Free Library, 207
Mary Roberts Rinehart Fund, 207
River City, 207
River Oak Review, 208
River Styx, 208
Robinson Jeffers Tor House Foundation, 208
Rockefeller Foundation, 208
Rocky Mountain National Park, 209
Rocky Mountain Student Theater Project, 209
Rome Arts and Community Center, 209
St. Martin's Press, 209
Salmon Run Press, 210
Salt Hill Journal, 210
Constance Saltonstall Foundation for the
    Arts, 210
San Francisco Chronicle, 210
San Jose Center for Poetry and Literature, 211
Sarabande Books, 211
Sasquatch Books, 211
Scholastic, 211
Schomburg Center for Research in Black
    Culture, 212
Schoolcraft College, 212
Scripps Howard Foundation, 212
Seattle Arts Commission, 214
Seattle Post-Intelligencer, 214
The Seattle Times, 214
Serpentine, 215
Seventeen Magazine, 215
The Sewanee Review, 215
Sewanee Writers' Conference, 215
Shenandoah, 216
Shenandoah International Playwrights
    Retreat, 216
Joan Shorenstein Center on the Press, Politics,
    and Public Policy, 216

Siena College, 217
Sierra Repertory Theatre, 217
Silverfish Review Press, 217
Sitka Center for Art and Ecology, 218
Slipstream, 218
Gibbs Smith, Publisher, 218
The Smithsonian Institution, 218
Snake Nation Press, 219
Soapstone, A Writing Retreat for Women, 219
Social Science Research Council, 219
Society of American Historians, 220
Society of American Travel Writers
	Foundation, 220
Society of Children's Book Writers, 221
Society for Historians of American Foreign
	Relations, 221
Society for the History of Technology, 221
Society for the Study of the Short Story, 222
Society for the Study of Social Problems, 222
Sons of the Republic of Texas, 222
Source Theatre Company, 223
South Carolina Academy of Authors, 223
South Carolina Arts Commission, 223
South Coast Repertory, 224
South Dakota Arts Council, 224
Southeastern Theatre Conference, 224
Southern Appalachian Repertory Theatre, 225
Southern Environmental Law Center, 225
Southern Historical Association, 225
Southern Oregon University, 226
The Southern Poetry Review, 226
The Southern Review, 226
The Southerner, 226
The Southwest Review, 227
Sow's Ear Poetry Review, 227
SPAIN: Cultural Office, 227
Spoon River Poetry Review, 228
Spuyten Duyvil, 228
SQUARE magazine, 228
STAGE (Society for Theatrical Artists'
	Guidance and Enhancement), 228
Stanford University (John S. Knight
	Fellowships), 229
Stanford University (Wallace E. Stegner
	Fellowships), 229
State Historical Society of Wisconsin, 229
Story Line Press, 230
STUDIO for Creative Inquiry, 230
Sundance Institute, 231
Sunset Center, 231
SWEDEN: Swedish Information Service, 231
SWITZERLAND: Château de Lavigny
	International Writers' Colony, 232
Syracuse University, 232

Syracuse University Press, 232
Tanne Foundation, 233
Mark Taper Forum, 233
John Templeton Foundation, 233
Tennessee Arts Commission, 233
Tennessee Writers Alliance, 234
Texas Institute of Letters, 234
Thanks Be to Grandmother Winifred
	Foundation, 235
Theatre Communications Group, 235
Theatre Conspiracy, 236
Thorngate Road, 236
Thunderbird Films, 236
James Thurber Residency Program, 236
tnr—The New Renaissance, 237
Towson State University, 237
Harry S. Truman Library Institute, 237
Truman State University Press, 238
Trustus Theatre, 238
Tulsa Library Trust, 238
Tupelo Press, 238
Ucross Foundation, 239
Ukiah Players Theatre, 239
Unicorn Theatre, 239
Unitarian Universalist Association, 239
United Daughters of the Confederacy, 240
UNITED KINGDOM: Boardman Tasker
	Charitable Trust, 240
UNITED KINGDOM: British Centre for
	Literary Translation, 240
UNITED KINGDOM: Forward Publishing, 240
UNITED KINGDOM: International Retreat for
	Writers at Hawthornden Castle, 241
UNITED KINGDOM: Orange Prize for
	Fiction, 241
UNITED KINGDOM: Reuters Foundation, 241
UNITED KINGDOM: Royal Society of
	Literature of the United Kingdom, 242
UNITED KINGDOM: Stand Magazine, 243
UNITED KINGDOM: Translators
	Association, 243
UNITED KINGDOM: University of
	Cambridge, 244
UNITED KINGDOM: University of East
	Anglia, 244
UNITED KINGDOM: University of
	Edinburgh, 245
UNITED KINGDOM: Wiener Library
	Unlimited, 245
United Methodist Communications, 245
United States Civil War Center, 246
United State Holocaust Memorial Museum, 246
United States Institute of Peace, 247
United States Naval Institute, 248
United States Trotting Association, 249

University of Akron Press, 249
University of Alabama, 249
University of Alabama in Huntsville, 250
University of Alaska Southeast Explorations, 250
University of Arizona, 250
University of Arkansas Press, 251
University of California at Irvine, 251
University of California, Los Angeles, 251
University of Chicago, 252
University of Evansville, 252
University of Georgia Press, 252
University of Hawai'i, 252
University of Hawai'i at Manoa, 253
University of Iowa Press, 253
University of Kansas, 253
University of Massachusetts, 254
University of Massachusetts Press, 254
University of Michigan, 254
University of Michigan Press, 255
University of Missouri, 255
University of Nebraska-Kearney Theatre, 255
University of Nebraska Press, 255
University of Nevada, 255
University of New Hampshire, 256
University of New Mexico, 256
University of North Texas Press, 256
University of Notre Dame Press, 256
University of Pittsburgh Press, 257
University of Rochester, 257
University of Southern California, 257
University of Texas. See Dobie-Paisano Project
University of Virginia, 258
University of Wisconsin Press, 258
Unterberg Poetry Center of the 92nd Street Y, 258
Urban Stages/Playwrights Preview Productions, 258
Utah Arts Council, 259
Utah State University Press, 259
The Valley Players, 259
Vermont Arts Council, 259
Vermont Studio Center, 260
Verse, 260
Very Special Arts, 260
Veterans of Foreign Wars National Headquarters, 260
Villa Montalvo, 261
Virginia Center for the Creative Arts, 261
Virginia College Stores Association, 261
Virginia Commonwealth University, 262
Virginia Quarterly Review, 262
Visiting Writers Program, 262
Ludwig Vogelstein Foundation, 262

Wagner College, 263
Lila Wallace-Reader's Digest Fund, 263
Edward Lewis Wallant Book Award, 263
Washington Center for Politics & Journalism, 263
Washington Independent Writers, 264
The Washington Post, 264
Washington State Arts Commission. See Artist Trust
Water-Stone, 264
Frank Waters Foundation, 265
Thomas J. Watson Foundation, 265
Wesleyan Writers Conference, 265
West Coast Ensemble, 266
West Virginia Commission on the Arts, 266
Western History Association, 266
Whetstone, 267
White Eagle Coffee Store Press, 267
White Pine Press, 268
Mrs. Giles Whiting Foundation, 268
Wichita Falls Backdoor Players, 268
Elie Wiesel Foundation for Humanity, 268
Tennessee Williams/New Orleans Literary Festival, 269
Woodrow Wilson International Center for Scholars, 269
Wind Publications, 269
Wisconsin Arts Board, 270
Wisconsin Institute for Creative Writing, 270
The Thomas Wolfe Society, 270
Carter G. Woodson Institute for Afro-American and African Studies, 270
Word Works, 271
World Hunger Year, 271
World Literature Today, 271
Writers Colony at Dairy Hollow, 271
The Writers Community, 272
Writers' Conferences & Centers, 272
Writer's Digest, 272
The Writer's Voice of the West Side YMCA, 273
Writers at Work, 273
WritersBlok, 274
Helene Wurlitzer Foundation of New Mexico, 274
Wyoming Council on the Arts, 274
Xeric Foundation, 274
Yaddo, 275
Yale University Library, 275
Yale University Press, 275
Young Adult Library Services Association, 275
Young Playwrights, 276
Zoetrope: All-Story, 276
Zone 3, 276

INDEX OF CATEGORIES

FICTION/Ⓕ

Edward Abbey Short Fiction Award, 32
Sam Adams Short Story Contest, 276
Aga Khan Prize for Fiction, 183
Nelson Algren Awards for Short Fiction, 53
American Literary Review Short Fiction Contest, 15
Ariadne Press Fiction Prize, 22
Isaac Asimov Award for Undergraduate Excellence in Science Fiction and Fantasy Writing, 25
Authors in the Park Short Story Contest, 30
Emily Clark Balch Awards, 262
Bananafish Short Story Contest, 31
Bellwether Prize, 162
Best First Private Eye Novel Contest, 209
Black Caucus of the American Library Association Literary Award, 36
James Tait Black Memorial Prizes, 245
Black Warrior Review, 36
Boston Review Short Story Contest, 38
Boulevard Short Fiction Contest for Emerging Writers, 39
Paul Bowles Prize for Short Fiction, 80
Bill Boyd Library Literature Award, 14
Brazos Bookstore Short Story Award, 234
Capricorn Novel Award, 273
Carolina Novel Award, 31
Raymond Carver Short Story Contest, 99
Willa Cather Fiction Prize, 94
Chekhov Award for Short Fiction, 64
Chelsea Award Competition, 52
Chicago Literary Awards, 21
Chinook Prize, 211
Mary Higgins Clark Mystery/Suspense Short Story Contest, 78
Community Writers Association International Writing Competition, 61
James Fenimore Cooper Prize for Historical Fiction, 220
A. E. Coppard Prize for Long Fiction, 267
Dana Awards, 66
Discover Great New Writers Award, 32
David Dornstein Memorial Creative Writing Contest for Young Adult Writers, 58
Jack Dyer Fiction Prize, 64
Eaton Literary Award, 74
Willard R. Espy Award, 77

Evergreen Chronicles Novella Contest, 77
Explorations Awards for Literature, 250
Ferro-Grumley Awards, 202
Robert L. Fish Memorial Award, 153
Fish Short Story Prize, 116
F. Scott Fitzgerald Literary Conference Short Story Contest, 79
H. E. Francis Award, 250
Miles Franklin Award, 30
Friends of American Writers Literary Adult Awards, 83
Georgia State University Review Writing Contest, 85
Glimmer Train Fiction Open, 89
Glimmer Train Short Story Award for New Writers, 89
Glimmer Train Very Short Fiction Award, 89
Jeanne Charpiot Goodheart Prize for Fiction, 216
Gulf Coast Short Story Prize, 91
Hackney Literary Awards, 35
Heartland Prizes, 53
HEArt Quarterly Short Fiction Contest, 93
Drue Heinz Literature Prize, 257
Hemingway Foundation/PEN Award, 189
Lorian Hemingway Short Story Competition, 94
Winifred Holtby Prize, 242
Hurston/Wright Award, 99
IHS Film & Fiction Scholarships, 104
Indiana Review Fiction Prize, 102
Inkwell Short Fiction Contest, 103
International Impac Dublin Literary Awards, 108
Iowa Short Fiction Award, 253
Charles Johnson Awards for Fiction and Poetry, 102
James Jones First Novel Fellowship, 122
Jesse H. Jones Award, 234
Janet Heidinger Kafka Prize, 257
Robert F. Kennedy Annual Book Award, 128
Kestrel Writing Contest, 78
Kiriyama Pacific Rim Book Prize, 51
Lawrence Foundation Prize, 143
Lesbian Writers' Fund Awards, 28
Literal Latte Fiction Award, 133
Mary McCarthy Prize in Short Fiction, 211
John H. McGinnis Memorial Awards, 227
Madison Review/Chris O'Malley Fiction Award, 138

Malahat Review Novella Prize, 46

Malice Domestic Best First Novel Contest, 209

Mentor Series Contest, 134

Milkweed National Fiction Prize, 144

Mississippi Review Prize in Fiction, 146

Jenny McKean Moore Writers Program, 85

National Steinbeck Center Short Story
Competition, 161

Nebraska Review Fiction Prize, 163

Negative Capability Short Fiction Award, 163

New Letters Fiction Prize, 167

New Voice Fiction Award, 273

New Writer Awards, 90

New York Stories Fiction Prize, 170

New York University Press Prize for Fiction, 171

North American Authors and Fiction Writers
Contest, 201

Novel Writing Contest, 161

Flannery O'Connor Award for Short Fiction, 252

Frank O'Connor Fiction Award, 69

Louis Littlecoon Oliver Memorial Award for
Short Fiction, 162

Omaha Prize, 30

Open Voice Scott Sommer Fiction Award, 273

Opus Magnum Discovery Awards, 49

Orange Prize for Fiction, 241

Kenneth Patchen Competition, 193

Paterson Fiction Prize, 184

William Peden Prize, 147

PEN/Faulkner Award for Fiction, 189

PEN/Naylor Working Writer Fellowship, 187

Peregrine Prize, 19

Julia Peterkin Award, 62

Playboy College Fiction Contest, 194

Katherine Anne Porter Prize for Fiction, 173

Premio Aztlán, 256

PRISM international Fiction Contest, 47

Pushcart Press Editors' Book Award, 203

Quarterly West Novella Competition, 204

Renwick-Sumerwell Award for Short Fiction, 64

Harold U. Ribalow Prize, 92

River City Writing Awards in Fiction, 207

River Oak-Hemingway Foundation Short Story
Contest, 207

Renee Sagiv Fiction Prize, 192

Louise E. Reynolds Memorial Fiction Award, 237

Salt Hill Journal Short Short Fiction Prize, 210

Marjory Bartlett Sanger Award, 21

Sandstone Prize in Short Fiction, 178

Serpentine Annual Short Story Contest, 215

Seventeen Magazine Fiction Contest, 215

Michael Shaara Award for Excellence in Civil War
Fiction, 246

John Simmons Short Fiction Award, 253

Elizabeth Simpson Smith Award, 52

Society for the Study of the Short Story Contest, 222

South Carolina Fiction Project, 223

The Southern Review/Louisiana State University
Short Fiction Award, 226

Stand Magazine's Short Story Competition, 243

Wallace E. Stegner Fellowships, 229

Richard Sullivan Prize in Fiction, 256

Tamarack Award, 146

Peter Taylor Prize for the Novel, 130

Three Oaks Prize for Fiction, 230

Reginald S. Tickner Writing Fellowship, 89

Tupelo Press Award for the Best Novel-Length
Fiction, 238

Steven Turner Award, 234

Mark Twain Award for Short Fiction, 206

Brenda Ueland Prose Prize, 264

UNESCO/Françoise Gallimard Prize, 112

Van Lier Fellowships, 24

Edward Lewis Wallant Book Award, 263

Cornelia Carhart Ward Fellowship, 232

Robert Penn Warren Prize for Fiction, 226

Frank Waters Voices of the Southwest Writing
Award, 265

Willamette Award, 56

Gertrude Johnson Williams Writing
Contest, 122

Wind Magazine Short Story Competition, 269

L. L. Winship/PEN New England Award, 189

Wisconsin Institute for Creative Writing
Fellowships, 270

Thomas Wolfe Fiction Prize, 175

Tobias Wolff Award for Fiction, 33

David T. K. Wong Fellowship, 244

Charles B. Wood Award for Distinguished
Writing, 48

Writers Exchange Program, 199

Writers of the Future Contest, 98

WritersBlok Short Story Contest, 274

Zoetrope Short Fiction Contest, 276

POETRY/Ⓟ

Akron Poetry Prize, 249

American Literary Review Poetry Contest, 15

American Poetry Review/Honickman First Book
Prize, 16

American Poets Fund, 1

Anamnesis Poetry Chapbook Award
Competition, 20

Anhinga Prize for Poetry, 20

Arvon International Poetry Competition, 106

Atlanta Review International Poetry Competition, 28
Backwaters Prize, 30
Emily Clark Balch Awards, 262
Barnard New Women Poets Prize, 32
Elinor Benedict Poetry Prize, 183
Beyond Baroque Poetry Chapbook Contest, 35
Black Warrior Review, 36
Blue Lynx Poetry Prize, 137
Bluestem Award, 76
James Boatwright III Prize for Poetry, 216
George Bogin Memorial Award, 198
Bordighera Bilingual Poetry Prize, 205
Boston Review Poetry Contest, 38
Bright Hill Press Poetry Award, 40
Brittingham Prize in Poetry, 258
Dorothy Brunsman Poetry Prize, 33
Bucknell Seminar for Younger Poets, 41
Witter Bynner Foundation for Poetry, 43
Gerald Cable Book Award, 217
Campbell Corner Poetry Prize, 44
Capricorn Poetry Award, 273
Hayden Carruth Award for Emerging Poets, 62
Cave Canem Poetry Prize, 49
Center for Book Arts Poetry Chapbook Competition, 50
Chelsea Award Competition, 52
Chicago Literary Awards, 21
John Ciardi Lifetime Achievement Award in Poetry, 118
John Ciardi Prize for Poetry, 35
Colorado Prize, 59
Betsy Colquitt Award for Poetry, 69
Community Writers Association International Writing Competition, 61
Bernard F. Conners Prize for Poetry, 183
Crab Orchard Award Series in Poetry, 64
Dana Awards, 66
Diane Decorah Memorial Award for Poetry, 162
Alice Fay Di Castagnola Award, 198
James Dickey Prize for Poetry, 80
"Discovery"/The Nation Poetry Contest: Joan Leiman Jacobson Poetry Prizes, 258
Milton Dorfman Poetry Prize, 209
Eckerd College Review Poetry Contest, 74
Sue Saniel Elkind Poetry Contest, 124
T. S. Eliot Prize, 238
Verna Emery Poetry Competition, 203
Maurice English Poetry Award, 76
Eve of St. Agnes Award in Poetry, 163
Explorations Awards for Literature, 250
Norma Farber First Book Award, 198
Field Poetry Prize, 177

49th Parallel Poetry Award, 33
Forward Poetry Prizes, 240
Four Way Award Series in Poetry, 83
Four Way Books Intro Prize in Poetry, 83
Robert Frost Poetry Award, 84
Georgia State University Review Writing Contest, 85
John Gilgun Poetry Award, 99
Allen Ginsberg Poetry Award, 184
Gival Press Chapbook Competition, 89
Glimmer Train Poetry Open, 89
Green Rose Prize in Poetry, 166
Greg Grummer Poetry Award, 192
Gulf Coast Poetry Prize, 91
Violet Reed Haas Poetry Prize, 219
Hackney Literary Awards, 35
Hanks Chapbook Award, 82
Beatrice Hawley Award, 119
HEArt Quarterly Poetry Contest, 93
ICARUS Poetry Competition, 99
Inkwell Poetry Competition, 103
Iowa Poetry Prizes, 253
IRA Lee Bennett Hopkins Promising Poet Award, 114
Randall Jarrell Poetry Prize, 174
Charles Johnson Awards for Fiction and Poetry, 102
Juniper Prize, 254
Barbara Mandigo Kelly Peace Poetry Awards, 176
Jane Kenyon Award, 165
Jane Kenyon Chapbook Award, 119
Jane Kenyon Poetry Prize, 264
Kestrel Writing Contest, 78
Harold Morton Landon Translation Award, 1
James Laughlin Award, 1
Ledge Annual Poetry Chapbook Competition, 131
Ledge Poetry Award, 131
Nikolaus Lenau Prize, 86
Lesbian Writers' Fund Awards, 28
Larry Levis Editor's Prize in Poetry, 147
Levis Poetry Prize, 83
Levis Reading Prize, 262
Ruth Lilly Poetry Fellowships, 197
Literal Latte Poetry Award, 133
Frances Locke Memorial Poetry Award, 35
Loft Awards in Poetry, 134
Amy Lowell Poetry Travelling Scholarship, 136
Lullwater Prize for Poetry, 136
Lyric Poetry Award, 198
MacGuffin National Poet Hunt, 212
Naomi Long Madgett Poetry Award, 135
Madison Review/Phyllis Smart Young Prize in Poetry, 138

Magellan Prize, 42

Malahat Review Long Poem Prize, 45

S. J. Marks Memorial Poetry Prize, 16

Marlboro Review Poetry Prize, 139

Lenore Marshall Poetry Prize, 2

Tom McAfee Discovery Feature in Poetry, 147

Elise G. Mead Fellowship, 232

Lucille Medwick Memorial Award, 198

Mentor Series Contest, 134

Jim Wayne Miller Prize in Poetry, 129

Vassar Miller Prize in Poetry, 256

Mississippi Review Prize in Poetry, 146

Jenny McKean Moore Writers Program, 85

Marianne Moore Poetry Prize, 94

Samuel French Morse Poetry Prize, 175

Kathryn A. Morton Prize in Poetry, 211

Mudfish Poetry Prize, 39

National Poetry Competition, 122

National Poetry Series, 158

Nebraska Review Poetry Prize, 163

Howard Nemerov Sonnet Award, 82

Pablo Neruda Prize for Poetry, 173

New England/New York Award, 119

New Issues First Book of Poetry Prize, 166

New Letters Poetry Prize, 167

New Voice Poetry Award, 273

New Writer Awards, 90

New York University Press Prize for Poetry, 171

Frank O'Hara Ward Chapbook Competition, 235

Ohio State University Press/The Journal Award in Poetry, 178

Ohioana Poetry Award/Helen and Laura Krout Memorial, 179

Open Voice Poetry Award, 273

Natalie Ornish Award, 234

Guy Owen Poetry Prize, 226

William and Kingman Page Poetry Book Award, 200

Passager Poetry Contest, 183

Kenneth Patchen Competition, 193

Paterson Poetry Prize, 184

Paumanok Poetry Award, 262

Pavement Saw Press Transcontinental Poetry Award, 185

Pearl Poetry Prize, 185

PEN/Joyce Osterweil Award for Poetry, 187

PEN/Voelcker Award for Poetry, 188

Peregrine Prize, 19

Julia Peterkin Award, 62

Philbrick Poetry Award, 201

Poetry Center Book Award, 197

Poetry Center Prize, 57

Poetry Magazine Awards, 197

Poets Out Loud Prize, 199

Felix Pollak Prize in Poetry, 258

Ezra Pound Poetry Award, 183

Quarterly Review of Literature Poetry Book Awards, 204

Rainmaker Awards in Poetry, 276

Raiziss/de Palchi Translation Award, 2

Red Rock Poetry Award, 206

Refined Savage Poetry Competition, 206

River Oak Poetry Contest, 207

River Styx International Poetry Contest, 208

Robinson Jeffers Tor House Foundation Poetry Prize, 207

Nicholas Roerich Poetry Prize, 230

Salmon Run National Poetry Book Award, 210

Salt Hill Journal Poetry Prize, 210

Benjamin Saltman Poetry Award, 206

San Jose Center for Poetry and Literature Poetry Prize, 211

Ernest Sandeen Prize in Poetry, 256

Say the Word National Poetry Competition, 75

Jerome J. Shestack Poetry Prizes, 16

Slapering Hol Press Chapbook Competition, 98

Slipstream Annual Poetry Chapbook Contest, 218

Peregrine Smith Poetry Competition, 218

Richard Snyder Poetry Award, 24

Sow's Ear Chapbook Competition, 227

Sow's Ear Poetry Competition, 227

Spoon River Poetry Review Editor's Prize, 228

Spuyten Duyvil Book Award, 228

Stand Magazine's Poetry Competition, 243

Ann Stanford Poetry Prize, 257

Agnes Lynch Starrett Prize, 257

Wallace E. Stegner Fellowships, 229

Elizabeth Matchett Stover Memorial Award, 227

Hollis Summers Poetry Prize, 178

May Swenson Poetry Award, 259

Allen Tate Memorial Award, 269

Reginald S. Tickner Writing Fellowship, 89

Tnr Poetry Award, 237

Lena-Miles Wever Todd Poetry Series, 196

Kate Tufts Discovery Award, 56

Kingsley Tufts Poetry Award, 56

Tupelo Press Poetry Award, 238

Daniel Varoujan Prize, 164

Verse Prize, 260

Villa Montalvo Biennial Poetry Competition, 261

Chad Walsh Poetry Award, 33

Robert Penn Warren Awards, 21

Robert Penn Warren Poetry Prize, 65

Washington Prize, 271

White Pine Press Poetry Prize, 268

Walt Whitman Award, 2
Stan and Tom Wick Poetry Prize, 128
Richard Wilbur Award, 252
Willamette Award, 56
William Carlos Williams Award, 198
Robert H. Winner Memorial Award, 198
Wisconsin Institute for Creative Writing
  Fellowships, 270
Charles B. Wood Award for Distinguished
  Writing, 48
Writers Exchange Program, 199
Yale Series of Younger Poets, 275

DRAMA/Ⓓ

ACT/Hedgebrook Women Playwrights Festival, 1
American Shorts Contest, 80
Anchorage Press Theatre for Youth Playwriting
  Award, 125
Annual Backdoor Theatre New Play Project, 268
AT&T East West Players New Voices Playwriting
  Competition, 74
Auricle Award, 194
Roy Barker Playwriting Prize, 209
Beverly Hill Theatre Guild Plays for Children's
  Theatre Competition, 34
Susan Smith Blackburn Prize, 36
Border Playwrights Project, 37
Boulder Museum of Contemporary Art One-Act
  Festival, 39
Jane Chambers Playwriting Award, 126
Robert Chesley Award for Lesbian and Gay
  Playwriting, 202
Clauder Competition for Excellence in
  Playwriting, 57
David Mark Cohen National Playwriting
  Award, 125
Cornerstone Dramaturgy and Development
  Project, 190
Cunningham Prize for Playwriting, 68
Dayton Playhouse FutureFest, 66
DramaRama, 195
Emerging Playwright Award, 258
Ensemble Studio Theatre/Alfred P. Sloan
  Foundation Science & Technology Project, 76
Shubert Fendrich Memorial Playwriting
  Contest, 193
Festival of Firsts Playwriting Competition, 231
Florida Playwrights' Process, 80
Fourth Freedom Forum Playwriting Award, 125
Miles Franklin Award, 30
Full-Length Play Competition, 266
John Gassner Memorial Playwriting
  Competition, 164
Charles M. Getchell New Play Award, 224

Goshen College Peace Playwriting Contest, 90
Great Plains Play Contest, 253
Great Platte River Playwrights' Festival, 255
Paul Green Playwrights Prize, 174
Lorraine Hansberry Award, 125
Aurand Harris Children's Theatre Fellowships, 54
Aurand Harris Memorial Playwriting
  Competition, 165
Julie Harris Playwright Competition, 34
High School Playwriting Contest, 31
Hispanic Playwrights Project, 224
Hudson River Classics Annual Playwriting
  Contest, 98
IHS Film & Fiction Scholarships, 104
International Herald Tribune/Singapore
  Repertory Theatre International Playwriting
  Competition, 111
Janusfest, 249
Jerome Playwright-in-Residence Fellowships, 195
Jewel Box Theatre Playwriting Award, 121
KC/ACTF College Musical Theatre Award, 125
KC/ACTF Sí TV Playwriting Award, 126
Marc A. Klein Playwriting Award, 48
Lee Korf Playwriting Awards, 52
Kumu Kahua Playwriting Contest, 253
Frank K. and Janet Levin Award, 57
McKnight Fellowship, 195
McLaren Memorial Comedy Playwriting
  Competition, 144
Manhattan Theatre Club Playwriting
  Fellowships, 139
Maxim Mazumdar New Play Competition, 5
Midwest Theatre Network Original Play
  Competition/Rochester Playwright Festival, 144
Mill Mountain Theatre New Play Competition, 145
Musical Stairs Competition, 266
George Jean Nathan Award for Dramatic
  Criticism, 63
National AIDS Fund CFDA-Vogue Initiative
  Award for Playwriting, 126
National Children's Theatre Festival, 3
National Hispanic Playwriting Contest, 22
National New Play Award, 99
National One-Act Playwriting Contest, 72
National Play Award, 159
National Playwrights' Award, 239
National Playwrights Conference, 179
National Student Playwriting Award, 126
National Ten-Minute Play Contest, 4
National Theatre Artist Residency Program, 235
National Youth Theatre Playwriting
  Competition, 102
NEA/TCG Theatre Residency Program for
  Playwrights, 235

Dr. Henry and Lillian Nesburn Award, 34

New American Comedy Festival, 239

New Directors/New Works, 72

New Dramatists, 164

New Harmony Project, 165

New Plays Festival, 57

New Playwrights' Program, 249

New Professional Theatre Writers Festival, 167

New Works for a New World, 254

Onassis International Prize, 110

Mildred and Albert Panowski Playwriting Award, 175

PEN/Laura Pels Foundation Awards for Drama, 187

Peterson Emerging Playwright Competition, 49

Robert J. Pickering Award for Playwriting Excellence, 58

Pilgrim Project, 193

Playhouse on the Square New Play Competition, 194

PlayLabs, 195

Plays for the 21st Century, 196

Playwright Discovery Award, 260

Playwrights First Award, 195

Francesca Primus Prize, 68

Princess Grace Awards Playwright Fellowship, 201

Promising Playwright Award, 58

Lois and Richard Rosenthal New Play Prize, 55

Janet and Maxwell Salter Award, 34

Morton R. Sarett Memorial Award, 255

Shenandoah International Playwrights Retreat, 216

Reva Shiner Full-Length Play Contest, 36

Short Play Awards Program, 126

Short Play Festival, 135

Siena College International Playwrights' Competition, 217

Dorothy Silver Playwriting Competition, 121

Jean Kennedy Smith Playwriting Award for the Best Play Written on the Theme of Disability, 126

Source Theatre Company Literary Prize, 223

Southern Appalachian Playwrights' Conference, 225

Southern Playwrights Competition (Center for Southern Studies), 51

Southern Playwrights Competition, 119

STAGE Festival of New Plays, 228

Stanley Drama Award, 263

Sundance Institute Feature Film Program, 231

Sundance Institute Theater Laboratory, 231

Mark Taper Forum, 233

Marvin Taylor Playwriting Award, 217

TCG Extended Collaboration Grants, 235

Ten-Minute Play Festival, 126

Theatre Conspiracy Annual New Play Contest, 235

TheatreFest Regional Playwriting Contest, 150

Towngate Theatre Playwriting Competition, 177

Trustus Playwrights' Festival, 238

Mark Twain Comedy Playwriting Award, 126

UBC Creative Writing Residency Prize in Stageplay, 47

U.S. West TheatreFest, 68

Vermont Playwrights Award, 259

Theodore Ward Prize for Playwriting, 59

"We Don't Need No Stinkin' Dramas" Playwriting Contest, 147

Tennessee Williams/New Orleans Literary Festival One-Act Play Competition, 269

Year-End-Series New Play Festival, 175

Young Playwrights Festival, 276

Yukon Pacific New Play Award, 200

Anna Zornio Memorial Children's Theatre Playwriting Award, 256

JOURNALISM/ⓙ

AAAS Science Journalism Awards, 8

American Legion Fourth Estate Award, 13

APSA Congressional Fellowships Program, 16

ASCAP-Deems Taylor Awards, 18

Asia Fellowships, 252

Associated Press Summer Minority Internship Program, 25

Banff Centre Creative Nonfiction and Cultural Journalism Program, 45

Whitman Bassow Award, 182

James K. Batten Award for Excellence in Civic Journalism, 191

Burton R. Benjamin Fellowship in Broadcast Journalism, 254

Robert Spiers Benjamin Award, 182

Worth Bingham Prize, 112

Blethen Family Newspaper Internship Program for Minorities, 214

Robert Bosch Foundation Fellowship Program, 38

Hal Boyle Award, 182

Broadcasters Awards, 249

Heywood Broun Award, 172

Daniel B. Burke Fellowship, 254

Arthur F. Burns Fellowship, 113

Business/Economic Reporting/William Brewster Styles Award, 212

Maria Moors Cabot Prizes, 60

Rosalynn Carter Fellowships for Mental Health Journalism, 48

Harry Chapin Media Awards, 271

Chicago Reporter Minority Fellowship in Urban Journalism, 53

Evert Clark Award, 159

Commentary Award, 212

Bob Considine Award, 182

Courage in Journalism Award, 115

Ed Cunningham Memorial Award, 182

Dart Award, 143

Jon Davidoff Scholarships for Journalists, 265

Joe and Laurie Dine Award, 182

Everett McKinley Dirksen Award for Distinguished Reporting of Congress, 159

Dow Jones Newspaper Fund Business Reporting Program, 71

Editorial Writing/Walker Stone Award, 213

Environmental Reporting/Edward J. Meeman Awards, 213

Malcolm Forbes Award, 182

Ford Environmental Journalism Fellowships, 113

Ford Transportation Technology Fellowship, 254

Morton Frank Award, 182

French-American Foundation Journalism Fellowship Program, 83

Fund for Investigative Journalism Prize, 84

Dick Goldensohn Fund, 90

Goldsmith Prize for Investigative Reporting, 216

James T. Grady-James H. Stack Award for Interpreting Chemistry for the Public, 9

Senator John Heinz Fellowship in Environmental Reporting, 113

O. Henry Award, 234

John Hervey Awards for Writing Excellence, 249

High School Journalism Teacher of the Year, 71

High School Workshop Writing Competition, 71

Sidney Hillman Foundation Prize Awards, 95

Roy W. Howard National Reporting Competition, 213

Human Interest/Ernie Pyle Writing Award, 213

ICFJ-KKC Journalism Fellowship in Japan, 113

ICIJ Award for Outstanding International Investigative Reporting, 114

Inter American Press Association Scholarship Fund, 105

Jefferson Fellowship Program, 73

Journalists in Europe, 109

Robert F. Kennedy Journalism Awards for Outstanding Coverage of the Problems of the Disadvantaged, 128

Donald E. Keyhoe Journalism Award, 85

Kiplinger Reporting Program, 129

John S. Knight Fellowships, 229

Knight Fellowships in Specialty Reporting, 254

Knight International Press Fellowships, 113

Knight Science Journalism Fellowships, 141

Knight-Bagehot Fellowship Program in Economics and Business Journalism, 60

Knight-Ridder Internships for Native American Journalists, 129

Livingston Awards for Young Journalists, 254

Gerald Loeb Awards for Distinguished Business and Financial Journalism, 133

Bobbi McCallum Memorial Scholarship, 214

John J. McCloy Fund, 138

Missouri Lifestyle Journalism Awards, 255

Felix Morley Journalism Competition, 105

Robert T. Morse Writers Award, 17

Frank Luther Mott-Kappa Tau Alpha Journalism and Mass Communication Research Award, 124

Edward R. Murrow Fellowship, 63

George Jean Nathan Award for Dramatic Criticism, 63

National Arts Journalism Program, 153

National Association of Black Journalists, 153

National Association of Hispanic Journalists, 154

National Awards for Education Reporting, 74

National Fellowship in Education Reporting, 74

National Press Club Scholarship for Minorities in Journalism, 158

Native American Journalists Association, 162

New York Public Library Helen Bernstein Book Award for Excellence in Journalism, 169

New Yorkers Need to Know Prizes for Journalism, 171

Lucius W. Nieman Fellowships for Journalists, 173

Alicia Patterson Foundation Fellowship Program, 184

Ethel Payne Fellowship, 154

Leonard M. Perryman Communications Scholarship for Ethnic Minority Students, 245

Phillips Foundation Journalism Fellowship Program, 192

Politics & Journalism Semester, 263

Pope Foundation Journalism Awards, 200

Public Policy Journalism Fellowships, 254

Public Service Reporting/Roy W. Howard Awards, 213

Pulliam Journalism Fellowships, 203

Reuters Fellowships in Medical Journalism, 241

Reuters-IUCN Media Awards, 242

Reuters Oxford University Fellowships, 242

Madeline Dane Ross Award, 182

William B. Ruggles Journalism Scholarship, 157

Cornelius Ryan Award, 182

San Francisco Chronicle Internships, 210

Science in Society Journalism Awards, 154

Ted Scripps Environmental Fellowship Program, 50

Scripps Howard Foundation Internships, 213

Seattle Times Summer Newsroom Internships, 214

Philip Shehadi New Writers Award, 143

Spanish Language Fellowships, 159

Sports Reporting Fellowship, 254

Stoody-West Fellowship in Religious Journalism, 245

Lowell Thomas Travel Journalist Awards, 220

Time-Warner Fellowship, 254

Lawrence Wade Journalism Fellowship, 95

Stanley Walker Award, 234

Mike Wallace Fellowship in Investigative Reporting, 254

Washington Post Summer News Program, 264

Edward Weintal Prize for Diplomatic Reporting, 105

GENERAL NONFICTION / Ⓝ

AAR Research Grants Program, 7

ABC-Clio America: History and Life Award, 180

Herbert Baxter Adams Prize, 10

Age Studies Award, 87

Amy Foundation Writing Awards, 20

Anthem Essay Contest, 205

Vincent Astor Memorial Leadership Essay Contest, 248

Robert G. Athearn Book Award, 266

Atlas Shrugged Essay Contest, 205

Bancroft Prizes, 59

Mrs. Simon Baruch University Award, 240

George Louis Beer Prize, 11

Berkshire Conference of Women Historians Publication Awards, 34

Myrna Bernath Book Award, 221

Stuart L. Bernath Book Prize, 221

Albert J. Beveridge Award, 11

Ray Allen Billington Prize, 180

Binkley-Stephenson Award, 180

Paul Birdsall Prize, 11

James Tait Black Memorial Prizes, 245

Black Caucus of the American Library Association Literary Awards, 36

Herbert Eugene Bolton Memorial Prize, 61

James Henry Breasted Prize, 11

Philip Brett Award, 15

Frank S. and Elizabeth D. Brewer Prize, 18

British Council Prize, 174

Bross Prize, 131

John Nicholas Brown Prize, 141

Arleigh Burke Essay Contest, 248

Campbell Corner Essay Prize, 44

Capricorn Nonfiction Award, 273

Vernon Carstensen Award, 4

Thomas H. Carter Prize for the Essay, 216

Caughey Western History Association Prize, 266

Chinook Prize, 211

James L. Clifford Prize, 18

Coast Guard Essay Contest, 248

Morton N. Cohen Award, 147

Carr P. Collins Award, 234

Albert B. Corey Prize in Canadian-American Relations, 11

Avery O. Craven Award, 180

Merle Curti Award, 180

Cushwa Center for the Study of American Catholicism Publication Awards, 65

Watson Davis and Helen Miles Davis Prize, 96

Dexter Prize, 221

Annie Dillard Award for Nonfiction, 33

Frederick Douglass Book Prize, 88

John H. Dunning Prize, 11

Eaton Literary Award, 74

Educator's Award, 67

Everett Edwards Award, 4

Alfred Einstein Award, 15

Charles C. Eldredge Prize, 158

Ernest M. Eller Prize in Naval History, 162

Van Courtlandt Elliott Prize, 141

Ralph Waldo Emerson Award, 191

Enlisted Essay Contest, 248

Willard R. Espy Award, 77

Evans Biography Award, 151

Evans Handcart Prize, 151

Exemplary Papers in Humility Theology Program, 233

John K. Fairbank Prize in East Asian History, 11

Herbert Feis Award, 11

Morris D. Forkosch Prize, 123

Morris O. Forkosch Prize, 11

The Fountainhead Essay Contest, 205

Dixon Ryan Fox Manuscript Prize of the New York State Historical Association, 170

Fraenkel Prize in Contemporary History, 245

Friends of the Dallas Public Library Award, 234

Christian Gauss Award, 191

Lionel Gelber Prize, 45

Leo Gershoy Award, 12

Robert H. Goddard Historical Essay Award, 160

Goldsmith Book Prize, 216

Louis Gottschalk Prize, 18

Judy Grahn Award, 202

Guideposts Young Writers Contest, 91

John Guyon Literary Nonfiction Prize, 64

John Whitney Hall Book Prize, 26

Clarence H. Haring Prize, 12

Haskins Medal, 142

Ellis W. Hawley Prize, 180

Heartland Prizes, 53

Hendricks Manuscript Award, 84

O. Henry Award, 234

Sidney Hillman Foundation Prize Awards, 95

History of Women in Science Prize, 96

International League of Antiquarian Booksellers Bibliography Prize, 108

International Navies Essay Contest, 248

W. Turrentine Jackson Award, 267

J. Franklin Jameson Prize, 12

Jamestown Prize, 179

Kaiser Media Fellowships in Health, 123

Kaiser Media Internships, 123

Kaiser/National Press Foundation Media Mini-Fellowships, 123

Joan Kelly Memorial Prize in Women's History, 12

Robert F. Kennedy Annual Book Award, 128

Otto Kinkeldey Award, 16

Kiriyama Pacific Rim Book Prize, 51

Katherine Singer Kovacs Prize, 147

Dorothea Lange-Paul Taylor Prize, 50

Waldo G. Leland Prize, 12

Richard W. Leopold Prize, 181

Joseph Levenson Book Prizes, 26

Literal Latte Roy T. Ames Essay Awards, 133

Littleton-Griswold Prize, 12

James Russell Lowell Prize, 147

J. Anthony Lukas Prize, 136

J. Anthony Lukas Work-in-Progress Award, 136

Mark Lynton History Prize, 136

John H. McGinnis Memorial Awards, 227

Maclean-Hunter Endowment Award for Literary Nonfiction, 46

Marine Corps Essay Contest, 249

Beryl Markham Prize for Creative Nonfiction, 230

Helen and Howard R. Marraro Prize, 12

Howard R. Marraro Prize, 148

Horace Samuel & Marion Galbraith Merrill Travel Grants in Twentieth-Century American Political History, 181

Kenneth W. Mildenberger Prize, 148

C. Wright Mills Award, 222

H. L. Mitchell Award, 225

Eric Mitchell Prize, 110

Mitchell Prize for the History of Art, 110

Modern Language Association Prize for a Distinguished Bibliography, 148

Modern Language Association Prize for a Distinguished Scholarly Edition, 148

Modern Language Association Prize for a First Book, 148

Modern Language Association Prize for Independent Scholars, 148

Frank Luther Mott-Kappa Tau Alpha Journalism and Mass Communication Research Award, 124

National Jesuit Book Award Competition, 27

Frederic W. Ness Book Award, 26

Allan Nevins Prize, 220

New Jersey Council for the Humanities Book Award, 166

New Letters Creative Nonfiction Prize, 167

New Voice Nonfiction Award, 273

New York Public Library Helen Bernstein Award for Excellence in Journalism, 169

Thomas Newcomen Book Award in Business History, 172

North American Indian Prose Award, 255

Eli M. Oboler Memorial Award, 14

Open Voice Nonfiction Award, 273

Opus Magnum Discovery Awards, 49

Frank Lawrence and Harriet Chappell Owsley Award, 225

Robert Troup Paine Prize, 92

Francis Parkman Prize, 220

Louis Pelzer Memorial Award, 181

PEN/Martha Albrand Award for the Art of the Memoir, 186

PEN/Martha Albrand Award for First Nonfiction, 186

PEN/Architectural Digest Award for Literary Writing on the Visual Arts, 186

PEN/Jerard Fund Award, 186

PEN/Spielvogel-Diamonstein Award for the Art of the Essay, 188

Pfizer Award, 96

Phi Beta Kappa Award in Science, 191

Paul A. Pisk Prize, 16

Forest C. Pogue Prize, 75

Colin L. Powell Joint Warfighting Essay Contest, 249

Premio Anual de Ensayo Literario Hispanoamericano Lya Kostakowsky, 108

Premio del Rey, 11

Pushcart Press Editors' Book Award, 203

James A. Rawley Prize, 181

Rear Admiral John D. Hayes Pre-Doctoral Fellowship, 163

Phillip D. Reed Memorial Award for Outstanding Writing on the Southern Environment, 225

James Harvey Robinson Prize, 12

Elliott Rudwick Prize, 181

Theodore Saloutos Award, 4

Barbara Savage/"Miles from Nowhere" Memorial Award, 152

Aldo and Jeanne Scaglione Prize for Comparative Literary Studies, 149

Aldo and Jeanne Scaglione Prize for French and Francophone Studies, 149

Aldo and Jeanne Scaglione Prize for Studies in Germanic Languages and Literatures, 149

Aldo and Jeanne Scaglione Prize for Studies in Slavic Languages and Literatures, 149

Aldo and Jeanne Scaglione Prize in Italian Literary Studies, 148

Henry and Ida Schuman Prize, 96

Peter Seaborg Award for Civil War Nonfiction, 246

Mina P. Shaughnessy Prize, 150

Randy Shilts Award, 202

Frances Butler Simpkins Award, 225

John Ben Snow Foundation Prize, 174

John Ben Snow Prize, 232

Society for the History of Technology Popular Book Prize, 222

Stork Search, 131

Charles S. Sydnor Prize, 225

Amaury Talbot Fund Annual Prize, 111

Texas History Essay Contest, 223

Harry S. Truman Book Award, 237

Frederick Jackson Turner Award, 182

Brenda Ueland Prose Prize, 264

Vice Admiral Edwin B. Hooper Research Grant, 163

Voice of Democracy Audio Essay Competition, 260

Wesley-Logan Prize, 12

Elie Wiesel Prize in Ethics Essay Contest, 268

Kemper and Leila Williams Prize in Louisiana History, 96

Writing Award in Physics and Astronomy, 13

Lamar York Prize for Nonfiction, 52

CHILDREN'S LITERATURE/©

AJL Sydney Taylor Book Awards, 27

AJL Sydney Taylor Manuscript Award, 27

John and Patricia Beatty Award, 43

Beverly Hills Theatre Guild Plays for Children's Theatre Competition, 34

Book Publishers of Texas Award, 234

Boston Globe-Horn Book Awards for Excellence in Children's Literature, 97

Children's Literature Association Research Fellowships and Scholarships, 54

Marguerite de Angeli Prize, 31

Delacorte Press Prize for a First Young Adult Novel, 32

Margaret A. Edwards Award, 275

Joan Fassler Memorial Book Award, 27

Friends of American Writers Young People's Literature Award, 83

Aurand Harris Children's Theatre Fellowships, 54

Aurand Harris Memorial Playwriting Competition, 165

Highlights for Children Fiction Contest, 95

Highlights Foundation Scholarship Program, 95

International Reading Association Children's Book Awards, 114

IRA Lee Bennett Hopkins Promising Poet Award, 114

Barbara Karlin Grant, 221

Ezra Jack Keats/Kerlan Collection Memorial Fellowship, 54

Ezra Jack Keats New Writer Award, 73

Coretta Scott King Award, 14

Coretta Scott King/John Steptoe Award for New Talent, 14

Anne Spencer Lindbergh Prize in Children's Literature, 132

Milkweed Prize for Children's Literature, 145

National Children's Theatre Festival, 3

John Newbery Medal, 28

Scott O'Dell Award for Historical Fiction, 177

Ohioana Award for Children's Literature/Alice Wood Memorial Award, 178

Paterson Prize for Books for Young People, 184

PEN/Norma Klein Award, 187

PEN/Naylor Working Writer Fellowship, 187

Pockets Fiction Writing Contest, 197

QPBC/Estés International Storyteller Prize, 204

Pleasant T. Rowland Prize for Fiction, 196

Society of Children's Book Writers Work-in-Progress Grants, 221

Joan G. Sugarman Children's Book Award, 264

Teddy Book Award, 29

UNESCO Prize for Children's and Young People's Literature in the Service of Tolerance, 111

Paul A. Witty Short Story Award, 115

Anna Zornio Memorial Children's Theatre Playwriting Award, 256

TRANSLATION/Ⓣ

ALTA National Translation Award, 15

Arabic Translation Awards, 251

ASF Translation Prize, 17

ATA German Literary Translation Prize, 19

Aurora Borealis Prize for Outstanding Translation of Fiction Literature, 107

Aurora Borealis Prize for Outstanding Translation of Nonfiction Literature, 107

Bordighera Bilingual Poetry Prize, 205

British Centre for Literary Translation Awards, 240

Pierre-François Caillé-FIT Foundation, 107

Pierre-François Caillé Memorial Medal, 107

Karel Capek Medal, 107

Finnish Literature Information Center, 79

John Florio Prize, 243

Soeurette Diehl Fraser Award, 234

French-American Foundation Translation Prize, 83

Lewis Galantiere Prize, 19

Italian Government Translation Prizes and Grants, 118

Japan-U.S. Friendship Commission Prize for the Translation of Japanese Literature, 125

Gregory Kolovakos Award, 185

Korean Literature Translation Award, 130

Harold Morton Landon Translation Award, 1

Astrid Lindgren Translation Prize, 107

Scott Moncrieff Prize, 243

National Endowment for the Arts Translation Project Grants, 156

Nordmanns-Forbundet, 176

NORLA-Norwegian Literature Abroad, 176

PEN Award for Poetry in Translation, 186

PEN/Book-of-the-Month Club Translation Prize, 186

Renato Poggioli Translation Award, 188

Premio Valle Inclan, 244

Raiziss/de Palchi Translation Award, 2

A. K. Ramanujan Book Prize for Translation, 26

Sasakawa Prize, 243

Aldo and Jeanne Scaglione Prize for Literary Translation, 149

Schlegel-Tieck Prize, 243

Bernard Shaw Prize, 243

Inger Sjöberg Award, 17

Snorri Sturluson Icelandic Fellowships, 100

Teixeira-Gomes Prize, 244

Translation Project Grants,

Vondel Translation Prize, 244

SCREENWRITING/Ⓢ

American Dreamer Script Competition, 9

Austin Film Festival Screenwriters Competition, 29

Chesterfield Film Company/Writers' Film Project, 53

Christopher Columbus Screenplay Discovery Awards, 49

Cyclone Productions Screenwriters Project, 65

Walt Disney Studios Fellowship Program, 69

Final Draft International Screenwriting Competition, 78

Humanitas Prize, 98

IHS Film & Fiction Scholarships, 104

Low-Budget Feature Project, 65

Maui Writers Conference National Screenwriting Competition, 141

Monterey County Film Commission Screenwriting Competition, 151

National Screenwriting Competition, 160

New Century Writer Awards, 179

Don and Gee Nicholl Screenwriting Fellowships, 2

SQUARE magazine Screenwriting Award, 228

SQUARE magazine Television Award, 228

Sundance Institute Feature Film Project, 231

Thunderbird Films Annual Screenplay Competition, 235

MULTIPLE LISTING/Ⓜ

Alligator Juniper Writing Contest, 5

American Awards for Literature International Award, 62

Anisfield-Wolf Book Awards, 57

Artist Trust Fellowships, 23

Artist Trust GAP (Grants for Artist Projects) Program, 23

Artists in Michigan Program, 24

Arts & Letters Prizes Competition, 23

AWP (Associated Writing Programs) Award Series, 25

Bakeless Literary Publication Prizes, 40

Neltje Blanchan Award, 274

Boardman Tasker Prize, 240

Boston Authors Club, 38

Boston Book Review Literary Awards, 38

Brody Arts Fund Fellowships, 40

BRIO (Bronx Recognizes Its Own) Fellowships, 40

Bush Artist Fellows Program, 42

California Arts Council, 43

California Book Awards, 61

Cambridge Arts Council Arts Lottery Grants, 44

Chicano/Latino Literary Contest, 251

Colorado Council on the Arts and Humanities Artist Fellowship Awards in Literature, 58

Connecticut Commission on the Arts Artist Fellowships, 61

Crossing Boundaries Writing Awards, 114

Violet Crown Book Awards, 29

Delaware Division of the Arts Individual Artist Fellowships, 66

District of Columbia Commission on the Arts and Humanities, 69

Frank Nelson Doubleday Memorial Award, 274

William Faulkner Creative Writing Competition, 193

Florida Division of Cultural Affairs Individual Fellowships, 80

Florida Review Editors' Awards, 80

Gay, Lesbian, Bisexual, and Transgendered (GLBT) Book Award, 14

Gerty, Gerty, Gerty in the Arts, Arts, Arts Award, 150

Andreas Gryphius Prize, 86

John Simon Guggenheim Memorial Foundation Fellowships, 91

Fannie Lou Hamer Award, 150

Headwaters Literary Competition, 168

Heinemann Award for Literature, 242

Idaho Commission on the Arts, 100

IHS Young Communicators Fellowships, 104

Illinois Arts Council, 101

Joseph Henry Jackson Award, 116

Joan and John Jakobson Scholarships, 265

Kansas Arts Commission, 124

Kentucky Arts Council Artists' Fellowships, 128

Lincoln Prize, 56

Loft Awards in Creative Prose, 134

Loft Awards of Distinction, 134

Louisiana Division of the Arts, 135

McKnight Artist Fellowships for Writers, 134

MAMMOTH press, 139

Richard J. Margolis Award, 37

Marin Arts Council, 139

Maryland State Arts Council, 140

Massachusetts Cultural Council, 140

Masters Literary Award, 51

Frederic G. Melcher Book Award, 239

James A. Michener Fellowship, 142

James A. Michener Prize in Writing, 155

Michigan Author Award, 143

Mid-List Press First Series Awards for the Novel, Poetry, Short Fiction, and Creative Nonfiction, 144

Minnesota Voices Project, 168

Minnesota Writers' Career Initiative Program, 134

Mississippi Arts Commission, 146

Money for Women/Barbara Deming Memorial Fund, 150

Montana Arts Council, 150

Mountains and Plains Booksellers Association Regional Book Awards, 152

National Book Awards, 154

National Endowment for the Arts Fellowships in Creative Writing, 155

National Jewish Book Awards, 121

National Self-Publishing Awards, 272

National Sephardic Literary Contest, 118

Larry Neal Writers' Competition, 70

Nebraska Arts Council, 163

Nevada Arts Council, 164

New Century Writer Awards, 179

New Hampshire State Council on the Arts, 165

New Hampshire Writers and Publishers Project, 165

New Jersey State Council on the Arts Fellowship Program, 166

New Jersey Writers Project, 166

New Millennium Awards, 167

New York Foundation for the Arts Artists' Fellowships, 168

NLAPW Scholarship for Mature Women in Letters, 158

North American Native Authors First Book Awards, 162

North Carolina Arts Council, 174

Ohio Arts Council, 177

Oregon Arts Commission, 180

Oregon Book Awards, 133

Oregon Literary Fellowships and Women Writers Fellowship, 133

PeaceWriting International Writing Awards, 185

PEN Center USA West Literary Awards, 188

Peninsula Community Foundation, 190

Pennsylvania Council on the Arts, 190

Pew Fellowships in the Arts, 191

James D. Phelan Award, 116

Poets & Writers Readings/Workshops Program, 199

Prairie Schooner, 200

Pulitzer Prizes, 203

Pushcart Prize, 203

Rhode Island State Council on the Arts, 207

Mary Roberts Rinehart Fund, 207

Summerfield G. Roberts Award, 222

Juan Rulfo International Latin American and Caribbean Prize for Literature, 110

Carl Sandburg Literary Awards, 84

Saskatchewan Writers/Artists/Colony, 47

Seattle Artist Program, 214

Short Grain Writing Contest, 46

South Carolina Academy of Authors, 223

South Carolina Arts Commission, 223

South Dakota Arts Council, 225

Tennessee Arts Commission, 233

Tennessee Writers Alliance Literary Awards, 233

Towson University Prize for Literature, 237

2001 Writing Prize, 167

Utah Original Writing Competition, 259

Vermont Arts Council, 259

Visiting Fellowships for Historical Research by Creative and Performing Artists and Writers, 8

Weatherford Award, 33

Wesleyan Writers Conference Scholarships, 265

West Virginia Commission on the Arts, 266

Whetstone Prize, 267

Wisconsin Arts Board Fellowships, 270

World of Expression Scholarship Program, 34

Writers Community of the YMCA National Writers Voice, 272

Writer's Digest Annual Writing Competition, 272

Writers at Work, 273

Wyoming Council on the Arts Literary Fellowships, 274

WRITERS' RESIDENCES/®

American Antiquarian Society Long-Term and Short-Term Fellowships, 7

Acadia National Park, 3

Edward F. Albee Foundation, 5

Altos de Chavon, 70

Mary Anderson Center for the Arts, 20

Apostle Island National Lakeshore, 21

Artists-in-Berlin Program (Berliner Künstlerprogramm), 86

Asian Cultural Council, 25

Atlantic Center for the Arts, 28

AWP/Prague Summer Seminars Fellowships, 26

Berlin Prize Fellowships (American Academy in Berlin), 5

Blue Mountain Center, 37

Bogliasco Foundation, 37

Margery Davis Boyden Writing Residency, 189

Bread Loaf Writers' Conference, 39

Camargo Foundation, 44

Centrum, 52

Château de Lavigny International Writers' Colony, 232

Djerassi Resident Artists Program, 70

Dobie-Paisano Fellowship Project, 70

Dorland Mountain Arts Colony, 71

Dorset Colony, 71

Willard R. Espy Literary Foundation, 77

Fine Arts Work Center in Provincetown, 79

Tyrone Guthrie Centre, 117

Hambidge Center, 92

Headlands Center for the Arts, 93

Hedgebrook, 93

Institute on the Arts & Civic Dialogue, 103

International Retreat for Writers at Hawthornden Castle, 241

Isle Royale National Park, 117

Jerome Playwright-in-Residence Fellowships, 195

Journalists in Europe, 109

Ledig House International Writers' Colony, 131

Leighton Studios for Independent Residencies, 45

MacDowell Colony, 138

McKnight Fellowship, 195

Millay Colony for the Arts, 145

Montana Arts Refuge, 150

National McKnight Artist Fellowship for Interdisciplinary Artists, 106

NEA/TCG Theatre Residency Program for Playwrights, 235

New Harmony Project, 165

New York Mills Arts Retreat, 169

Lucius W. Nieman Fellowships for Journalists, 173

Norcroft, 174

North Carolina Arts Council Fellowships, 174

Northwood University Summer Resident Fellowship Program, 176

Ragdale Foundation, 204

Jennings Randolph Program for International Peace, 247

Rockefeller Foundation, 208

Rocky Mountain National Park, 209

Rome Prize Competition, 7

Philip Roth Residence in Creative Writing, 41

Constance Saltonstall Foundation for the Arts, 210

Sewanee Writers' Conference, 215

Frances Shaw Fellowship for Older Women Writers, 205

Shenandoah International Playwrights Retreat, 216

Sitka Center for Art and Ecology, 218

Soapstone, A Writing Retreat for Women, 219

STUDIO for Creative Inquiry, 230

Richard H. Thornton Writer-in-Residence, 137

James Thurber Residency Program, 235

UBC Creative Writing Residency Prize in Stageplay, 47

Ucross Foundation, 239

UNESCO-Aschberg Bursaries for Artists Program, 112

University of Arizona Poetry Center, 250

Vermont Studio Center, 260

Villa Montalvo Artist Residency Program, 261

Villa Montalvo Biennial Poetry Competition, 261

Virginia Center for the Creative Arts, 261

Walden Residency Program, 226

Writers on Site, 199

Writers Colony at Dairy Hollow, 271

Helene Wurlitzer Foundation of New Mexico, 274

Yaddo, 275

BY INTERNAL NOMINATION ONLY/[IN]

Abby Award, 9

Academy Awards, 5

Ambassador Book Awards, 76

Award of Merit Medal of the American Academy of Arts and Letters, 5

Bingham Poetry Prize, 38

Bollingen Prize, 275

Michael Braude Award for Light Verse, 5

Cleanth Brooks Medal for Distinguished Achievement in Southern Letters, 78

Bryan Family Foundation Award for Drama, 78

Buxtehude Bulle, 86

Witter Bynner Award for Poetry, 5

Cohen Award in Poetry and Fiction, 196

Common Wealth Awards, 60

Conch Republic Prize for Literature, 94

John William Corrington Award for Literary Excellence, 50

Cino del Duca World Prize, 106

John Dos Passos Prize for Literature, 134

T. S. Eliot Award for Creative Writing, 103

"Evil Companions" Literary Award, 59

Fellowship of the Academy of American Poets, 1

Fellowship of Southern Writers Award for Nonfiction, 78

Fellowship of Southern Writers New Writing Award, 78

Antonio Feltrinelli International Prize, 107

Fisk Fiction Prize, 38

Foundation for Contemporary Performance Arts, 82

Josette Frank Award, 31

Frost Medal, 198

Brendan Gill Prize, 152

Goethe Prize, 87

Gold Medal of the American Academy of Arts and Letters, 5

Grand Prix des Biennales, 110

Friedrich Gundolf Prize, 87

Sarah Josepha Hale Award, 207

Hanes Prize for Poetry, 78

O. B. Hardison, Jr., Poetry Prize, 81

John Hay Award, 182

Heinz Awards, 93

Peggy V. Helmerich Distinguished Author Award, 238

Hillsdale Prize for Fiction, 78

Howells Medal of the American Academy of Arts and Letters, 5

International Rainer Maria Rilke Prize for Poetry, 108

Irish American Cultural Institute Literary Awards, 117

Irish Times International Fiction Prize, 109

Irish Times Irish Literature Prizes, 109

Rona Jaffe Foundation Writers' Awards, 119

Jerusalem Prize, 109

Sue Kaufman Prize for First Fiction, 5

Robert Kirsch Award, 135

Koret Jewish Book Awards, 130

Claudia Lewis Award, 31

Lifetime Achievement Awards for Literature, 162

Ruth Lilly Poetry Prize, 197

Los Angeles Public Library Literary Award, 135

Los Angeles Times Book Prizes, 135

Lyndhurst Prize, 137

MacArthur Fellows Program, 137

Maryland Author Award, 140

Addison M. Metcalf Award in Literature, 5

James A. Michener Memorial Prize, 142

Harriet Monroe Poetry Award, 252

Neustadt International Prize for Literature, 271

New Visions Award, 204

New Voices Award, 204

New York State Edith Wharton Citation of Merit, 170

New York State Walt Whitman Citation of Merit, 170

The New Yorker Literary Awards, 171

PEN/Malamud Award for Excellence in Short Fiction, 190

PEN/Nabokov Award, 187

Daniel A. Pollack-Harvard Review Prize, 92

Rea Award for the Short Story, 73

Rea Nonfiction Prize, 38

Arthur Rense Poetry Prize, 5

Rome Fellowship in Literature, 5

Richard and Hilda Rosenthal Foundation Award, 5

Art Seidenbaum Award, 135

Shelley Memorial Award, 198

Flora Stieglitz Straus Award, 31

James Still Award for Writing, 78

Mildred and Harold Strauss Livings, 5

Tanning Prize, 2

Aiken Taylor Award for Modern American Poetry, 215

University of Michigan Press Book Award, 255

Johann Heinrich Voss Prize for Translation, 87

Harold D. Vursell Memorial Award, 5

Lila Wallace-Reader's Digest Writers' Awards, 263

Robert Penn Warren Prize for Fiction, 78

Washington Post/Children's Book Guild Nonfiction Award, 54

Richard M. Weaver Award for Scholarly Letters, 103

Bill Whitehead Award, 202

Whiting Writers' Awards, 268

Morton Dauwen Zabel Prize, 5

John C. Zacharis First Book Award, 196

Charlotte Zolotow Award, 62